Mr. Pepys of Seething Lane

Mr. Pepys of Seething Lane

A NARRATIVE BY

CECIL ABERNETHY

McGRAW-HILL BOOK COMPANY, INC.

NEW YORK   TORONTO   LONDON

MR. PEPYS OF SEETHING LANE

FIRST EDITION

Endpaper map of London and Westminster, by T. Porter, circa 1660, published by London Typographical Society in 1898. Probably based on earlier map, 1630–1640, mistakenly ascribed to Ryther.

For my brother John

PREFACE

EVERY PERIOD in time must seem crucial to its contemporaries, but the events of history are not a chain, one link as strong and as essential as the next. Human history can be more aptly compared to a lace, a complication of links: involved, complex, only ultimately yielding its pattern—even then, various patterns to various men.

Some claim can be made that the period of the Restoration was crucial in the history of the English-speaking people. Only then, it seems to me, in the last half of the seventeenth century, did the Middle Ages at last begin to release their hold on the minds and habits of Englishmen. Monarchy finally gave way to constitution; sectarianism won its fight for establishment; empirical science made its great and persuasive exhibit; the bourse replaced the manor as the center of social as well as economic authority.

But there are other, incongruous elements in the emerging pattern. King Charles II continued to practice the ancient rite of healing. More than one Cambridge don regarded the comet of 1665 as a supernatural portent. Even so sophisticated a man as the poet John Dryden argued that the great fire of 1666 was a judgment upon the citizens of London. If the medieval hand was slipping from the garment of England, the fingertips still clutched.

King Charles was, ultimately, an anachronism. He managed to hold his throne by his wit and King Louis' money. He was, in reality, only an irrelevant—if colorful—hiatus between Cromwell and William III, sovereigns by the grace of Parliament. James II, who did not share his brother's wit, was a historical accident, quickly corrected.

Or so it seems from the wise distance of 300 years. Now the pattern seems clear and inevitable; but in the 1660s, to the men who lived and suffered and rejoiced in the daily events of King Charles's reign, the Royal Society was merely an intriguing novelty, the Duke of York's Catholicism a danger to the Parliament, the Parliament an impertinent hindrance to the Crown, the new Royal Exchange a marvelously convenient place to transact business. That time was to prove them—Society, Chapel, Hall, and Exchange—vital symbols of a new England, they could not know.

But they could suspect, consciously or subconsciously. John Locke suspected consciously and wrote his two *Treatises of Government* announcing the theory of revocable contract. Mr. Samuel Pepys, I suggest, suspected subconsciously, and in his famous *Diary* revealed a self-image of the new man—rational, materialistic, clerkly, and ambitious.

The miracle of the *Diary* is that such a person, in the quick jottings of a busy decade, could paint so complete a portrait of an essential man at this crucial point in time. But Pepys did, for he was not only essential, he was aesthetic. He had the instinctive ability to feel the significant and to give it lasting expression, even in the nonaesthetic form of the diary. No other diarist, I believe, has ever done this; and many poets and novelists, with aesthetic form to guide them, have failed to come as close to this kind of truth.

It is now almost exactly 300 years since Mr. Pepys sat down in his lodgings in Axe Yard, Westminster, and made his first entry in the famous *Diary,* January 1, 1660: *Blessed be God, at the end of the last year I was in very good health, without any sense of my old pain, but upon taking of cold. I lived in Axe Yard, having my wife, and servant Jane, and no more in family than us three.*

Nothing could be more simple, direct—and unpromising. But for nine and a half years, day after day in a busy life, he filled the pages in his meticulous shorthand, well over a million words, six thick quarto volumes. It is not the length of the diary, however, that is impressive—any clerk could write that many words in a decade. Nor its duration. Mr. Evelyn's diary extends for half a century. The marvel of Mr. Pepys's *Diary* is its composition. Any reader who has the time and the patience to submit himself to the fullness of the *Diary* will find himself caught up and swept along by the same kind of narrative drive that moves a fine novel from its early development to its significant climax.

It is the purpose of this book not only to extract that essential portrait of Mr. Pepys from the 3,000 pages of the *Diary* but also to tell, as truly as possible, the story of the man who lived its vivid years. I have occasionally taken a novelist's liberties. I have adopted a third-person point of view for the narration. I have frequently brought the focus of dramatic attention to bear more closely upon a scene than the diarist did. I have added some dialogue. It is this last liberty that gave my conscience its greatest struggle. The practice is anathema to the historian. But this is not a history or a biography; it is a narrative, an attempt to represent dramatically the aesthetic quality of the *Diary*.

No one man makes a book. The collaboration is so extensive that the writer quails before the responsibility of specifying and expressing proper gratitude to his creditors. Not a word of this book could have been written without the tremendous amount of work previously performed by the Pepysian scholars. I have tried to indicate at least the extent of my debt to them in the Selected Bibliography at the end of the book. I would be remiss, however, not to make special mention of the invaluable work of Mr. H. B. Wheatley, the nineteenth-century editor of the *Diary,* and of Sir Arthur Bryant, the twentieth-century biographer of Mr. Pepys. Any investigation of the *Diary* and of Pepys begins with them.

My indebtedness also extends to the directors and staff of the British Museum, the Library of Congress, and the Folger Shakespeare Library for the many courtesies they have shown me in the course of my research. I am especially grateful to the Folger for a grant-in-aid which allowed me the pleasure of spending a summer in that delightful library. The small but excellent collection of Londoniana in the library of my own college was indispensible to me throughout. Nor was it only research materials that Birmingham-Southern College provided me. It gave me research grants to finance my studies, leave from my teaching duties to write the book, and continual encouragement to keep me going.

A part of Chapter III, in a somewhat different form, originally appeared in the *Saturday Review* for May 30, 1953, under the title, "Mr. Pepys Goes to the Coronation." I am indebted to the editors for permission to use it here.

My gratitude to Margaret Hughes for making the index is boundless.

C. A.

CONTENTS

We must have a little patience

ON HIS THIRTIETH *birthday, May 29, 1660, King Charles II returned to London. After a four-day progress from Dover, he entered the City by way of London Bridge at two o'clock in the afternoon, at the head of a procession of ten thousand soldiers and
shouting citizens. The long train of bright robes and shining arms
clumped over the wooden floor of the old bridge and turned westward, making its way slowly through the clamoring streets, conducting the King to his palace at Whitehall. The cobbles of Cornhill and Cheapside were strewn with flowers. The public fountains
in St. Paul's Churchyard ran red with wine, and the windows of the
houses in Fleet Street were filled with screaming girls in white
waistcoats and crimson skirts. For seven hours, until nine o'clock at
night, the procession wound its way through the jubilant crowds in
the packed streets. The City of London, weary of civil war and the
strictures of a Puritan government, shouted out its raucous welcome
to Charles Stuart—and the restoration of order and prosperity.*

*At Dover, seventy miles away from the happy scene of the
King's return, Admiral Sir Edward Montagu leaned against the rail
of the* Royal Charles *and scanned the almost empty shore. Only
two weeks before, Admiral Montagu, as commander of the fleet,
and upon orders from the Parliament of Great Britain, had greeted
Charles Stuart at The Hague and offered the services of the fleet in
bringing His Majesty home to England. Only a week before, the*
Royal Charles, *hurriedly rechristened from its now hateful old Protectorate name of* Naseby, *had anchored at Dover and delivered its
royal charge to the glittering thousands who jammed the shoreline
to receive their king from his exile. Now the shore was almost
empty. The royal procession had moved on inland to escort the*

I

King to London. For his service in bringing the royal family from Holland, Montagu had received the Garter, the choice of an earldom, and the promise of His Majesty's grateful bounty. He had only to wait for orders to leave his fleet and come to Whitehall to receive his honors and his fortune.

But the waiting was tedious. The glory had gone ahead and the Admiral was left with nothing better to do than watch the natives of Dover build their bonfires on the lofty cliffs. Sir Edward looked at the cloudless sky and struck the rail with his fist. He ordered his barge and strode down the deck to the captain's hatchway.

Below, in a narrow cabin just off the gun deck, he found his secretary, Mr. Samuel Pepys, bent low over a table, writing his journal, making his entry for the day with painful care in neat, meticulous cryptogram. The round-faced young man looked up from his work when the Admiral entered the cabin, his eyes blinking in the light of the two candles that gave the only light in the dark little room. With one hand the secretary quietly closed his journal and waited for his master to speak.

Sir Edward smiled. "It is too dark to write in a lightless cabin, Samuel, and too fine a day to stay cooped up in an idle ship. Put up your work. We need air and exercise. Let us go explore the cliffs of Dover."

Mr. Pepys took up his book and carefully locked it in his sea chest. He did not hurry. Admiral Montagu was his cousin and patron as well as his master. Although Sir Edward came from a distinguished landed family and had won honors and esteem during the Protectorate, while Samuel was the son of a London tailor and had been a schoolboy and family dependent during most of the interregnum, only eight years separated their ages. For five years Samuel had been Sir Edward's protégé, confidential clerk, and companion. They did not stand upon ceremony with each other, although Samuel never presumed upon his employer's kindness. He stood in considerable awe of his cousin's title and position; but he did not underestimate his own value. If his father was a tailor, he was from a fine old county family. Samuel had himself earned a degree from Cambridge and his Latin was better than Sir Edward's. There was much that gave him no reason to underestimate himself and his value to Edward Montagu. He put the key to the sea chest

2

carefully into his pocket, fixed his hat on his head, threw his boat cloak over his shoulders, and nodded his head that he was ready.

The two men left the Charles and rode companionably in the captain's barge into Dover. They obtained a pair of horses at the public stables and spent the afternoon riding through the fields above the cliffs of Dover. They watched the farmers build their great bonfires for the night's celebration, and late in the afternoon they drew up at the edge of the highest cliff and looked down upon the rocky shingle. The Admiral, full of exuberance, swept the scene with his gloved hand and said that this must be the highest point above the sea in the south of England. Mr. Pepys, born and reared within earshot of the bells of St. Mary-le-Bow, shook his head and said that he doubted it. St. Paul's Cathedral in London was higher.

The Admiral cocked his eye at the stocky little man beside him. "There may be some wonders in the world," he said, "greater than any to be seen in London."

"I have not seen them," Samuel replied placidly.

"There is time enough, perhaps, in the days of your life to meet a few. In the meantime, we will go down to the shore and measure this little altitude that fails to impress you."

They turned their horses and rode back to Dover. At the foot of the cliff the Admiral dismounted and searched about until he found two sticks. He was very proud of his skill in navigation, triangulation, and measurement. While the skeptical Samuel sat silently on his horse, Sir Edward arranged his sticks, sighted, calculated for a moment, and then announced, "This cliff is at least thirty-five yards high."

Samuel looked up at the cliff, squinted, and shook his head. "It is indeed a great height, high enough to kill a man if he should have the misfortune to fall. But it is not as high as the tower of St. Paul's."

Sir Edward tossed his sticks into the surf and jumped back onto his horse. He bobbed his heels against the horse's belly and galloped off along the beach, leaving Samuel to follow in the spray of sand at his own pace.

When they returned to the Charles at dusk, Samuel went down immediately to his cabin and unlocked his sea chest. He searched through the books he had bought in Holland a week ago. Among them he found what he wanted, a history of St. Paul's Cathedral.

3

By the light of the candles he turned the pages, scanning quickly. In five minutes he had what he needed. He dipped his pen and marked the passage. The tower of St. Paul's was 285 feet high. Now let Sir Edward learn the truth.

Taking the book with him to Sir Edward's cabin, his finger inserted at the proper page, Samuel announced that St. Paul's was higher than Dover's cliff, 285 feet or 95 yards, almost three times the height.

The Admiral took the book and read the passage for himself. He flipped back through the pages and looked at the title. Slapping the book with contempt, he threw it upon the table and walked over to the open porthole.

"The cliff is a natural elevation," he protested.

"They were both made by God," Samuel suggested piously.

Sir Edward snorted. "You argue like a Jesuit," he snapped.

Samuel hurried back down to his cabin and fetched his lute. Nothing pleased his patron so much when he was fretted as a quiet evening of music.

That night, while the bonfires burned along the Kentish coast, Samuel and Sir Edward sat in the captain's cabin and sang madrigals, ate supper, and talked of the state of the nation. Edward Montagu had been, during the Civil Wars, a strong Parliament man. He had had no part in and no sympathy for the beheading of King Charles I, but he had an admiration that amounted almost to idolatry for the bluff virtues of his county neighbor, Oliver Cromwell. And he had prospered under the Protector. He had fought at Naseby as a colonel of foot soldiers. He had received a baronage and he had been appointed joint-commander of the Commonwealth fleet. Montagu was a Cromwellian but not a regicide. He had opposed any injury to the person of the King, and he had set himself against the Protector when Cromwell infringed upon the rights of the Parliament.

He was basically a conservative man. He believed in a stable government, the established church, and the traditional rights of landowners. That he had found himself aligned with regicides, Puritans, and city merchants was only the result of the strange accidents wrought by the twisted politics and theology of the mid-seventeenth century.

As soon as Oliver Cromwell died and his son Richard proved inadequate to rule a united kingdom, Montagu threw in his lot with General George Monck and worked for the return of the exiled Charles Stuart. As the restored King was interested in and able to govern a stable kingdom, Edward Montagu was his servant.

Samuel Pepys had been a schoolboy of nine when the wars broke out in 1642. The great battles of Marston Moor, Naseby, and Langport meant less to him than a day's holiday from his studies at St. Paul's school or a trip with his father to Huntingdon to visit his country relatives. But he had stood in the street before the Banqueting House at Whitehall in 1649 and watched the beheading of the King. The overzealous piety of a sixteen-year-old London schoolboy made him announce righteously to his schoolmates that if he were to preach a sermon upon the event he would use the text: "The memory of the wicked shall rot."

The memory of his own foolish piety did not soon rot, however. For the rest of his life he repented his stupidity and feared that some schoolfellow with a long memory might recall his announcement and quote it to his injury.

At Cambridge he kept better guard on his tongue and devoted his attention to his studies. He was more concerned with Cicero and Vergil and Ovid than he was with Dunbar and Worcester. When he came down from Cambridge in 1655 with no prospects but the tailoring shop in Salisbury Court, and no money but what he could pick up delivering clothes to his father's customers, he looked to his cousin Montagu for help. He needed lodgings as well as help, for he had, with the impetuosity that always contended with his streak of caution, married a portionless fifteen-year-old girl, Elizabeth St. Michel, the daughter of an improvident French artisan.

Montagu gave him help and lodgings. He installed Samuel and his youthful bride in a room in his Whitehall house and gave him the job of attending to his household affairs in London while he was away on his duties as joint-commander of the fleet.

This was five years before, in the heyday of Cromwell's rule. Since that time Samuel had served a tenure as clerk to one of the Tellers of the Exchequer Court, had learned to write in shorthand, and had survived the ordeal of an operation to remove a stone the

*size of a tennis ball from his bladder; he had resigned himself to
the conviction that he would have no descendants, and had rented
a house in Westminster. He was one of a little army of government
clerks that helped to make the wheels go round in Whitehall, a cog
in a machine that was not overpoweringly concerned with whether
the machine was royal, parliamentary, or dictatorial.*

*There was one difference, however, between Samuel and the rest
of the army of clerks. He had ambition.*

He had also, of course, his cousin, Edward Montagu.

*Long after the bonfires on the cliffs had burned out and the good
country people on the land had gone to bed, Samuel and Sir Edward sat and talked.*

*They talked of their families and briefly of religion, but prin-
cipally they talked about London—and their future. Any future
that Samuel could conceive of had to be in London. This was his
city, the only world he knew or cared about knowing. London was
also the seat of the government, the residence of the King. Any
preferment that Sir Edward could expect would come from London, and any hope that Samuel had that he too would profit from
the Admiral's favor with the King involved itself with London.*

*There were many places in the King's household that Sir Ed-
ward could have for the asking, places of profit and honor—Master
of the Horse, or the Wardrobe, Treasurer of the Household—all
of them honorable, profitable sinecures. When he got to Whitehall, the Admiral said, he could survey the ground and take his
pick of what was available to him: these in addition, of course,
he pointed out to Samuel, to a place on the Privy Council and
command of the fleet. The King's brother, the Duke of York,
would be the Lord High Admiral; but there was no reason to think
that he, Edward Montagu, would not be commander of the fleet.*

*There were all kinds of perquisites available to a knowing and
deserving man. And an honorable man saw to it that his friends
and servants prospered with him. He tapped Samuel upon the
knee.*

*"We must have a little patience, Samuel, and we shall rise
together. In the meantime, I will do you all the good jobs I can."*

They waited a week to hear from Whitehall. It was June 7

6

when word came for Sir Edward to come to the Court. They packed all their belongings, their clothes and gear and the presents they had bought in Holland for their families. And at five o'clock the next morning, they set out on horseback for London— and the uncertain but hopeful future.

The place of the Clerk of the Acts

THE LONDON to which Sir Edward Montagu and Mr. Samuel Pepys rode so eagerly was in fact two cities—the ancient City of London and the royal city of Westminster. Only the first of these bore the honor of the capital letter. The City was always London; Westminster was just Westminster, the seat of the royal palace, a mile to the west and around the southward bend of the Thames. But more than space divided the two cities.

London was a compact arc of narrow streets and ancient timbered houses and shops fixed like a clinging growth to the hilly north bank of the river. Anchored on the east by the jutting gray battlements of the Tower and on the west by the polluted stream of the Fleet, the dense mass of the City bulged out northward along the encircling line of the old Roman wall. Dominating this "square mile" of the City, St. Paul's Cathedral with its square-stubbed tower (exactly 285 feet high) loomed grandly over the low-gabled houses and the sharp-pointed spires of the hundred parish churches of London. St. Paul's was the pivot of the traffic of the turbulent river port. The only broad streets of the City had their origin here, Cheapside to the east, Aldersgate to the north, and Fleet Street to the west.

London had long ago outgrown the confining limits of the Roman wall and had pushed eastward through Aldgate into the fields of Whitechapel. Its principal growth, however, had been westward through Ludgate and Newgate, across the Fleet, and into Salisbury Court, Holborn Hill, and West Smithfield. The space between Ludgate and the Inns of Court near Chancery Lane had filled up with shops and houses and parish churches. To the ninety-seven parishes of old London, sixteen "Liberties," and seventeen "Outparishes," were added to the authority of the Lord Mayor. But the westward growth stopped short at the Inns of Court. The Temple Bar became the dividing line; beyond that lay Westminster and the King's authority. Nor was there any growth northward beyond the wall. Moorfields and the low, well-wooded hills to the north reminded the City that England was still essentially a rural country.

A mile beyond the Temple Bar, around the turn of the river, lay Westminster. Here in the green parks and on the broad avenues walked the more elegant subjects of the King. Here was Whitehall Palace, Westminster Abbey, St. James's Park, Westminster Hall. The King lived here with his royal household. Parliament met in the great Hall. The courtiers and the ladies of the court had their dwellings in the dozen scattered buildings of the royal demesne. The clerks and footmen and porters and laundresses of the Court lived in narrow rooms in little side-streets and cul-de-sacs that fringed the royal premises. They drank their ale side by side with the courtiers in the dozen taverns on King Street between the great gatehouses, but they took their orders directly from the Crown and lived under the authority of the King.

For many years the two towns had existed side by side in mutual suspicion, separated by a mile of open ground and three centuries of divergent tradition. Westminster was autocratic, spendthrift, and libertine. London was democratic, mercantile, and conservative. Both were strong-willed, hot-headed, and powerful, each jealous of its own prerogatives. The power of London lay in its wealth, the power of Westminster in its traditional authority. The success of the movement to restore King Charles to his throne had, to a great extent, depended upon the reception that London had given to General Monck when he came south from Coldstream with his army. London had been hospitable, and the plan for the Restoration continued on to its successful culmination.

During the period of the Commonwealth the burghers of London had come to Westminster and learned the pleasure of governing. For more than a decade they had sat in Westminster Hall and controlled England. It was a taste of power they would not soon forget. But with the failure of Richard Cromwell, they had assented to the return of the King. They were interested in one thing: a stable government. Only with stability and peace could profit and prosperity endure. These hard-fisted, tough-spirited Londoners were, first of all, merchants. Their theology, their politics, their society, all were formed upon the central principle of free and independent trade. A Crown government could insure their happiness if it knew how to govern in the interest of trade. Young King Charles II had had time enough to consider the errors of his martyred father. He was entitled by law and tradition to the opportunity, but the City reserved its own final judgment and was resolved to keep its suspicious eye closely upon the King.

Connecting the two disparate towns was one broad street, the Strand, which followed the westward curve of the river as far as Charing Cross. Charing Cross was a wide intersection, a meeting place of three important streets: the Strand from the east, Cockspur Street from the north, and King Street from Whitehall to the south. On the north side of the circus stood the Royal Mews, the great stables of the King's thousand horses. In the center of the road King Charles had erected an equestrian statue of his martyred father as a mute warning and a memorial. No one came from London into Westminster without seeing this statue of a king who was beheaded by his own people.

Between the Strand and the river, from the Temple to Charing Cross, stretched the broad estates of Savoy, Somerset, York, Northumberland: the noble houses of the great lords of the kingdom, surrounded by expansive gardens, equipped with their own private river stairs, and guarded from the Strand by locked iron gates.

North of the wide avenue, new streets and neighborhoods had begun to develop: Covent Garden, Soho, Bloomsbury. Some of the more prosperous merchants had moved outside the cramped shops of the City and built fine houses on the uncrowded squares. Courtiers unhappy with the restrictions of Court residence leased new lodgings near Covent Garden, and artists and professional men who sought their trade in both directions set up shop midway between the two centers of profit. The single cord between London and Westminster had become a slender neck connecting the head and the body of the growing metropolis.

Sir Edward Montagu had excellent lodgings, furnished him by the King, across the road from the Privy Gardens of the Palace, in a corner of the scramble of buildings that separated the Palace from the Park. But Samuel Pepys and his wife Elizabeth lived in Axe Yard, one of the little cul-de-sacs that led off King Street. They had lived there for two years, ever since Samuel and his bride had left his patron's narrow rooms in 1658 and sought out a house of their own with a parlor, a kitchen, and a private study for Samuel. There was not much more to it than that: a little dressing room and an inside privy; but it was a house, an independent lodging where Samuel could imagine that he was master of a household. There really was no household, one servant, no children. Elizabeth was probably barren, Samuel thought, and he did not mind too much. He could not afford children—yet.

Elizabeth was not barren. She was a healthy, vigorous young girl of twenty, quick-tongued, vivacious, and shrewd. She was not very talented. She had had very little schooling: a few years in a village school in Somerset and less than a year in a French convent. She could write, although her spelling was hilarious, and she could read. She loved to read, but her taste was one-sided. She read only French romances. Fortunately for Elizabeth, there was no lack of her favorite matter available. The French *romanciers* kept the presses busy turning out the multivolumed, endless stories of Cassandre, Cléopâtre, and Clélie.

Samuel thought that Elizabeth was extremely pretty, but she was not pretty exactly. She had a very good figure, full-bosomed, narrow-waisted; she was almost as tall as Samuel. Elizabeth's chief claim to beauty was her flair for clothes. She knew how to wear the plainest dress with distinction. She could take Lady Montagu's hand-me-downs, tighten the bodice, lower the neckline, sew a little lace on the full-skirted petticoat, and look handsomer in it than Sir Edward's sweet but plain wife ever had. It was not that Elizabeth liked hand-me-downs; she much preferred to go to the tailoring shop of her friends the Unthanks in Charing Cross and have a dress made. But Samuel not only discouraged, he forbade. He was still infatuated with Elizabeth's attractions, but he was also very careful of his purse. He kept a firm hand on Elizabeth's love of expensive finery.

He also kept a jealous eye on her fondness for wearing her neckline too low. He admired her impressive breasts, but he felt it was not seemly for her to expose so much of them to the public view.

It was not Elizabeth's daring vanity that gave Samuel the most trouble; it was her temper that frightened him. She was usually affectionate and sweet-natured, but she did have a temper. Samuel attributed it to her being French. She was not really French, or rather she was only half French. Her mother was English—and good English, the daughter of a landed family. But her father was French, an artisan who had come over from France with Henrietta Maria, the queen of King Charles I. Alexander St. Michel had been converted to Protestantism and lost his place in the Queen's household. Thereafter he had led a precarious, ne'er-do-well existence, always impoverished, but always on the threshold of some ingeniously conceived fortune which never materialized.

Elizabeth had been born in Devonshire and brought up in Somerset but she had spent a year in France, could read and speak French like a native, and could dress like a Parisian. So Samuel always thought of her as French; that is, he always thought of her as French whenever she displeased him, forgot to wash his shirts, asked for money to buy gloves, quarreled with him for leaving her so much alone, or gave him the edge of her tongue for accusing her of flirting.

But in reality she was no more French than Samuel's sister Pall. She was merely brighter, prettier, more sophisticated; and Samuel was just an Englishman who was suspicious and jealous of everything that came from the land of King Louis XIV. He knew very little about women, having actually known, intimately, before he married Elizabeth, only his dowdy, slow-witted mother and his unpromising sister Pall. Elizabeth was still something new and unpredictable to him. He did not like the unpredictable, but he loved Elizabeth.

On July 4, almost a month after his return to London from Dover with Sir Edward, Samuel and Elizabeth left their little house in Axe Yard and walked down King Street to the Gatehouse. It was a clear and sunny morning. They turned east, skirted the side of the royal lodgings of Mrs. Palmer, the King's mistress, and made their way along the path that ran between the Bowling Green and the Privy Gardens toward the public stairs on the river bank.

At the Privy Garden stairs a dozen watermen pressed forward to claim their patronage. Samuel guided Elizabeth to a boat on the outside of the landing platform and helped her into the narrow, flat-bottomed little craft. The hard-faced young waterman who owned it quickly jumped in after them, pushed off from the stairs with his oars, and sculled out into the stream while his disappointed colleagues on the shore kept up a barrage of blasphemous comment on his seamanship.

The river was the best avenue for traffic in London. The City streets were narrow, often too narrow for the passage of a single coach, and the going was slow through the thick congestion of carts, vendors, and countless porters. Samuel, and most people who had business between the two towns, usually used the river boats for passage from Westminster to London. The fare was cheap, the boats plentiful, the watermen garrulous and full of gossip.

Holding well to the left bank, the waterman made the sharp eastward turn of the river, regaling his customers all the while with the news of the City: a reception the Lord Mayor had given to the King at the Guildhall, a fire that had broken out during the night at the Hercules Pillars, a fight among the apprentices in Smithfield markets. Samuel always enjoyed the news of the City from the watermen, and sometimes he paid a little extra when the waterman was especially newsy or amusing.

In fifteen minutes they pulled in to the Whitefriars Stairs, and Elizabeth was handed out. Samuel had business near the Tower and she had agreed to go to the tailoring shop and visit in Salisbury Court with the Pepyses until he returned for her at noon. She kept the boat waiting a minute while she impressed upon her husband the necessity for coming promptly at noon. If she stayed too long in Salisbury Court, somebody always started a quarrel. She stressed the *somebody* strongly enough to make it clear that it was not *she* who started the quarrels.

Samuel waved agreeably to her and the little boat pushed back into the stream and continued on its way down toward the Bridge.

There was only one bridge across the Thames at London, and it was therefore called *the* Bridge. But it was more than a bridge. It was a well-populated street, heavy with houses and shops and even a chapel. Its wooden roadway was rough and broken from the constant traffic of carts, coaches, and thousands of daily feet. It was dangerous to cross the Bridge on foot at any time. But it was equally dangerous to go under it in a boat.

The four-hundred-year-old Bridge rested upon nineteen massive stone piers sunk firmly into the bed of the river. The great width of the piers made the passages between them extremely narrow, and the whole structure acted as a kind of dam in the tidal river. When the tide was running, the passages became precipitous rapids of rushing water and very dangerous. The young watermen prided themselves upon their skill in "shooting the Bridge" without capsizing—but it was seldom accomplished without soaking their passengers. Their more cautious fares, unless they were in a great hurry, usually preferred to land at the Old Swan Stairs and walk around the Bridge to the Billingsgate Stairs.

Samuel, who was cautious by nature, was not in such a hurry that he wanted to hazard the Bridge. He ordered his waterman to pull in to the Old Swan. He stepped out onto the slippery stone steps, gave his waterman an extra sixpence for his news of the King's feast at the Guildhall, and dismissed him. He would walk the rest of the way to the Tower.

He walked up Ebbgate Lane and turned into Lower Thames Street. Thames Street, like most of the streets in the City, was a narrow little way, hemmed in on both sides by half-timbered buildings, shops below and houses above. The low-gabled roofs jutted out above the street to catch the little light that came into the neighborhood and succeeded only in shutting out the sky. The housewives threw their slops from the overhanging top windows down onto the cobbles, where they ran down the shallow channels, or kennels, in the middle of the street. A stench of excrement, fish offal, and strong ale hung constantly in the air and blended with the salty smell of the riverside. The combination of the elements was not a pleasant odor, but Londoners were used to it and did not notice.

But all was not ugliness in the street. The dozens of shop signs that creaked and swayed in the breeze were colorful and gay, bright reds and greens, orange and purple, blue and yellow. The colors were strong and primitive, the designs bold and romantic—mailed fists, green dragons, roses, shocks of wheat, purple dogs—all bold and fantastic to catch the eye of the customers, most of whom could not read, but could remember the sign of the Golden Cow.

And the shops, too, were colorful and interesting, loaded to the doors and outside the doors onto trestles: swords, guitars, lace from Germany, boots from Italy—the varied objects that people need or desire and find the means to buy. Samuel loved to wander before the shops and look at the infinite products of man's ingenuity.

But most of all he loved the people, the noisy, quarrelsome, kind-hearted, loyal people of London. They were his people. He had grown up among them and recognized them as his neighbors. The shopkeepers standing in the doors of their shops haggling with a customer, the apprentices brawling in the road, the porters scurrying with heavy boxes on their backs, the vendors filling the air with their rhythmic chants:

"What d'ye lack? What d'ye lack?"
"I'll change you pins for coneyskins."
"Hot pippin pies. Hot pippin pies."
"What d'ye lack? What d'ye lack?"

There was a music in it and Samuel liked to hear it when he walked in the streets.

He picked his way through the crowd, pressed close to the wall to avoid the inevitable cascade of slops. He darted once across the road and was nearly run over by a cart heavily loaded with empty oystershells. He stopped to examine a curious dagger in an iron-monger's stall and to wipe the slop from his good leather boots. He watched a fight between two cursing, wheel-locked cart drivers, but it was only a battle of words, neither cartman troubling himself to get down off his seat to support threats with fists. At the sign of the Salutation in Billingsgate, Samuel went in to drink his morning draught of ale and, incidentally, to look down the bosom of the girl who filled the tankard.

It was nearly ten o'clock when he arrived in the neighborhood of the Tower. He stopped for a moment in the shade of the ancient little church of All Hallows Barking and wiped the perspiration from his forehead. The morning had become hot and his walk had been strenuous. Fanning himself with his hat, he looked up the length of the street called Seething Lane. It seemed like a village street, motionless and peaceful, plumped down here strangly in the midst of the teeming riverside neighborhood.

He ran his finger around the inside of his wilted linen neckband. In his twenty-seven years of exploring the lanes and byways of the City, he had only once or twice before passed along this way; and he had never taken a second glance at the quiet gentility of Seething Lane. It had once, in the days of Queen Elizabeth, been a distinguished street, containing the London residences of a Lord Mayor, Sir John Allen, and of a Privy Councilor, Sir Francis Walsingham. The great Earl of Essex had been christened here when he was an infant by no less a priest than the famous Lancelot Andrews.

It was a short street, running only from Great Tower Street northward one block to Crutched Friar's Street, but it was well guarded by houses of God. All Hallows stood at the south end and on the opposite side at the far end stood the lovely parish church of St. Olave's, six centuries old, tiny but venerable.

The rest of the street was not so venerable. The old houses had fallen into disrepair and neglect. A few taverns had invaded the neighborhood, the White Horse, the Crown, the Blue Raven; there was a hemp shop just behind St. Olave's. But most of the street was dominated by the buildings of the Navy Office, the residences of His Majesty's Principal Officers and Commissioners of the Navy Board. These were relatively new, built of good brick, airy and solid. They gave the street its official, genteel look.

Samuel put his hat back on his head and walked slowly up the quiet street. A stocky little man, about five feet six, he carried himself very erect. There was something almost dandyish in his stride, a kind of assumed stateliness which probably came from much recent association with courtiers and which sorted oddly with the general disarray of his clothes. They were good clothes, as became the son of a tailor: a well-cut purple shag coat, black silk breeches, and good worsted stockings. But no matter how thoughtfully he selected them, his clothes always had a distressing way of looking as if he had picked them up on the run. He could start out from home immaculately dressed, and in an hour his stockings would be twisted, his breeches bagging below the knees, and the lace at his cuffs limp as dish clouts.

No one loved order and neatness more than Mr. Pepys and no one tried harder to maintain it; but his own conflicting nature defied him. In the externals of the world, his accounts, his letters, the tidy cipher of his diary, things over which his mind could exercise control, he could be orderly with the most painstaking exactness. But in the things that touched him inwardly, his emotions, his temper, his desires, he always, or nearly always, lost the battle; and his impulses broke through his armor of restraint and left him with emotions taut and stockings twisted.

His face mirrored this essential conflict. It was a rather large face, bland and immobile most of the time. The nose was long and imposing: a Pepys nose, his father said, a nose of dignity, one well worth looking down. It was the eyes and the lips that revealed his inner nature. The lips were full and sensuous and the eyes were eager and piercing. He had trained himself to keep them well shuttered by half-closed lids; but when the crises came, or sudden excitement, the eyes opened wide and showed the inner fire that always simmered beneath the thoughtfully composed surface.

When he came to the gateway of St. Olave's churchyard, Samuel sat down on the stone steps and gazed at the Navy residences. They were what he had come to see.

Sir Edward had spent a busy month since his arrival at Whitehall, attending the King, conferring with the Duke of York, the King's younger brother and Lord High Admiral, visiting with General Monck and the other great ministers of state. Only by industrious attendance upon the great did favors come; and Sir Edward, like all courtiers in England, was eager for favors. He had the Garter and an earldom, but they were portionless honors; he needed money or the sinecures that produced money.

With a liberal hand, the King had dispensed his favor. Monck got the dukedom of Albemarle, and also a handful of household places that were worth a fortune: Serjeant of the Silver Scullery,

Master of the King's Horse, and the gift of a dozen little offices which he could dispense at his pleasure to his own servants and kinsmen. Montagu went to the Palace assiduously, talked to the right people, pulled the right strings, and got the place he wanted: Master of the King's Wardrobe. He also received the gift of two minor places for his own dispense, Clerk of the Signet and Clerk of the Acts, and the promise of a few more as they became available.

It was the promise of the place of the Clerk of the Acts that Sir Edward had given Samuel. Samuel knew very little about the place. It was a position on the Navy Board, the civilian department of the Navy, and the work was secretarial. The Clerk of the Acts, apparently, was the Secretary of the Board. It was a good place, Sir Edward had told him, good enough to consider until a better came along. It had the advantage, to Sir Edward, of being Navy. The Admiral would like to have a protégé on the Board; he could be useful. So he had advised Samuel to come down to the Tower and consider it, and Samuel had come. Now he sat on St. Olave's steps and thought about it.

He had been brought up in London and had absorbed from his childhood the Londoner's suspicion of Westminster. He had a shopkeeper's mind, which scorned the loose, carefree ways of the Court. It was one thing to love and be loyal to the King, but it was another to approve of the King's high-handed, extravagant, libertine way of living—and to pay the bill for it. Samuel never felt comfortable in the environs of the Court. He was fascinated, intrigued, a little bit jealous; but the Londoner in him always felt abused and critical.

And yet—to live in London, the son of a tailor, was to live a circumscribed, penurious life. A shopkeeper's son learned his father's trade, lived in his father's house, inherited his father's business, worked, married, bred children, and ultimately died in exactly the same way his father had before him. It was a secure and respectable way to live and die. But Samuel could not do it. He had been to St. Paul's and to Cambridge and he had lived in Westminster. He had learned to love scholarship and music and good conversation at Cambridge. These academic pleasures were expensive and not to be found in Salisbury Court. But most of all he had learned, at Westminster, the excitement of ambition. He had observed the courtiers who came to his cousin's house, the energetic secretaries and clerks who came into the Exchequer, and the vivid and attractive placemen who flocked to Holland with the fleet to welcome the new King. There was excitement just being with these ambitious, well-educated, well-dressed young men. Cambridge and Westminster had spoiled him for London and the tailoring shop.

He had hoped his patron would find him a place at Westminster, some profitable sinecure that would permit him to live near the excitement and the splendor while he plotted in his practical mind how he could best turn preferment into fortune. For he was determined to have a fortune, a modest fortune, enough to keep him and his wife secure in a changeable world.

The best place Sir Edward had obtained for him so far was this place of the Clerk of the Acts of the Navy Board, and the office of the Navy Board was not at Westminster; it was as far removed from Westminster as one could get—the Tower.

There were two major departments of the Navy. The Admiralty was at Whitehall, in the chambers of the Duke of York, the Lord High Admiral. All business of command and strategy, appointment of major officers of the line, and plans for building or reducing the fleet centered in the Admiralty Office in the Palace. But the care and supply of the fleet was the business of the Navy Board, a civilian department located in Tower Ward. The Board office was located at the far end of the City for the practical reason of being near to its principal operations. The major supply and repair yards were situated on the lower Thames at Deptford and Woolwich, and the chief construction yards were at Chatham, on the river Medway, and at Portsmouth.

The several departments of the Board were themselves a little scattered, but scattered in the immediate neighborhood. The Pay Office was located in Broad Street, just north of the Royal Exchange; the Ordnance, the Victual, and the Commission for the Sick and Wounded were all on Tower Hill. These departments were accountable to the Board, but they operated under a commission appointed by the Crown. The business of the Board, in addition to supervising its separate departments, was to administer the orders of the Admiralty in the construction, supply, and repair of all ships, in the obtaining and payment of all personnel. Mates, doctors, and pursers were appointed by the Board; boatswains and other minor officers were also under its authority. The Board made contracts for all supplies and materials needed in the fleet or the yards. They kept records of all expenditures and all physical needs of the fleet. They were, in short, the business office of the Navy.

The Board was composed of seven members: four Principal Officers and three extra Commissioners. The four officers were a treasurer, a comptroller, a surveyor, and a secretary—the Clerk of the Acts. The extra commissioners did whatever was needed to be done, but their principal role was to represent the Admiralty and to balance the vote with the officers.

The Board operated under a set of regulations that were traditional rather than official. And the Board did its work in a two-story building that faced Crutched Friars Street to the north and was flanked on either side by a row of attached residences, three houses in each row.

Samuel looked at the front of the row that faced on Seething Lane. They were two stories high with flat, leaded roofs. They were built of neat red brick. Windows were plentiful and clean. The little stoops that led to the entries were scrubbed white. Judging from the outside, there being only three stoops in the long row, the apartments inside were spacious, much larger certainly than the tight little rooms of his house in Axe Yard. The Crown, with characteristically liberal hand, had built expansively when it built quarters for its officers in London. It was a spot of Westminster in London. That was something in favor of the place. He could have a good house, on royal property, even if it was a long way from Court.

Sir Edward had told him to come down to the Navy Office and talk to Sir George Carteret. Sir George was Treasurer of the Board, and as such his base of operation was at the Pay Office in Broad Street; but he had agreed to meet Sir Edward's cousin, Mr. Pepys, at the Navy Office during the morning. Samuel pulled his stockings back into shape and walked across the street to keep his appointment. He was a little intimidated at having to appear, hat in hand, before the distinguished Sir George Carteret, petitioning for approval. As he went through the Seething Lane gateway into the gardens and across the well-cropped grass into the building, he kept reminding himself that he was not a petitioner. The place was his by right, as a gift from Sir Edward and from the King, if he wanted it. *He* was to interview Sir George, not Sir George him. But he had a hard time persuading himself. Titled officeholders still frightened him.

Sir George received him in the large Board room that occupied most of the second floor.

"Welcome to Crutched Friars, Mr. Pepys," Sir George greeted him cordially. "Sir Edward told me you would come. But it is not Sir Edward any more, is it? What title has he taken for his earldom?"

Samuel was relieved that the conversation could begin on such easy and impersonal grounds.

"He is undecided at the moment between Portsmouth and Sandwich. Both have good naval implications, but he inclines toward Sandwich."

"Then we will have to call him 'Lord P or S' until he decides, won't we?"

"Perhaps we can just call him 'his lordship'," Samuel suggested.

" 'His lordship' it will be, and his lordship tells me that he is sending you to take the place of the Clerk of the Acts with us."

Samuel bridled a moment. He did not like the implication that he was being *sent* to take anything.

"I have come to inquire of the place," he said firmly.

Sir George sat up a little straighter in his chair and looked closely at his blunt young visitor.

"Yes," he said noncommittally. "And what would you have me tell you?"

"The duties," Samuel promptly told him. "The duties and the salary and the perquisites."

"It is the duty of the Clerk of the Acts," Sir George recited obediently, "to rate all bills (with the Board's approbation) and to record them, as well as all orders, contracts, and warrants; to make up and cast all accounts, to frame and write answers to all letters, orders, and commands from the Council and the Admiralty. He ought to be a very able accountant, well versed in Naval affairs and all inferior officers' duties."

"He is, then," Samuel said knowingly, although his head swam from the rapidity of Sir George's recital, "the secretary of the Board."

"Yes, as Mr. William Coventry can be called Secretary of the Admiralty because he is the secretary of the Lord High Admiral."

"But—the Clerk of the Acts is not secretary to any one man?"

"No, we are all equal here: Principal Officers and Commissioners."

"The Clerk of the Acts is equal? He votes with the rest?"

Sir George hesitated and considered his answer. It was a moot point. The regulations were ambiguous about it.

"That depends, Mr. Pepys. It depends upon the quality of the man, the man who is Clerk of the Acts."

"I see," said Samuel and he looked around the spacious room. There was a good fireplace, large and capacious, able to keep a man warm in the dead of winter if he could manage to get a place near the fire. The room was high-ceilinged and light, a half-dozen windows running down each side of the room. The clerks worked in smaller rooms below, but there were tables by the walls where the officers and their private clerks attended to their business.

"Who will occupy the other places?" Samuel asked.

"Admiral Batten comes in as Surveyor, Colonel Slingsby as Comptroller. With the Treasurer and the Clerk of the Acts, they compose the list of Principal Officers. Lord John Berkeley, Admiral Penn, and Mr. Peter Pett are the Commissioners."

Samuel's stomach tightened. These were impressive names, all of them titled, except Mr. Pett, and he was the most distinguished ship architect in England. All of them had years of distinguished service either in the Army or the Navy. What chance had he in contesting for preferment with these men? He had no claim to distinction except his connection with the Montagus; he had had no experience in the Navy except his brief voyage with the Restoration fleet. In this company he would be quickly reduced to a flunky, gratefully receiving crumbs from great men's fingers. The prospect depressed him, but he did not show it to Sir George.

"And the salary?" he asked.

"Three hundred and fifty pounds a year, paid quarterly."

That was heartening. He had only made £50 a year at the Exchequer and that was the only salary he had ever had, except, of course, for the bounty he had received from his cousin. He had to his name only £100 in this world. He could live well on £350 a year in a rent-free house. And of course there would be perquisites in addition to the house. Contractors always gave bounty to the men who helped them obtain contracts, and grateful mates, boatswains, pursers, and yardmasters would surely expect to give some evidence of their gratitude. The perquisites could be rich, but he was not hopeful that his seniors would permit them to seep down to him.

"The officers are entitled to lodgings in the residences, aren't they, Sir George?" Samuel asked.

"They are all entitled, but there is not room for all. There are only six. The three on the Seething Lane side are the most preferred, and I expect Penn and Batten will speak for two of those. The senior clerks, Turner and Gibson, and Griffin, the caretaker, all live in the back row. It would not be fair to ask them to move. But they could be moved," Sir George added unenthusiastically, "upon order of the Board."

Samuel shook his head silently to indicate his agreement that they should not be moved.

"Could I see the houses," he asked humbly, "or at least one of them?"

"I am sure you can," Sir George answered. "Mr. Griffin will be happy to show you any. Forgive me for not going with you, but I must return to Broad Street. Griffin will take care of you; and I hope, Mr. Pepys, you will come to join us on the Board." Sir George stood up to end the interview.

Samuel also arose and went to the door. "Thank you, sir, I will decide," he said briefly and went down stairs to find Griffin and look at the houses.

He spent the rest of the morning inspecting them, counting the rooms, measuring the size of the parlors, the bedrooms, the kitchens, and the closets he could make into a private study. He went down in the cellars and examined the pits that received the refuse from privy and kitchen, to see that they did not leak. He went up on the roof to walk on the leads and sample the view. To the east he could see the battlements of the Tower: Beauchamp Tower, Devereaux Tower, the White Tower. To the west he could see St. Paul's in the distance and, nearer at hand, the spires of St. Lawrence Poultney, St. Magnus Martyr, St. Katherine Coleman.

It was a good view. The tile roofs glimmered in the sun, the smokepots sent up little puffs of smoke that quickly melted and dispersed into the general haze that hung over the City. Samuel stayed on the roof an hour trying to identify the distant steeples and debating with himself whether he should accept this place and trust to being able to hold his own against these experienced, established men, or whether he should refuse it and wait for his patron to find him another place, less removed from Westminster, less complicated with superior competitors. He stayed on the roof until he was hungry and needed dinner.

He went up Mark Lane to Fenchurch Street, to the Mitre, and ordered a plate of mutton, and while he ate he wrestled with his decision.

Three hundred and fifty pounds a year, a good house with a view from the roof, the intimate company of admirals and baronets, the chance to watch for opportunity and build a fortune on the gifts from contractors: the place was almost irresistible, but the great flaw was those colleagues in the office. They would think of him as an underling, a servant of the Montagus, a commoner, a clerk. They would push him aside, intimidate him, keep him submerged in the trivia of office routine while they consorted with the contractors, dined with the captains of the fleet, talked shop with each other and embarrassed him with his ignorance of the Navy. That kind of life would not be worth the salary or the fine house.

He was brought up from his meditations and his dinner by a sudden commotion outside the window. A coach with a liveried coachman had brushed against a porter, knocked his box from his shoulders and spilled its contents of apples onto the dirty cobbles of the street. The porter now stood gripping the front wheels of the coach and screaming at the coachman sitting high on his box. The porter was a little man. He scarcely stood as high as the wheels of the coach, but he gripped the spokes firmly and held on for dear life while he screeched his wrath at the careless coachman.

The coachman, splendid in his livery, sat aloof on his box trying to pretend that the porter was not there. He clucked to his pair of horses, but the furious little porter clung to the spokes and increased the volume of his tirade.

"Come down. Come down, you bloody whoreson spawn of a mangy bitch, and I'll crack your head open for you until your bloody brains run out on the cobbles—like you made my bloody pippins do!"

The coachman was a large man, a little stout but tall and impressive looking. He flicked his horses with the tip of his whip and looked straight down the street as if he were unaware of the fury at his wheels.

The coach gave a lurch and the porter let out an anguished yelp. Running to the side of the street he grabbed up a long iron spike that rested against the side of the building. He was back at the coach before it had moved ten feet. He jammed the spike through the spoke and locked it against the axle. Two spokes broke through quickly and the coach came again to a sudden halt. When the coachman jumped from his seat to come down and protect his wheel, the little porter grabbed at the apples lying scattered at his feet and began to throw them. He hit the coachman flush in the face with the first one, knocked off his hat with the second, and continued to lambast him with accurate shots until he had thrown every apple within reach, and the hulking coachman cowered helplessly behind the protection of his high box.

When the apples were all gone and the porter's wrath apparently spent, the little fellow dusted off his hands, shouted a final "bloody bastard" at his cowering enemy, and skipped off the battlefield through a tiny alley that disappeared behind the Ironmongers' Hall.

Samuel watched the whole scene in fascination. It was as good as a play acted out in its entirety before his eyes, just outside the window. He had been afraid that the little porter had tackled something larger than he could handle. The coachman had size

25

and height and better weapons, but the porter had by quickness of wit, agility, and fierce determination completely routed him. It was a typical London fight, Samuel chortled: brain and determination over size and position.

He suddenly stopped short and laid down his knife.

"By God, I'll take it," he announced out loud to the startled room.

He hailed the first hackney coach he found and ordered the driver to drive him straight to Axe Yard, Westminster. He would tell Elizabeth before he announced it to Sir Edward. She would like the house with its large parlor and room for servants, a cook, an extra maid, and an errand boy. She would like the chance to live next to titled neighbors and to give dinners and make calls and sit in their own pew at church.

And then he remembered. He had forgotten her. He looked at his watch and it was past three o'clock. He was to have met her at the tailoring shop at noon.

He did not know where the time had gone—or his mind. It was too late now to go to Salisbury Court. She would have had Tom take her home long since. Elizabeth was not the sort to sit quietly and wait. She would already be at home nursing her injury.

When he opened the door to his house in Axe Yard, she stood in the middle of the entry, her hands on her hips, her face red and angry. Assuming the most thoughtful expression he could manage, he walked casually past her without a word and put his foot on the first step of the stairs. Elizabeth whirled around and started to open her mouth, but before she could say a word, he turned and put out his hand.

"Mrs. Pepys," he said, "you must go to Unthank's and order a velvet dress. As the wife of the Clerk of the Acts of his Majesty's Navy, you must hereafter wear clothes more befitting the company of knights and ladies."

Without waiting to see the effect of his prepared announcement, he turned and walked up the stairs, humming the air of Mr. William Byrd's *What Pleasure Have Great Princes.*

At noon home to dinner

THE BUSIEST PLACE in London during the first months of King Charles's restoration was the Office of the Privy Seal. A horde of place-seekers besieged Whitehall clamoring for the hundreds of offices, great and small, made available by the change of government. The Crown was quick in replacing the late Commonwealth officeholders with loyal supporters. But the road between the grant of a patent of office by the King and the official verification of that patent by the government was beset by intricate barriers of inviolable, traditional procedure. Kings could change and governments fall, but the ancient customs of the Office of the Privy Seal did not alter—or hurry.

As soon as Samuel decided that he would accept the place of the Clerk of the Acts, Sir Edward informed Mr. Coventry, the Lord Admiral's secretary; and the Lord Admiral issued a warrant for Mr. Pepys' claim upon the office. The Attorney General passed the warrant and issued a patent in the King's name for the place of the Clerk of the Acts to be occupied by Mr. Samuel Pepys. Then the Office of the Privy Seal took charge. The patent would require the Privy Signet and then the Privy Seal before the Lord Chancellor could apply the Great Seal and make the patent official.

"These matters take time, Mr. Pepys. Be patient."

But the Navy and the Privy Council did not have as much time available as the Privy Seal apparently had. At the request of the Duke of York, the Council ordered the Navy Board to proceed at once to organize itself and begin its work of surveying the condition of the fleet.

Samuel set about equipping himself with assistants. Since he knew nothing about the Navy Office and since he did not plan to keep himself cooped up there away from further opportunity for preferment in these opportune times, he went back to Seething Lane and interviewed the clerks of the office. He needed a clerk who knew the routine, was anxious to remain, and willing to do most of the work of the Clerk of the Acts. After a consultation with Sir George Carteret and an afternoon of careful quizzing, he selected Mr. Thomas Hayter, an experienced, serious-minded clerk, who was happy to stay in the office as clerk to Mr. Pepys.

Samuel also needed a personal clerk, a young man to attend to his personal affairs, accompany him about the town, run errands. He visited old Mr. Robert Blackburne at the Admiralty Office and asked him if he could recommend a young man who would like the opportunity of rising in the world by associating himself as a servant to the new Clerk of the Acts. As a matter of fact, Mr. Blackburne said, he had a young nephew, named Will Hewer, a boy of seventeen, who needed a good connection. Mr. Blackburne promised to talk to the boy and send him to Mr. Pepys whenever he wanted him.

Equipped now with two clerks, Samuel was ready to tackle the office and see about getting a house in Seething Lane.

The Navy Board met for the first time on July 11. Samuel went down the river early to get himself a suitable place at the table before the other officers arrived. He selected a place in the middle of the table, near the fireplace, so that he could have the advantage of the warm fire to his back in the winter and a good view of the trees out the windows in the summer. He summoned Mr. Hayter and told him to sit beside him and take notes throughout the meeting. He was ready to inspect his colleagues and see what he had to contend with.

They arrived one by one, straggling in leisurely. Sir George Carteret was the first to arrive, trim and handsome in a blue velvet coat, and gracious and friendly to the young protégé of Admiral Montagu.

"Portsmouth or Sandwich?" he asked Samuel, as soon as he had taken his seat at the head of the table.

"Sandwich," Samuel told him pleasantly. "His lordship's patent is at the Privy Seal now, with mine, waiting for perfection."

"The Privy Seal is a great trial," Sir George pronounced cheerfully. "But we will refer to Lord Sandwich and call you the Clerk of the Acts without waiting on the tediousness of my Lord Privy Seal."

The others came in shortly and took their seats at the table. Samuel greeted each one cautiously and scanned them closely, making terse shorthand notes about each of them.

Sitting next to Sir George was Sir William Penn. Samuel had a slight acquaintance with Penn. He had seen him on board the flagship in May when Montagu had called a conference of all the flag-officers before the fleet put in to the Dutch coast. Penn was at that time just one of the many captains upon whose loyalty the climactic action of the King's restoration depended. For his services he had received a knighthood and this place as extra Commissioner on the Navy Board.

He was a large man, broad-chested, full-faced, and given to gout and strong language. Despite the fact that he was only thirty-nine years old, he looked like a veteran past his prime and ready to enjoy the soft rewards of peace and retirement. He had an amiable, easygoing manner that Samuel was not sure he could trust. Those gray eyes of Sir William had a way of cutting sharply at one while his fat, weather-stained face seemed to sleep in smiling indifference. Samuel made a note to take his time with Penn.

Sitting next to Penn and straight across from Samuel was Sir William Batten, a little man, no taller than Samuel, but almost as large around as he was tall. Batten had come up from nowhere in the early days of the Civil Wars and had endeared himself to the Parliament by making a ruthless attack on the Dutch ship in which Queen Henrietta Maria was escaping to France. Although he had failed to sink the ship, his boldness had won him the rank of rear admiral.

When the winds of restoration began to blow westward after Cromwell's death in 1658, Batten reversed his ship and put it and himself at the services of Admiral Montagu. Because of this timely tack, he was present at Scheveningen with the Restoration fleet and received a knighthood and the place of Surveyor on the Board.

It occurred to Samuel that the road to a throne must be filled with hard decisions. For what reason had the King so honored the man who had tried to drown his mother? Whatever the King's reason, Samuel liked nothing that he knew of Batten and nothing that he saw now across the table from him. Batten was an arrogant little toad, sitting squat and alert in his chair, waiting to pounce upon any hand that touched his interest.

On Samuel's left sat a tall young man with a long angular face and thin graceful hands. This was Mr. Peter Pett, Master of the Navy Yard at Chatham, a distinguished son of a distinguished shipwright. The Petts for over a hundred years had enjoyed the reputation of being the best shipwrights in England; some Navy men said the best in the world. Mr. Pett had been put on the Board as an extra Commissioner to contribute his expert knowledge of ship architecture. As he sat there at the table, lacing and unlacing his long fingers, he seemed ill at ease and unhappy at the prospect of having to spend his time away from his ship models and his building yards at Chatham. Samuel felt a kindness to him. Pett seemed lost in this place among these sea dogs and titled men, as he himself felt.

The other two places were vacant. Colonel Sir Robert Slingsby, the Comptroller, was out of town concluding his affairs in the country; and Lord Berkeley, the third extra Commissioner, was too busy at Whitehall to waste his day at this distant end of town. Today the Board was to sit as a quorum of five.

Sir George, by virtue of his senior title and his length of service on the Board, presided and opened the meeting by announcing that the most pressing business of the Navy Board was to survey the financial condition of the Navy. Any sudden change of administration brought its problems, but this change from a Commonwealth and the authority of an admiralty commission to a unified command under a Lord High Admiral was a particularly complex shift. The fleet had to be paid and no one knew exactly how much money was available. The Board would have to make a full report to the Duke of York of the charges now current in the fleet and in the yards at Deptford and Woolwich, Chatham, and Portsmouth.

It was also necessary as soon as possible to survey the condition of the supply yards on the Thames, to make a complete inventory of all supplies of every kind on hand and an estimate of fresh supplies needed.

Finally there was the matter of the regulations. The organization of the Board was loose and ambiguous, inviting friction and inefficiency. A new study of the duties of each officer should be made and suggestions for reorganization or clarification sent to the Duke.

There was much to be done, he concluded, and each member should address himself to the task best suited to his talents and experience: Batten to surveying the yards, Penn to studying the regulations, Pett to estimating the charges in the fleet, while he himself would undertake to draw up an account of all expenses of the Board for the past year.

Batten immediately launched into a long-winded discourse on the necessity for searching out the best contractors, men who had in former days furnished hemp, silk, tar, pitch, and timber to the Navy, men who could be trusted to know the ways of the Navy. Samuel listened impatiently to this dull ramble of Batten's on his favorite subject. Batten was obviously interested in courting the contractors and filling his purse with gratuities. But what Samuel was interested in was the fact that Sir George, in suggesting the tasks that each might assume, had failed to mention a task for the Clerk of the Acts. It may have been an oversight; it may have been that he did not know what kind of task Mr. Pepys was fit for. At any rate, Samuel had been ignored, and he did not intend to be ignored on the Navy Board, even at the first meeting.

As soon as Sir William took a breath in his discourse, Samuel cleared his throat and lifted his finger. Batten popped his eyes at the interruption and stared at Samuel. Samuel took the stop as permission to speak.

"Before I can make a start in performing the duties of the Clerk of the Acts," he said, "I need to become acquainted at first hand with all the documents in the office that pertain to me. I propose that I and my clerk, Mr. Hayter, make a complete inventory of all letters, reports, and contracts left over from the former administration."

On the word *contracts,* Batten jerked in his chair, but Sir George interrupted to announce that it was noon and time to go to dinner.

They went in a body down to the Dolphin in Tower Street.

Sir George took Samuel by the arm. Batten and Penn walked on ahead and Pett brought up the rear, walking alone.

"Go ahead with the inventory, Mr. Pepys," Sir George told him quietly when they were out of earshot. "It is a reasonable task to perform and within your province. Batten is overly jealous of the word *contract*. You might try not to mention it in his presence any more than you have to."

Samuel thanked the tactful Treasurer and they went into the Dolphin to dine on a roast of veal and a half-dozen bottles of claret. They stayed at the tavern for two hours, Batten and Penn and Carteret recalling their adventures during the wars. Each man claimed to have been present at the "crucial action," and Samuel thought it odd that so many different events at so many different places could all be crucial. He held his peace and made no mention of himself having been on the *Royal Charles* with the King when the royal family came home.

It was past two o'clock when, full of food, wine, and lethargy, they all returned to the office to conclude their business. It occurred to Samuel that this was a fat and lazy life, well suited to the leisurely taste of courtiers; but he wondered when they ever got their work done.

Through the afternoon, while Batten droned on about conttracts, Samuel listened sleepily and drew designs in his notebook. Late in the afternoon he looked up to see a man in a plain brown coat slip quietly into the room and beckon to Penn. While the two men stood in the door and conversed in whispers, Samuel leaned over to Mr. Pett and asked who the stranger was. Pett whispered that he was Lord Berkeley's steward and that he had undoubtedly come down to select a residence for his lordship.

Samuel got up from the table hurriedly and went over to the windows. He could see the backs of the three houses in Seething Lane. If Penn and Batten had already decided to claim two of the houses and Lord Berkeley had now sent his steward down to look at the third, there would be no house for the Clerk of the Acts. And it was the house that gave this place its principal charm. If he expected to establish his claim, he had to act before Berkeley, with Penn's connivance, could beat him to it.

Gathering up his papers and his hat, he bade the table good

day and left the room. He hurried down to the river and told the waterman to get him to the Privy Garden stairs as fast as he could. As soon as he got to Whitehall, he ran home and told Elizabeth to give him a pair of sheets and a blanket. He was fighting, he explained, to establish his claim to one of the houses, and he intended to establish it by the law of possession. He would spend the night there, sleeping on the floor, and Lord Berkeley would have to remove him bodily if he meant to press his claim.

He hurried back to the river, where his waterman waited for him, and sped back down the river with the ebbing tide. At the Navy Office, he summoned Mr. Griffin, the doorkeeper, and ordered him to let him into his house.

He knew which house he wanted. Penn had bespoken the house at the north end and Batten would surely want the middle house. It had the best passage to the roof. Samuel was content to have the house at the south end, the one next to the gate, the Seething Lane gate. He had Mr. Griffin help him spread his sheets and blanket on the floor, and he asked that the doorkeeper inform his clerk, Mr. Hayter, to come to this house the next morning at seven before he went to the office. Mr. Pepys was in his house.

Samuel roamed the house alone that night. Mr. Griffin had given him some candles and brought him a tray of bread, cheese, and ale for his supper. He went up on the roof and watched the City go to sleep, lighted only here and there by the flash of occasional torches which the link boys used to light late passengers through the dark and silent streets.

When Mr. Hayter came the next morning, Samuel instructed him to stay there in the house all day and tell anyone who inquired that this was the house of the Clerk of the Acts. Mr. Pepys was abroad, but he had already established his claim to his house. Mr. Hayter asked what he should do about making the inventory of the office papers, and Samuel told him that he could begin that in good time, as soon as he had his house.

Mr. Hayter borrowed a chair from the office and sat down in the entry of the house to read a book of devotionals while he guarded Mr. Pepys' house for him. Mr. Hayter was a pious Dissenter.

While Hayter stood guard, Samuel dashed off to Whitehall.

Although he was Clerk of the Acts in fact, he was not yet Clerk of the Acts in theory. He would have to be both before he could forestall Lord Berkeley and claim his lodgings. He was not sure that he could forestall him even then, but he would have a better chance with his patent in his hand. He hurried to the Office of the Privy Seal and tackled the chief clerk. When could he have his patent?

The chief clerk was a crotchety little fellow named Beale, who had spent his life seeing to it that the rushing world did not slight the ancient requirements. He had held earls and dukes at bay until they had satisfied his meticulous demands. He was not going to be hurried by a junior officer of the Navy.

"Your patent has passed the Signet, Mr. Pepys. As soon as we can have it engrossed in Chancery hand, we will affix the Privy Seal and you will be ready for the Chancellor's Great Seal."

"How long will that take?" Samuel demanded.

"It will not take long, a day, as soon as we have a clerk available to engross it."

"There is no clerk available now?" Samuel asked urgently.

"None here, Mr. Pepys."

"Is there a clerk anywhere who can write Chancery hand?"

"Perhaps at the Six Clerks Office in Chancery Lane. Perhaps there you might find one who could engross it to our satisfaction." Mr. Beale did not sound optimistic about the possibility.

"Give me the patent and I will try the Six Clerks Office," he demanded.

Mr. Beale gave him the document *and* a long, unhurried discourse about the necessary niceties of Chancery. He could not insure, he said, that the document would be acceptable just because the Six Clerks Office engrossed it.

Samuel dared not anger the little martinet by rushing him, but as soon as Mr. Beale had made himself perfectly clear about what he would accept, Samuel dashed for the door and found a coach to take him to Chancery Lane.

At the Six Clerks Office they told him that they were much too busy to take on Mr. Pepys's patent for a week. But after Samuel had badgered them for thirty minutes, they remembered that one of their former clerks, an old man now retired, could write an acceptable Chancery, if he could be found. He lived somewhere in Westminster. His name was Mr. Spong and he used to live in Bell Yard.

It took Samuel the rest of the day to find him. He had to use every wile he knew to trace him down, quizzing porters, bribing tavern keepers, harrying landlords who remembered the old man. It was well after dark before he found him, and then not in Westminster at all, but in the City, near St. Paul's.

Samuel explained his case to Mr. Spong, impressed on him the necessity for his urgency, and offered him a handsome fee. Mr. Spong was sympathetic to the plea; he needed the money. He promised to sit up all night and have the patent ready by morning.

Samuel sent a porter with a message to Elizabeth and then went to Seething Lane to relieve Mr. Hayter. No one had come, the clerk reported. He had had a good quiet day, reading his devotions and meditating upon the goodness of God and the wickedness of man.

At eight the next morning, Mr. Spong had the patent copied in beautiful Chancery hand. Mr. Beale could find no fault with it, but he took his time in getting around to applying the Privy Seal. It was noon before he released Samuel with careful instructions about taking it to the Lord Chancellor for the Great Seal and then depositing it at the Rolls Office with a fee of nine pounds.

Samuel went back to the Tower by water, telling the waterman to shoot the Bridge. He wanted to get back to the office before the matter of the house came up for discussion, and he was willing to get wet under the Bridge if he could secure his house.

In Seething Lane Mr. Hayter reported that the morning had been as uneventful as the day before. Samuel summoned his patient clerk to come with him and they trotted across the garden and ran up the stairs. His four colleagues were so absorbed in their discussion that they did not seem to notice his entrance. He slipped around quietly and sat down in his chair near the fireplace. He was glad to see that no one had taken his place.

In a few minutes, Sir William Penn looked up and nodded pleasantly.

"Since the Clerk of the Acts has now come," he said, "I propose that we proceed to the matter of selecting our houses in the residence building."

Samuel smiled nervously. It was possible that Penn had been considerate in waiting for him to arrive before bringing up the business of the houses, but it was also possible that he was making an open point of his being late to the meeting.

Sir George asked Penn if he had decided what house he wanted for his family. Penn said that he had already spoken to Griffin about the house at the north end. His family was large and he would need a large house.

Sir George looked around the table and asked if there were any objections. Samuel joined the others, "No objections."

Now was the time for Penn to put in Lord Berkeley's claim for a house, but the amiable admiral, his own housing problem settled, relaxed into his chair and closed his eyes.

Batten promptly said that he wanted the house next to Penn's. He did not say why he wanted it. He just said that he wanted it, and sat back to await the Board's approval. The table again muttered, "No objections," and Samuel quickly jumped to his feet.

Holding his hands tight against his sides to keep them from trembling, he blurted out, "I request the third house for the Clerk of the Acts."

A long silence held the room. To Samuel it seemed that he was suspended in a void. Sir George looked at him steadily with an expression of amused curiosity on his bland face. Samuel began to feel a wave of anger mount upward through his body, and then Mr. Pett broke the stillness by saying, "No objections." There came a low rumble of assent from around the table and Samuel sank limply into his chair.

Nothing had been said of Lord Berkeley. In this place, apparently, every man was looking out for himself. There were no cliques. It was useful to know that.

The meeting broke up immediately. Samuel went down to Thames Street and found a coach. Urging the driver to make the best time he could, he drove straight to Worcester House, the Lord Chancellor's imposing residence in the Strand. In the crowded anteroom, he used Lord Sandwich's name freely and in fifteen minutes his patent was on its way in to the Chancellor to receive the Great Seal.

In another fifteen minutes a secretary handed him his hard-earned scroll, bravely adorned with the Great Seal, and he drove off to Axe Yard.

Elizabeth was dressed and waiting. Samuel hurried her into the coach and ordered the driver to get them to Chancery Lane quickly. In Fleet Street Samuel had the coach stop and wait for him while he ran up Chancery Lane to the Rolls Office. He paid his fee of nine pounds and walked back leisurely to the coach. Now he was indeed the Clerk of the Acts. He got into the coach with Elizabeth, and they drove off to examine together their new house in Seething Lane.

The Pepyses began to pack their possessions in Axe Yard the next day. While Elizabeth and her maid, Jane Wayneman, packed clothes and dishes and draperies into large wooden boxes, Samuel went through Westminster paying his neighborhood bills. He wanted to start his new life at the other end of the town free of debt and obligation in Westminster. He also went down to the docks in Thames Street and ordered a supply of coal to be delivered and stored in the cellar of the new house. When he got back to Axe Yard that night, Elizabeth and Jane had finished packing; but it had begun to rain.

It rained steadily for two days. Samuel and Elizabeth sat in the dismantled house and looked at the drenching clouds. They could not move their goods in the rain; they would all be ruined in the open cart. Elizabeth fretted that all her clothes were packed; she had only the one poor house dress she wore and that was not fit to go calling in. Samuel said that it was too wet to go calling anyway, so they sat in their dreary rooms, trapped by the rain, impatient to move to Seething Lane.

While they waited, Samuel arranged with Jane Wayneman to bring her young brother Will to help them move and stay on with them as houseboy if he proved worthy. He also went around to the Admiralty Office and interviewed Mr. Blackburne's nephew, Will Hewer. The young man seemed intelligent and well-mannered. After an hour's conversation with him, Samuel felt that Hewer would do for a personal clerk and told him to meet them at Seething Lane as soon as the rain held up and help them unload their furniture.

The rain finally broke, two days later, the heavy gray skies giving way to scattered rags of smutty clouds and intermittent periods of bright sunshine and brief showers. Jane and her brother Will began to carry the furniture and the wooden boxes down to the entry and Samuel summoned a cart.

Samuel stood in the street and supervised the lashing of the furniture to the side-rings. He was in the midst of testing the knot that held the bedframe in place, when he was touched on the shoulder by a gentle old man dressed in country clothes and holding his hat in his hand.

"I am Mr. Barlow," the old man said.

Samuel let out his breath. He knew who Mr. Barlow was and dreaded hearing the name. Mr. Barlow had been Clerk of the Acts of the Navy Board during the reign of King Charles I. Samuel had heard that the old man was still alive and had feared his sudden appearance. The old officeholder had a legal claim upon the place. It was not Barlow's fault that he had been removed from office with all the rest of the royal government in 1648. He still held a patent from Charles I, and some attention had to be paid to his claim.

Samuel said, "And I am Mr. Pepys. Let us go into the house and talk, Mr. Barlow."

Samuel and Mr. Barlow sat on wooden boxes in the almost empty parlor. Samuel let Mr. Barlow do the talking. Samuel was wary, not sure what the old man wanted. He would fight for his place on the Board, now that he had it; but he had to give the old man a hearing. There was no telling what kind of trouble Barlow could cause if he wanted to.

"I am an old man now," Mr. Barlow said haltingly. "I am too old to perform the duties of the Clerk of the Acts, but I do have a patent from King Charles saying that the office belongs to me."

"I too have a patent, from the present King Charles," Samuel said firmly, "affirming that the office belongs to me."

"I know," said the old man. "I know. But at Whitehall they told me that you were the cousin of the Earl of Sandwich and that they were sure you would do me justice."

Samuel began to breathe hard. "What justice do you expect, Mr. Barlow?"

"I have a little house in the country," Mr. Barlow explained placidly. "I have good neighbors and a nephew to run the place. It is a good place to live out a quiet life. I do not want much else, but I do think I am entitled to some reward for my loyalty to the King and some income from my claim on the office."

Samuel sighed. It was not as bad as he feared; but the old man meant to claim a part of that good £350-a-year salary. The place now was not worth what he had thought it would be when he took it. Of course, there was still the house, and Lord Sandwich could surely find him other emoluments to redeem the lost salary. The question was how much would Barlow demand. Samuel wanted time to prepare himself for that negotiation.

"As you see, Mr. Barlow," Samuel pointed out, "we are now in the midst of moving to Seething Lane. If you would come tomorrow morning to the Navy Office, I am sure we can work out something agreeable to both of us. This is a bad moment for business."

Mr. Barlow got up from his box and put his hat on his head.

"Those are good houses in Seething Lane," he said. "You are lucky to get one. I never had one."

"Yes," Samuel said, "I was lucky."

By noon the cart was all packed, every stitch and stick that Samuel owned lashed tight to the top-heavy little vehicle. Will Wayneman scrambled to the top of the pile and stuck his feet through the tight ropes. It was his job to see that nothing fell off, including himself. Jane rode in a coach with Samuel and Elizabeth, and the little entourage pulled off down toward King Street, Elizabeth waving frantically to her old neighbors who had gathered to see the Pepyses move out of Westminster. Samuel rode up with the coachman to show him the way and to see that he did not get too far ahead of the lumbering cart.

Will Hewer was waiting for them in Seething Lane when they pulled into the quiet street more than an hour later. He was standing at the door of the house talking to Mr. Griffin. Hewer was a strapping, awkward young man, looking younger than his seventeen years. He had a sensitive, pleasant face, but his arms were too long for his body and his legs seemed uncertain of their proper relation to the rest of him. He was at the ambiguous state between boyhood and manhood. A few more years would prove him either a handsome man or a lazy, spoiled lout. Samuel, seeing him standing there, lounging idly against the door, hoped for the former.

They spent the afternoon carrying the goods into the fine, new house: the two Wills, the carter, and a day-hire laborer unloading the furniture, Elizabeth and Jane Wayneman unpacking the clothes and the dishes, Samuel and Mr. Griffin directing the setting up of the new stove in the kitchen. The furniture that had filled the little rooms in Axe Yard did not come close to filling the space in these larger rooms. There were a sofa, two chairs, and a table for the large, airy parlor; but there was room for at least another sofa, three more chairs, and two more tables. The room looked hollow and cold with its few possessions. There was a good fireplace on one wall and a bank of three windws on the other side that let in a flood of bright light and overlooked the trees in the office garden below. It was an elegant room, but it was going to be expensive to furnish it the way it should be. Samuel thought of Mr. Barlow and shook his head.

On the ground floor just beyond the entry was a dining room large enough to accommodate a table for twelve and sideboards on either wall. To the right of the dining room was the kitchen, the washroom, and the privy, or the "house of office," as it was euphemistically called in those times. To the left of the dining room was a smaller room suitable for a servant's bedroom, and here Samuel established Will Wayneman. It was connected to the entry and convenient for the boy to answer the door. Behind the dining room was a larger bedroom; and since it was connected to the kitchen and the washroom, this became Jane Wayneman's room. At the back of the house was a smaller room and an entry from the garden. The room off the garden entry became Will Hewer's room.

The ground floor was the working part of the house: washroom, kitchen, and servants' quarters. The upper floor was the living part of the house: the fine parlor, two bedrooms, a storage room, and a little closet which Samuel could use as a study. The main stairway rose from the Seething Lane entry, but there was a back stair also from the garden entry.

It was a grand, large house, or so it seemed to Samuel. There was only one fault that he could see. The only entrance to the roof was through a door that led into the Battens' house. He could get up to the leads and enjoy that good view of London only by going into a hall on the second floor of the Battens' house and up the only stairs that led to the roof. If the Battens took it into their heads to keep the door locked or assumed that the roof stairs were their private possession, there would be trouble.

They ate their first meal of the day that night in the kitchen, a quarter of a lamb that Elizabeth and Jane had bought at the cook-shop in Crutched Friars Street. They all sat in the kitchen, Samuel and Elizabeth and Jane on the three chairs and the two boys on the floor, eating with their fingers. They teased Will Wayneman about getting grease all over his face, and Will Hewer took him into the washroom and doused him in the washing tub. Elizabeth combed Samuel's tangled hair with the kitchen comb, and Jane made Hewer help her wash and dry the dishes. They were a happy, carefree family, proud of their new house, when they went to bed that night.

The next morning Samuel took Hewer with him to the office to introduce him to Mr. Hayter and the other clerks. Mr. Hayter had already started to work assembling the office correspondence for Samuel's inspection. Samuel put Hewer to work helping the older clerk put the letters in order. And just at nine o'clock Mr. Barlow appeared, hat in hand.

Samuel took him down into the garden and sat him on a bench.

"I have been thinking of an arrangement between us, Mr. Barlow. Since you cannot perform the duties of the office and since I do have a patent for the place from the new King Charles, you will confess, I am sure, that I am entitled to the major benefit of the office. And yet," Samuel hurried on before the old man could interrupt, "and yet I would not injure you nor have you live in penury after your years of loyalty to the Crown. I thought perhaps you would be willing to settle your claims for . . ."

But the old man did interrupt him this time.

"I want an annual grant of £100," he said calmly.

"One hundred?" Samuel asked plaintively.

"One hundred," Mr. Barlow said firmly.

"Annually?" Samuel pleaded.

"Annually," the old man insisted.

Samuel sighed. "It is a great sum," he said sadly. "Almost a third of my total salary."

"That is less than half, Mr. Pepys. I could ask you to share the place with me jointly."

Samuel got up from the bench.

"Come upstairs with me, Mr. Barlow. We will draw the agreement and the clerks can witness it."

They went together up the stairs and Samuel drew up the agreement. He would pay to Mr. Barlow or to his agent £100 a year, to be paid quarterly as his own salary fell due. This consideration would clear all claims that Mr. Barlow had upon the office of the Clerk of the Acts, and would cease entirely upon the death of the said Mr. Barlow, his heir and assigns relinquishing all further interest in the place.

Samuel signed it and Mr. Barlow signed it. Hayter and Mr. Turner, the senior clerk of the office, witnessed it. Mr. Barlow put the agreement in his pocket and wished Mr. Pepys good day and joy of his house in Seething Lane.

"I never had one," he said wistfully as he went down the stairs.

Samuel watched him go—and thought that Barlow seemed unusually healthy for so old a man. He could not live forever, Samuel sighed, but in the meantime his income had been cut a hundred pounds a year.

At noon he went home to dinner. Jane had fixed a decent meal of lamprey pie, veal, and anchovies. Young Will served them in the dining room, and Will Hewer ate at the table with Samuel and Elizabeth. Samuel said a lengthy grace, corrected Hewer for putting his elbows on the table, and said they must lay in a stock of wine. There was a good rack for wine in the cellar.

Elizabeth said that they needed rugs, draperies, and furniture to fill the gaping rooms before they needed wine. Samuel answered her sharply that he had spent more money already than he could afford on getting this place and this house. They could wait a while on rugs and draperies.

"And on the wine," Elizabeth retorted, getting the last word.

After the meal was over and Elizabeth had gone out, with young Will in attendance, to explore the neighborhood, Samuel went up to his little closet and unlocked the metal box that held his journal. He sat down at the table and entered the events of the past two days, the move, his agreement with Mr. Barlow, his favorable opinion of his new servants. At the end, he dipped his pen again and added: *Blessed be God, all things continue well with me; but I pray God fit me for a change of my fortune.*

III

To see things of state and show

PRINCE CHARLES STUART had been a boy of twelve when the Civil Wars began. Bearing the honorary title of Captain of Horse, he had sat on his pony on a hillside overlooking the field on which the battle of Edgehill was fought. His tutor, Dr. William Harvey, the famous discoverer of the circulation of the blood, had removed him from the area of danger before Prince Rupert made the bold and reckless charge which won for the Royalists the first battle of the war.

At the age of fifteen he was General of the Army, with a Council that included the Duke of Richmond, the rigorously loyal Earl of Southampton, and the brilliant young Chancellor of the Exchequer, Mr. Edward Hyde. The young prince, whose father wished to "unboy him by putting him into some action," watched the Parliament troops, the Ironsides, under the inspiring leadership of Oliver Cromwell, withstand the first blow of Prince Rupert's cavalry charge, and then saw them methodically grind down the remnant of the hapless Royal army. The rest was slaughter and escape.

Charles escaped to France, where he studied mathematics under Thomas Hobbes and practical politics under Edward Hyde. In love he needed no tutor.

Three years later the King, having been tried and condemned by the purged Parliament as a tyrant, traitor, murderer, and enemy of the people, stepped through a window of the Banqueting House in Whitehall and faced his executioners with the cryptic warning, "Remember!" One blow of the ax was sufficient to sever the head of King Charles I from his body and to place the burden of kingship upon the back of the exiled Prince.

At twenty-one he was crowned at Scone, Charles II, King of England, Ireland, and Scotland; but Oliver Cromwell was headed north almost before the crown was comfortably on his head. On the fields of Worcester, Cromwell shattered the King's Scottish forces as relentlessly as he had shattered the Royal armies at Marston Moor, Naseby, and Dunbar. The army of the Parliament was again victorious, and the King of England was again in flight.

But this time the King escaped. Young Charles was more flexible, more agile than his father. In disguise, and accompanied by only a handful of loyal followers, he passed through the length of England, sleeping in the fields, hiding in forests, making narrow escapes from detection. In a breathless month he reached the Channel port of Shoreham and sailed for France. Meanwhile the officers of the Parliament scoured the countryside looking for "a tall man, above two yards high with dark brown hair scarcely to be distinguished from black." But they scoured in vain, for the tall man was finally safe in France with his widowed mother and his younger brothers and sisters.

For eight years the new King lived a life of aimless dependence. King Louis XIV was his uncle, and Louis kept a firm hand on the ambitions of the restless exiles. He had his own foreign policy to think of, and no move to restore King Charles to his throne was going to be encouraged or financed until it suited the convenience of France. So Charles and his brother James, Duke of York, wandered through Europe in search of entertainment while Edward Hyde kept in close touch with the temper of the English people under the Protectorate.

At last, in 1658, Oliver Cromwell died. Richard Cromwell lacked his father's skill in the field and in the Hall, and England began to think more and more of the exiled King. Hyde kept his spies and couriers busy. Loyal cavaliers in England began to speak out more openly. The merchants began to fret and complain of the unstable government.

The Parliament ordered General Monck to bring his army south from Coldstream and settle the restless City. Monck came—

and talked to the royal negotiators. Quick conferences and deputations and whispered orders filled the tense spring days. Admiral Montagu took command of the fleet. A guarded commission slipped across the North Sea, conferred cautiously in Breda with Mr. Hyde and the King and his brother York. Hurried word came back to London.

The Restoration was accomplished—quickly, quietly, bloodlessly.

As soon as Charles was back in Whitehall, after his ecstatic welcome in the fleet, at Dover, and in London, he looked out the window at the shouting throngs and smiled sardonically. "It can be nobody's fault but my own that I have stayed so long abroad," he said, "when all mankind obviously wished me so heartily at home."

The King was not bitter but he was filled with lassitude and world-weariness. He was willing to let Mr. Hyde and the Privy Council take their revenge on the regicides while he relaxed in the luxury of a full purse and a joyous Court. He played with his spaniels, teased the ladies-in-waiting, and enjoyed the calculated favors of his voluptuous mistress, Barbara Palmer.

Although the King had been crowned at Scone in 1651, he had not yet received an official coronation. That had been only a Scotch crowning, a Presbyterian induction. The Church of England and the ancient custom of the British crown still required an English coronation in Westminster at the hands of the Bishops, in the presence of the people of London. King Charles selected April 22 and 23, 1661, for the days of his ceremony, which gave the Court a year to make their preparations, to restore the crown jewels the rebels had destroyed, to order new robes, new plate, new coaches, to study the ancient ceremony, and to train the inductors. It was a year of feverish work. They had to start from scratch.

Mr. Samuel Pepys, now residing in Seething Lane, felt that he, too, had to start from scratch. He had a job and a house, but he had very little money. The job could take care of itself; Mr. Hayter was capable of attending to the simple chores of the office. Samuel appeared at the weekly meetings to see that no one encroached upon his rights, but he left the administration of his office in the hands of his clerk while he searched for money.

Lord Sandwich had been prospering during the summer. He had discovered that his earldom was worth £4,000 a year—in addition to the honor. The place of the Wardrobe was worth another annual £4,000 as well as a house on the premises of the Great Wardrobe on Carter Lane near St. Paul's. There were also the little sinecures at his disposal: Master of the King's Swans, Bailiff of Whittlesea Mere. When Samuel visited him at his Whitehall lodgings and told him of Mr. Barlow's rape of his salary, his lordship consulted his list of benefits and put his finger on a Clerkship of the Privy Seal.

"Here is a place worth something, Samuel," his lordship pointed out. "There is no salary, but there are fees. Would you like to be my proxy at the Privy Seal?"

"I have reason to know that the Privy Seal is a busy place these days," Samuel observed. "I think it is worth a hazard."

Samuel went every day for a month, working side by side with the meticulous Mr. Beale. The fees poured in, frequently at the rate of £3 a day. At the end of the month, when his lordship's term was up, he had collected over £500: £132 for himself and £400 for the Earl of Sandwich.

On the strength of his replenished purse, Samuel set about to fill the gaps in his house. He bought a stock of wine to occupy the racks in his cellar; but he also bought new draperies for the windows, new furniture to fill the space in his hollow rooms, and he had the painters come to redecorate the parlor. He had cabinets built in his little closet to hold his papers and his violins.

He also bought Elizabeth a new dress, giving her £5 to buy the material for the handsome petticoat that fronted the dress and made her look like a Whitehall lady. Samuel was so pleased at the figure she made that he gave her another £5 to buy a pearl necklace. Elizabeth was beside herself with her new-found luxury.

The spring of 1661 was unusually fine, warm, and dry. The rose bushes had been in full leaf since January, and by St. Valentine's day all the country roads were dusty and the flies swarmed everywhere. Samuel bought a new suit of clothes, lighter and cooler than the heavy wool he had been wearing all winter. It was made of camlet cloth, a good fabric of silk and wool, and he bought silk stockings to keep his legs from sweating as they had under his heavier winter stockings.

He needed new clothes, better, more elegant clothes, for he had begun to entertain his colleagues. He approached the duty cautiously. At the office he had put up a stiff, formal countenance before them, minding his own business, keeping his own counsel; and they had treated him with equal distance. But in the office garden or at the taverns, they unbent a little, told stories, joked, gossiped about one another. Samuel discovered that Carteret distrusted Penn; Penn suspected Slingsby; Slingsby was jealous of Batten; and Batten liked nobody. They were a divided, mutually antipathetic office; but in public they kept up a semblance of sociability, going together to the playhouses, dining at each other's homes.

The Penn household consisted of Sir William and Lady Penn and their three children: William, a pious young man now studying at Oxford, Peg, a lively, marriageable young girl of fifteen, and Dick, a scamp of a little boy. Elizabeth found Lady Penn somewhat imperious and forbidding, but Samuel enjoyed teasing young Peg, telling her the hardships of marriage and the great desirability of remaining a spinster and living her life in peace and profit by teaching children how to sew. Peg could answer him as saucily as he wanted, reminding him that *he* had not helped *his* wife to remain a spinster and teach children to sew. Samuel enjoyed bantering with young Peg, but he cared very little for the entertainment offered by the rest of the household.

He liked the Battens even less. Lady Batten was a slovenly housekeeper, a self-satisfied, ignorant woman—an appropriate mate for a coarse, ill-tempered man. Samuel found no pleasure in the company of either Sir William or Lady Batten. Their daughter Martha interested him a little. She was already a spinster, older than Elizabeth by two years, and without any immediate prospect of marriage. Samuel made no jokes with Martha about teaching children to sew. He felt sorry for her, wondering what in the world a woman did in this life who would not or could not get married. Elizabeth was not quite so sympathetic. If Martha had had any charms, she would have been married long since,

Elizabeth told him severely. If Martha would put by her haughty airs and recognize that she was a plain woman, lucky to get any husband at all, she could find someone to marry her.

But Samuel chided Elizabeth for her hardness, and when they gathered at the Battens' house on St. Valentine's eve to choose their Valentines, Samuel chose the unprepossessing Martha.

Something more—or less—than generosity moved Samuel to honor Mistress Martha. He did not want to choose Lady Batten or Lady Penn; they would require too great a gift. And he felt that he had to honor some member of the company, just for the sake of the occasion and good relations with his colleagues. So he chose poor Martha and took her to a mercer's shop in Lombard Street and bought her six pairs of gloves. He was relieved that she did not select silk stockings, but it was Martha's modest requirements that Samuel had been counting on.

Elizabeth got even with him for going against her judgment. She chose *him* for her Valentine, and Samuel had to buy her a dress of lustring silk to show his gratitude. And when Sir William Penn showed up with a dozen pairs of gloves, a pair of silk stockings, and a set of handsome garters for Elizabeth because he had chosen Mrs. Pepys for his Valentine, Samuel knew that Elizabeth had won the honors of the holiday. To show that he bore no grudge for Elizabeth's triumphs—and for Sir William's gallantry in giving his wife garters—he invited both households, the Battens and the Penns, to come to his house and drink Rhenish wine and sugar in his parlor and sing rounds until midnight.

But Lady Batten spoiled the seasonal harmony by locking the door that led to the roof and thus blocking Samuel from his view of London. He hinted and complained, but the door remained locked; and Samuel made plans to dig deeper into his shrinking purse and have a private passage made to the leads.

While the carpenters ripped out the wall and cut through the roof, the house became unlivable. Water came in through the open leads when it rained, dirt and sawdust covered everything, and the carpenters took over the house.

Elizabeth tried to stand it for a few days, and then she gave up.

"I cannot live in this mess and confusion," she protested to Samuel.

"Where will you go?" Samuel asked.

"We could rent lodgings elsewhere until the work is done," she suggested. "We could go back to Axe Yard."

"I cannot leave the premises while the workers are here, and the house in Axe Yard is leased. You could go to your father."

Elizabeth snorted. "You know I cannot go there. There is no room and my father lives like a pig."

Samuel knew she was right. Old St. Michel did live like a pig.

"Then there is only the tailoring shop. Will you go to live in Salisbury Court until the work is done?"

Elizabeth sighed heavily. "I suppose I will have to," she said. "There is no love for me in Salisbury Court, but a few weeks of chilly weather with your family will be better than being driven mad here. Will you ask them not to critize my clothes, my cooking, my conversation—everything about me that seems to irritate them?"

"I won't ask them to board you and then tell them how to behave in their own house. Why don't you try not to criticize Pall, ignore my mother, or argue with my father? It takes two to quarrel."

"Not in that house," Elizabeth snapped. But she went to live there while her own house was being altered. And, of course,— they quarreled. They always did, always had, ever since Samuel had gone against his father's judgment and married a "foreign" girl.

It really was not easy for Elizabeth to desist from quarreling with them. Samuel often did himself. They were a quarrelsome family.

Old John Pepys, Samuel's father, had about reached the end of his days as a London tailor. He was now sixty years old, worn out with the work and worry of keeping his little business going and providing for his family. Whatever health and prosperity he had once had was now spent. He was an old man, ready to retire, living out his tasteless life with a nagging wife, a graceless daughter, and three sons who had no interest in carrying on his business. He read his Bible, particularly the words of the gloomier prophets of the Old Testament, listened with approval to the stern sermons of the Presbyterian ministers, and resigned himself sadly to the increasingly apparent fact that the world no longer had a use for simple faith, hard labor, and strict conscience. It *was* hard for him to accept this girl that Samuel had married, frivolous, loose-tongued, and clearly incapable of bearing him a grandchild to continue the name of Pepys.

Samuel's mother was a family burden. She had married above herself and brought into the family a pack of aunts, uncles, and cousins who were a constant embarrassment. She must once have been attractive, perhaps pretty, but years of continuous child-bearing (eleven children in fourteen years) and the grief of having all but four die in infancy had reduced her to a pitiable hulk of whining unhappiness. She sat all day in her chair in the back parlor, complaining that Samuel ignored her, that Pall mistreated her, that her husband scorned her. When she was not complaining, which was not often, she talked about her sister, Katherine Fenner, whose daughters had done so well by marrying the Joyce brothers, and about her brother, William Kight, whose butcher shop in Whitechapel made a better living for his family than this tailoring shop did for the Pepyses, although the Pepyses held themselves so high because they were kin to landed people in Huntingdonshire. No good that she could see, she said, had ever come of it.

Samuel's brothers were more attractive. The charm in the family seemed to run in the male line. Tom was only one year younger than Samuel. He was a cheerful, exuberant young man who enjoyed roaming the town and frequenting the taverns better than he liked sitting cross-legged in the tailoring shop and learning his father's trade. Tom had not cared for books and study, and therefore felt no resentment that Samuel had been sent to Cambridge while he remained in the shop learning to cut cloth and sew a hidden seam. Nor did he now resent his younger brother John being sent to Cambridge. Tom just had no taste for the confining tedium of having to learn to earn a living. His father scolded him and Samuel lectured him, but Tom slipped away from the shop every chance that came and spent his afternoons in Smithfield or Southwark, away from work and from his father's sorrowful chiding.

Elizabeth liked Tom. He was gay and spirited and good company. She also rather liked John, who was away at Cambridge. John was more serious than Tom, but he was friendly and kind to her. Sister Pall she could not bring herself to like. She had tried in the early days to like her. She had tried to teach her to dress, to fix her hair, to make her look less like a scullery maid; but Pall had only taken her suggestions for criticisms and scorned her help.

And Pall did need help. She had the misfortune to look like the Pepyses. It was all right for the men to look like Pepyses—it became them—but for Pall to look like a Pepys only made her gross and unfeminine. She was phlegmatic by nature, dull of wit, and slow of understanding. She had picked up her whining voice by living with her mother. She added no light to the establishment in Salisbury Court; she was one of the reasons that Mr. Pepys lost himself in the Scriptures, Tom sought pleasure away from home, and Elizabeth dreaded to spend a few weeks with her in-laws.

With Elizabeth ensconced at Salisbury Court, Samuel was free to roam the streets and watch the progress of the Coronation preparations. The Coronation was a two-part ceremony. On the first day, the King made his entrance into the City and "presented" himself to his subjects in a long parade through the streets. This part of the ceremonial was an ancient custom, dating back to Saxon days when the new king was escorted around the village and shown to the people. By the seventeenth century, the "presentation" had become an elaborate ceremonial. Great arches were erected along the royal route from Aldgate through Leadenhall Street, Cheapside, past St. Paul's, down Fleet Street, and along the Strand. Entertainments were designed for each arch, where the King stopped and watched the pageant acted for his benefit. Trestles were built along the route to seat the people. The City's militia, the "trained bands," were drilled and uniformed. The guildmen shook out their traditional livery to remove the creases. The musicians practiced the formal fanfares, the drummers their ceremonial tattoos. The passage through the City was London's part of the Coronation, and they were jealous of it, willing to go to great expense and trouble to give it style and elegance.

On the second day of the Coronation the actual ceremonial of anointment and crowning occurred. This was Westminster's day, and the Church's: the Coronation in the Abbey in the morning and the ancient feast of St. George in the Banqueting House in the afternoon. Samuel intended to see both occasions: the London and the Westminster. He had never seen a coronation, and he might never have a chance to see another. And in addition, he had a feeling—vague and indefinite—which he was ashamed to acknowledge, that good fortune, his *personal* good fortune, somehow related to the happy conduct of these ceremonials.

Samuel Pepys prided himself on his rational view of the world. He scorned the old-fashioned, medieval superstitions that persisted in the imaginations and convictions of so many of his contemporaries. He believed that this was a reasonable world, containing a divine order, capable of human order, and not subject to the influence of arcane powers. These things he told himself, and by them he tried to live; but deep-rooted inside him were a cluster of inherited notions: that God's will was shown in the caprices of the weather; that evil could be warded off by charms; that the King, in some mysterious way, had personal contact with the Almighty.

Buried now in his mind was a disturbing conviction that his own good fortune in the years ahead was somehow mysteriously connected with the success of the King's Coronation. What kind of success he did not know. But he followed the progress of the preparations avidly, the under half of his mind probing and searching for omens, the top half, the rational half, scorning the signs it saw and rebuking itself for yielding to superstition.

The ceremonies of the Coronation could not begin until after Lent was over, and Easter did not fall until April 14. It had been a rainy spring. In the rain workmen repaired the great stone steps at the Tower, where the King would land after his descent from Whitehall in the royal barge and begin his progress through the City. The carpenters building the Navy arch in Cornhill cursed the wet lumber. The trained bands drilled on the soggy turf of Moorfields in a downpour. But it could not rain forever, and the Coronation had to proceed, rain or no rain.

Samuel went to Whitehall and admired the Earl of Sandwich's coronation clothes. The Earl was to carry the scepter in the ceremonies in the Abbey, and he had ordered his robes, brilliant scarlet and snowy ermine, from France. He had spent a thousand pounds on costumes for his family and servants. The boys, Edward and Sydney, had come down from Hinchingbrooke, and the Earl's house bulged with people. The older girls, Jemimah and Paulina, were now old enough to join in the festivities. Jem was fifteen and Paulina twelve. Samuel was never quite at ease with the boys. He treated them with formal dignity, addressing them and answering their questions seriously. They were not children to him. It was to the girls that he gave his heart, especially Jem. He had been nurse, physician, counselor, and companion to Jem during the two years he had attended to his cousin's London affairs in 1658 and 1659. He loved her and treated her like a favorite niece and she treated him like an honored older brother. It worried him to see that Jem, living so much now at Hinchingbrooke, was beginning to look like a country girl. It was almost time for her to take her place in the elegant world of Westminster and find a husband suitable to her rank.

Samuel also went to Salisbury Court and visited his own family. As soon as he stepped into the house he was in the midst of a pitched battle. His mother was standing by the table in the back parlor, screaming at the top of her lungs, while his father lay back in his chair weeping helplessly. Samuel stood at the door long enough to make some sense of the wild words his mother was screaming, and then shouted at her.

"Stop. For God's sake, stop. Are you out of your mind?"

His mother was accusing his father of *philandering*—with a sorry old crone of a woman who lived in the neighborhood.

Mrs. Pepys stopped, shocked by Samuel's sudden appearance and his raised voice. She waddled over to her own chair by the window and whimpered that she had never expected to hear her son turn against her.

"And I never expected you to be such a fool as to accuse my father of debauching—and with such an old baggage! You must have lost your mind."

"Because you have married a French woman and live with lords, you now despise your family," she retaliated hotly.

Samuel flinched under the charge. "I only despise the nasty way my family sometimes acts," he retorted.

The old woman collapsed into a flood of tears, and Samuel took his father by the arm and led him from the room.

"What caused this tempest?" Samuel asked when they were safely in the empty cutting room.

"Nothing," the shaken old man replied. "She is just getting old and losing her faculties. It comes and goes with her."

Samuel tried to think of something helpful to say, but he felt only disgust at the scene and a mounting shame that he had had to shout at his mother. He could recall her love and attention when they both were younger, her sitting up with him at night when he was sick, her slipping away from the tailoring shop, without a word to anybody, to buy the red shoes he had wanted and cried for when his father had said that they could not afford them. He remembered her sending him baskets of food at Magdalene when he complained that the suppers at the college were inedible. It was hard to connect this miserable, hag-riding old woman with the memory of his mother when he was a boy.

"Where is Elizabeth?" Samuel asked.

"She and Pall left the house when your mother started. Elizabeth said it was not good for Pall to hear."

"It is not good for anyone to hear," Samuel said shortly. When Elizabeth and Pall came back to the house an hour later, Samuel told her of his scene with his mother; and Elizabeth told him that it was not right to leave Pall in the house with such carrying on.

"She will never have a chance to be anything living here," Elizabeth said firmly.

"Where could she go?" Samuel asked.

"She could come to Seething Lane," Elizabeth told him.

Samuel was appalled. Elizabeth suggesting that Pall come to live at Seething Lane!

"Not as a guest," Elizabeth went on quickly. "As a servant. Jane needs help in the house. We can use an extra maid, and Pall needs to learn to live in a decent place. Pall can come as a maid. Do you object?"

"No," Samuel said slowly. "No, I don't object, but what of Pall? Would she be willing?"

"I have already asked her," Elizabeth said brightly, "and she is anxious to come."

55

"Well," said Samuel, an edge of exasperation to his voice. "You might have asked me first. But since Pall is willing, she can come."

"No one can come, however, for a while," he hastened to say. "The rains have delayed the carpenters. You will both have to stay on here until after the Coronation."

Elizabeth's eyes began to narrow and her breath came quick.

"You are lying!" she exploded.

Samuel picked up his hat and headed for the door. "You may go down and see for yourself," he shot at her as he left the room. "Go and see for yourself if you doubt me."

The sun finally broke through on Easter morning. As Samuel was coming out of church at noon, the clouds pulled back and sunshine spilled down on the wet cobbles. Samuel looked up at the opening sky. It was odd that the rain should stop at this moment. He knew that at Court they would count it an omen of the Lord's blessing of the King; but in the City churches, where the old Presbyterians still held the pulpit, nothing would be said of it. They would think it blasphemy to make any connection between the Resurrection and the Restoration. Samuel thought so, too; but he *hoped* these breaking clouds were an omen, at least, of a week of fair weather.

But there was not a week of fair weather. It rained again on Monday and then cleared on Tuesday. Brief showers dampened the City's spirits Wednesday, and a hard drizzle fell all day Thursday. Samuel began to retire into that mystic part of himself that believed that weather was fate.

He followed avidly all the activity that preceded the great moment of the Coronation. He went to the Banqueting House and watched the King practice the ancient custom of healing the afflicted. The King stood on a dais while a long line of crippled, diseased people passed before him and stopped to be touched by the King, in whose right hand was believed to exist the same power that had healed Lazarus. It was a simple-minded, revolting scene, Samuel thought; and he was surprised to see the sophisticated King taking it so seriously, gravely touching the withered arm of a cripple, the scrofulous neck of a harridan.

The induction of the Knights of the Bath and of the new barons and earls in the Henry VII Chapel was more to his taste. The

King had granted an earldom, finally, to his indefatigable mentor and Lord Chancellor, Edward Hyde. The first minister would hereafter be the Earl of Clarendon, and Samuel stood in awe in the Banqueting House and watched the crusty old man being led up to the King by the heralds and five old earls to receive his vest, sword, and coronet from the hands of the sovereign whom he had made. With his new honor, the Lord Chancellor now had the privilege of standing covered before His Majesty. Samuel thought that it would take a brave man to dare stand covered before the Earl of Clarendon.

But throughout the week of healing and touching and investiture, the rains flirted with the City. The preliminary ceremonies had all been held indoors; but thereafter the success of the Coronation—as a spectacle—depended on the clemency of the fickle weather. The sun would shine for an hour and then give way to dark clouds, black and threatening. By the end of the week the prospect of a drenched and wretched Coronation hovered darkly over London.

When young Will Wayneman awoke Samuel at dawn on the morning of April 22, there was no sign of a sun; only thick gray clouds were visible out the window. With Will's help, Samuel put on his new silk suit, fresh stockings, a new lace neckband, lace cuffs, and freshly cleaned boots. He slipped on his new velvet cloak and was reaching for his new beaver hat when Lady Batten pounded on the locked door to her house and shouted to him that they were ready to go. Samuel made an ugly face at her toward the closed door, shouted back that he was ready, "my lady," and went down the stairs to join his neighbors.

Sir William Penn and his pious son from Oxford met them in the street, and they all walked together up Mark Lane toward Fenchurch Street—Batten, his lady, and his daughter Martha; Penn, his lady, and his son William; Samuel and his houseboy, Will Wayneman.

Mr. Young, a flagmaker in Cornhill with aspirations toward Navy contracts, had graciously supplied the Navy Board with an upper room in his shop, with a good view of the Navy arch. He greeted them at his flag shop, escorted them upstairs with ceremony, and showed them to the chairs he had arranged for them at the windows. Down below they could see the elaborate arch, with its design of ships, dolphins, and mast flags, its running fountains, and brightly draped platform-stage. On the trestled stands along the edge of the street, the honorable guildsmen in their colorful liveries found their reserved places, the Grocers, the Mercers, the Merchant Tailors. Bright carpets and brilliant pennants hung from the windows of all the buildings along the street. The trained bands marched up and down the freshly graveled cobbles, keeping the way clear.

There were four triumphal arches along the royal route: the first in Leadenhall Street, the second in Cornhill, the third in Cheapside, and the fourth at the Temple Bar. Each arch had been designed and executed by the ingenious Mr. John Ogilby, as well as the dumb show and orations that explained the significance of each. Samuel spotted a man dressed all in green behind the platform of the Navy arch practicing his oration. He was the River Thames, Mr. Young explained, his flowing green beard representing the undulating channel of the river and his contorted arms and outstretched fingers signifying the several creeks and streams that fed the mighty river.

Samuel's busy eyes were more entertained, however, by the movement and excitement of the growing crowd. Tall, willowy girls in long white robes posed and postured on the platform. These, according to Mr. Young, were River Nymphs, a part of the dumb show. Younger girls in new holiday dresses sat on the front row of the guildsmen's stands and threw flowers from their May baskets out onto the street. The City soldiers kept a close eye on them to see that they threw nothing else; and the girls' fathers and uncles in their honorable livery kept *their* eyes alert to see that the soldiers did nothing about it.

It was ten o'clock when they heard the cannon at the Tower let out its thunder, announcing that the King had landed at the Tower. A hush fell in the street. They all listened for the trumpets and the drums that led the vanguard up Tower Hill to Aldgate and the beginning of the royal progress into the City.

In the distance they could hear the parish churches begin to peal their bells—St. Katherine Cree, St. Katherine Coleman, St. Andrew Undershaft. The trumpets' fanfares came closer and more frequent, and then there was a long pause while the King stopped at the first arch to see the guildsmen's show.

Suddenly there was a loud rumble on the cobbles, a pealing of the bells of St. Peter's and St. Michael's, an abrupt fanfare by the trumpeters at the Navy arch, and the Duke of York's Horse Guard burst into view. Samuel clutched hard to the sill of the window.

The cheering became an advancing cloud of noise as the 136 Esquires of the Knights of the Bath, arrayed in crimson and silver, appeared in the street, moving quickly with that practiced, nonchalant swagger that marked them Whitehall and not London. There followed the minor officials of the King's household, the Clerks of the Signet, the Privy Seal, the Council, the ushers, the carvers, the waiters, the cup-bearers.

The line of march became more spectacular with the appearance of the Gentlemen and the Grooms of the King's Bedchamber closely followed by the sixty-eight Knights of the Bath in their richly embroidered crimson robes. A great shout went up for the sudden splendor of the Knights of the Bath.

"Nothing," Samuel whispered to Martha, "could be more magnificent than this."

But the procession became more magnificent and rich as the peers of the kingdom approached the arch. Jewels, embroidery, velvet, cloth of silver and gold, ermine, and damask lined with crimson blazed the procession as the barons, the viscounts, earls, marquises, and dukes of the realm passed by with their heralds. The Lord Chancellor and the Lord High Steward came together, the representatives of the Dukes of Normandy and Aquitaine, the Lord High Constable and the Lord Great Chamberlain—the great of the land in pairs, walking solemnly along Cornhill, treading the strewn daisies.

And then came the King!

He was preceded by his brother, James, Duke of York, Lord High Admiral of the British Navy, and by the Earl Marshal bearing the sword. The Duke of York was a handsome man, not so tall as his brother, nor so thin. There was a resemblance between them; but King Charles looked more foreign, more French, like his mother, while his brother James seemed more English, fairer with more flesh on his Stuart bones. The King sat his horse with an easy grace, sweeping his hand gracefully toward his screaming subjects, an amiable smile beneath the thin, black mustache on his upper lip.

The King and his immediate escort pulled up at the Navy arch and turned to face the platform-stage where the River Thames and his eight maiden nymphs stood poised to pay their tribute to the sovereign. Samuel could see only their backs as they watched the green-robed River deliver his oration, his green beard bobbing in time to his eulogy, and his white-robed nymphs trembling under the appraising gaze of the King. The oration lasted only a few minutes. The King's equerry threw a bag of gold onto the stage and the royal party wheeled and moved on through the arch. As the King came under Mr. Young's window, he suddenly looked upward, smiled broadly, and swept an elaborate salute to the Principal Officers of the Navy.

Samuel clutched Martha's hand tightly and bit his lips. The King had saluted him, had taken the trouble to look upward, recognize, and salute the Navy Board in the midst of the cheering thousands. His membership on the Board had never seemed so important before, so worthy of his thought and labor. He felt like weeping.

There was another quarter-mile of the procession: George Monck, Duke of Albemarle, Master of the King's Horse, with his heralds, the Vice-Chamberlain, the King's Horse Guard, the Foot Guard, the Volunteers, other officers and gentlemen. But they were anticlimactic.

Samuel slipped away from the window, thanked his host, and made his way through the jam-packed streets to the river. He was to spend the night at Whitehall, sleeping at Lord Sandwich's house, with Mr. Shepley, his lordship's steward of his country estate at Hinchingbrooke. He hoped Elizabeth had a good place to see the show at the Temple Bar arch. He wished now that she could have been with him in Cornhill, to see the King salute him. She would not believe him when he told her.

When Mr. Shepley awoke him at four o'clock next morning, as Samuel had asked him to do, the windows were still dark. If he was to see the Coronation, he had to get to the Abbey early. He had no certificate of admission. He would be able to get in only by his wit and his diligence, and he would need to be early to exercise either.

The Abbey Yard was already full of people, however, when he got there at dawn. He made a complete circuit of the great building. There were not only tradesmen and maids, who had been here all night to get a glimpse of the "great" entering the Abbey. There were ladies and gentlemen arriving by coach, eager to get a seat in the galleries as soon as the door opened. They either had certificates—or influence—or high hopes of their own wit and diligence.

Samuel moved away from them and surveyed the situation. He would get nowhere crowding in with them. Not many were going to find a place in the sparse seating around the Coronation Theatre. He walked down toward the gateway and entered King Street. The taverns were already open, preparing for the day and serving the petty officials who had been up all night doing their last-minute duties. More business could be conducted, Samuel knew from old experience, by finding the proper man in a King Street tavern than by waiting for hours in an official's anteroom. Samuel walked the length of the street, peering into the taverns, looking for someone who could help him. And in the last one, he found his man. Mr. Cooper, a clerk in the office of the Surveyor of the King's Works, was taking his morning draught before going to the Abbey to begin his exacting work in the back chambers of the church.

Samuel had drunk his morning draught often with Mr. Cooper in the old days. They had been fellow clerks in the great labyrinth of Whitehall; they had been Westminster colleagues, set apart from the rest of the world, joined by a common bond of petty, anonymous labor. For all Mr. Cooper knew, Mr. Pepys was still of the fellowship. Now there was no hurry; Samuel's problem was solved. He would just stick with Mr. Cooper; and when he went into the Abbey to perform his duties for the day, Samuel would go with him, letting Mr. Cooper and the doorkeepers think that he had business there. Mr. Cooper was his certificate for the coronation.

The Coronation Theatre in the Abbey was a raised platform built in the space between the choir and the sanctuary at the central crossing of the nave and the transepts. The platform was raised to the height of the sanctuary, and the throne was placed in the exact center facing the high altar. The coronation chair, where the crowning would occur, was placed nearer the altar. In the north and south transepts, tiered stands had been built to accommodate the hundred or so people who were fortunate enough to get inside the Abbey on coronation morning but not fortunate enough to have a seat reserved for them among the mighty in the choir and the nave. It was one of those few places in the transepts that Samuel had in mind for his view of the coronation. With Mr. Cooper to get him inside the building, he felt sure that he could manage.

Mr. Cooper got him inside. As they walked together past St. Margaret's Church and to the North Door, Mr. Cooper made a confident signal to the doorkeeper, and he and Samuel walked in as easily as if they had been bishops. When Mr. Cooper proceeded into the choir to go to his place in the crypts, Samuel bade him good day and scrambled up into the tiers in the north transept. He found space for himself on the end of a bench about halfway up the stands, nodded agreeably to the gentlemen and ladies already seated near him, and settled back to wait for the show. Admission to a restricted place was not difficult if one knew how to manage.

While he waited, Samuel surveyed the scene below him. He had an excellent view of the throne, part of the choir, and of the dignitaries in the south transept. He could not see the chair or the high altar. He felt this was regrettable—but inevitable.

There was ample time for Samuel to drink his fill of the colorful scene. The coronation would not begin until eleven; he had five hours. He clothed himself in patience and noted everything in sight: the red carpeting of the Theatre, the details of the throne, the footstool above the seat that inclosed the Stone of Destiny, the fiddlers in their red vests, the hushed efficiency of the vergers as they moved swiftly about their mute and mysterious business of preparing the altar. It was a long wait and Samuel grew weary of the hard seat, the constriction of his legs, the embarrassed emptiness of his stomach.

Promptly at eleven o'clock the chapter of Westminster Abbey, the Dean and Prebends, followed by the Bishops of the Church of England, came in through the North Door. Stately resounding music soared up into the beautiful, lofty ribbing of the vaulted roof, and the procession of priests in cloth-of-gold copes moved into Samuel's view. They bore in their arms the royal vestments, which they delivered ceremonially to the several peers who had taken their places on the Theatre platform. Then came the peers of the realm, their coronets in their hands, and bearing the King's symbols of sovereignty—Buckingham with the Orb, Albemarle with the Sword, and Lord Sandwich with the Scepter. Their great coronation robes, crimson and ermine, swayed majestically as they walked down the choir and up the steps to the raised Theatre. The Prebends, having delivered the King's vestments, filed back into the choir and began to sing the anthem as the King, followed by his brother York, entered the choir and mounted the Theatre. He stepped easily up to the throne and sat facing the altar, his Gallic face swarthy and sharp, his black head bare. Two bishops came immediately to stand on either side of him, and Gilbert Sheldon, Bishop of London, moved to the front of the Theatre and began his ceremony of Recognition.

The Coronation ceremony was composed of three basic parts: the Recognition of the new king by the people, the Anointing and Vestiture by the Bishops, and the Crowning by the Archbishop of Canterbury. Since Archbishop Juxon of Canterbury was too old and infirm, his offices were performed by Bishop Sheldon.

The Bishop faced the choir and intoned in a mellifluous voice his traditional query. Would the people have Charles Stuart for their king and do him homage? The people responded with the traditional but necessary answer: "God Save King Charles the Second!" He turned to the south transept and repeated his question. The people intoned their assenting response. He turned to the north, and Samuel joined the shout that answered, "God Save King Charles the Second!"

Most of the ceremony thereafter took place out of Samuel's view at the high altar: the Anointing, the Investiture, and the Crowning; but in between the King's ceremonial trips into the sanctuary, Samuel could hear the anthems and listen to the sermon of the Bishop of Worcester.

When the King, anointed and invested in coif, cobbium, and tunic, spurred, sworded, and crowned, came back to his throne, the Lord Chancellor read a general pardon for the King's late enemies; and Lord Cornwallis, Treasurer of the King's Household, flung silver medals into the audience. Samuel stretched mightily to catch one of the tokens of the King's largesse, but none came near enough for him to grab without toppling his neighbors from the precarious seats. By this time, however, after nine hours in the scaffold, nature had gained a victory over his stout will. Samuel made his way down the stands, through the North Door, and out into the crowded street while the choir and the organs poured out the joyous *Te Deum*.

After attending to what he had to attend to, Samuel pushed his way through the crowd that packed the way through which the King would proceed, on a path of blue cloth, to the Banqueting House and the Feast of St. George.

Samuel skirted the crowd and ran down King Street to the Banqueting House. He wanted to be sure that Elizabeth had found a place in the galleries. He was hungry. And he was anxious to see the last great show of the Coronation. The sky had become even darker than it had been at dawn—but still no rain. He touched his left ear for luck and hurried on into the House.

The central floor of the hall was filled with dozens of long tables, most of them lengthwise in the room, but one long table extended across the hall at one end. This table, raised upon a dais, was the place for the King and his Household. Servers and cupbearers scurried around the floor dressing the tables. Ushers patrolled the floor to see that no one came near the King's table. The high walls were hung with bright tapestries; the beautiful Rubens ceiling shone dimly in the light of the thousand candles. Small galleries had been fitted for visitors above the room; and it was high up in one of these that Samuel saw Elizabeth, surrounded by a knot of her old Axe Yard neighbors, looking up and down the room trying to spot her foot-loose husband. Samuel waved brightly three or four times and finally caught her eye and pointed to the north door, where he wished her to meet him after the Feast. Elizabeth waved back and shook her fist at him. He understood the fist to mean that he had *better* be there when the time came.

As soon as the Coronation at the Abbey was concluded, the King, walking under a canopy supported by the Barons of the Cinque Ports, crossed the path of blue cloth leading to the Westminster Stairs, and decended the river in his royal barge to Whitehall. The procession landed at the Privy Stairs and proceeded through the Palace to the Banqueting House. It was after one o'clock when the King and his Household, escorted by the Knights of the Garter, entered the hall to celebrate the Feast of St. George.

Samuel found a place in one of the side stalls with the Earl of Sandwich's secretary, John Creed, and watched the strange ceremony. The three rulers of the ceremony, the Earl Marshal, the Lord High Constable, and the Lord High Steward, clattered in on horseback and took their places at the far end of the room. The Duke of Albemarle, accompanied by heralds, made his official visit to the kitchens, as Serjeant of the Scullery, and tasted the first dish that was to be served the King. His Grace, having vouched that no one had poisoned the King's dinner, came back to his place with the happy knowledge that for his simple task he would receive all the plate, silver and gold, used that day at the Feast.

The Knights of the Garter had the honor of serving the King the first course. Led by the three noble horsemen, the Knights descended the hall and placed the first course of swan and venison before the King.

It was a fascinating ceremony to Samuel, full of dignity and honor; but his own stomach was behaving very badly, for it waited for more humble food to be made available to the servants of the servants of the King.

As soon as the King and his table were properly served, the waiters and the cup-bearers descended upon the tables occupied by the Knights of Bath, the Knights of the Garter, and the princes of the Church. Samuel and Mr. Creed slipped by the ushers to Lord Sandwich's table. The Earl passed them four rabbits, a pullet, and a loaf of bread. Samuel and Creed hurried back to their stall and ate their dinner while the King's Champion, Sir Edward Dymock, Lord of the Manor of Scrivelsby, escorted by the Marshal, the Constable, and the Steward, rode into the room on his white horse. He shouted out the traditional challenge to any man that dared gainsay the right of Charles Stuart to occupy the throne of England. And then he threw his gauntlet crashing to the floor.

A herald recovered it for him, and he rode forward and again shouted out his challenge and threw his gauntlet to the floor. When, after the third challenge and the third casting of the gauntlet, no man had gainsaid him, he rode up to the King's table, drank the King's health in a gold cup, and rode off to store his trophy, along with all the others of the ancient family, at Scrivelsby.

The elaborate ceremony and the heavy feasting lasted in the Banqueting House all the afternoon. At six o'clock Samuel walked out onto the floor. He waved vigorously to Elizabeth and pointed to the door. Elizabeth waved back frantically and hurried out of the gallery. She had had her fill of watching the King and Samuel eat their ceremonial dinner. She had had nothing all day.

As they left the Banqueting House, Elizabeth protesting that she had to get a bite to eat somewhere, the heavens opened and the rain came down in buckets. Elizabeth covered her head with her scarf and ran for shelter under the Gatehouse.

"No dinner," she panted when they had found cover. "No dinner, no fireworks, no celebration."

A flash of lightning blinded them for a moment and then a crash of thunder sent Elizabeth's hands to her ears.

"It is like a portent," she gasped, holding tightly to Samuel's arm. "It is a sign of God's blessing that he withheld the storm until the King was crowned."

"Nonsense," Samuel snorted, shaking her hand from his arm. "It is a sign that the clouds were ready to rain. You are a fool to believe such village superstition. It rains because it rains."

After the storm had abated a little, Samuel took Elizabeth's arm and led her through the flowing streets. King Street was a mass of roistering celebrants. Bonfires blazed; men and women, arms linked, stormed against the crowd. In front of the Leg Tavern, a group of gallants drinking the King's health stopped Samuel and made him and Elizabeth get down on their knees on the wet cobbles and drink a toast to His Majesty before they let them up again.

In Axe Yard three great bonfires burned in the street. They went up to the roof of Mrs. Hunt's house and looked out over the Court. A thin shower of bright needle rain laced the air. The rain had spoiled the King's fireworks and spoiled the night spectacle in St. James's Park; but there in the distance, London loomed, encircled by a line of bonfires, faint and magical, like a "ring of glory."

IV

I have newly taken a solemn oath

EARLY IN NOVEMBER 1661 a British frigate stationed near the Buoy of the Nore sighted a Swedish man-of-war coming out of the Thames estuary into the opening waters of the North Sea. On the quarterdeck of the patrolling vessel, Captain Robert Holmes kept his glass fixed on the rigging of the passing Swede. The man-of-war proceeded on course without a wrinkle in its topsails, and Holmes ordered a shot fired across the bow of the negligent foreigner. The shot splashed in the water well forward and considerably beyond the Swede. In a moment the man-of-war came about and stood across the wind, its sails flapping lightly. Through his glass Holmes could see a barge being lowered over the sides. When he saw the barge making a course toward him, he left the deck and went to his cabin, telling the mate to show the visitors to his quarters when they came aboard. In ten minutes two Swedish gentlemen were piped aboard and promptly led to Holmes's cabin.

The spokesman introduced himself as secretary to Count Brahé, the Swedish ambassador to the Court of King Charles, who was on his way to Stockholm. At the moment, however, he was curious about the shot that the English captain had seen fit to send across his bow. Holmes asked that his greetings be tendered to the Ambassador, but he had orders to fire upon any ship that failed to strike topsails upon passing an English vessel in the open seas. The Secretary said that he was sure that the Captain's zeal would be rewarded by the Lord Admiral, but Count Brahé had permission of His Majesty, King Charles, to dispense with the customary tribute of lowered topsails. Holmes said that he was glad to hear it, but would the Secretary be good enough to show him the King's order which countermanded his own standing orders. The permission, the gentleman said, was verbal.

Holmes stared at his visitor. "Verbal permission?" he asked.

"Yes," said the Secretary, "verbal permission."

Holmes was in a dilemma. He had had command long enough to know that a captain did not lightly omit an order as fixed and jealously guarded as the order that all passing foreigners pay tribute to his King's oceanic sovereignty. No British captain in his right mind would hesitate to fire upon a foreigner who failed to strike topsails. But Sweden was a friendly power and an ambassador was not a person to be trifled with. There could just possibly be some delicate Whitehall reason for giving the Count permission to omit the traditional salute. But how was an English captain, ten days from London, to know that his orders had been changed?

"Upon what assurance," he asked his visitor, "can I make the exception you claim?"

"Upon the word and honor of an ambassador," the Secretary replied coolly.

Holmes lifted his brows. He looked hard for a moment at the Swedish gentlemen, and then shrugging his shoulders, he got up and extended his hand.

"I wish you a pleasant voyage," he said. "I will, of course, return to Woolwich at once and report to Whitehall. My voyage may not be quite so pleasant as yours. There may be hell to pay at the Admiralty, but under the circumstances, I see no alternative but to accept your word. *Bon voyage*, gentlemen."

Two days later in Whitehall, Holmes had reason to rue his prescience. The King disclaimed giving the Count permission of any kind to omit the salute of acknowledgment of his dominion of the ocean seas. The Duke of York read the captain a raking reprimand for disobeying his standing orders upon the *word* of anyone, and the Admiralty clapped him in prison to consider in the quiet of a cell the dangers of gullibility.

While Holmes languished in jail, the Duke of York set about the task of mending diplomatic fences. Representations had to be made to Sweden, but before the Crown could take a firm position, the Duke needed to make sure of his ground. He began to summon everyone who had ever had any experience with the traditional claim of the British Crown to oceanic sovereignty. Late in the month he sent word down to Seething Lane that he wanted the Principal Officers and Commissioners to meet with him privately and at once on a matter of the gravest importance. Mr. Pepys made the journey up the river with his colleagues, curious and a little frightened. A sudden summons by the Duke could have disturbing consequences.

Mr. Coventry, the Duke's secretary, met them in the Stone Gallery and ushered them into the Duke's presence. The Lord High Admiral thanked the officers for making the journey up the river on short notice and related to them the whole story of Holmes and the Swedish ambassador.

Samuel knew Holmes and had heard that he was in trouble. On the face of it, he was inclined to be sympathetic with the unfortunate captain who had suddenly had an international incident thrust upon him. Anyone could have made the same mistake that Holmes had made. It was one of the hazards of officeholding and just as likely to happen to an officer of the Navy Board as to a frigate commander in the Nore. But he could tell from the chilly tone of the Duke's narration that more was involved here than the career of one unfortunate captain. The Duke was concerned about the prestige of the Navy and of the Crown. The eyes of Europe, the Duke said, were watchfully fixed upon the King, to see what strength the new government had and what role the King intended to play in the politics of the Continent. Holmes was unimportant, but the strength of the English Navy was highly important. One show of weakness now, however slight, he said, might lead to untold danger later.

It was for the purpose of receiving their knowledge of the tradition of striking sail that he had summoned them. Before committing itself to any action against Sweden, the Privy Council needed to be certain of its legal ground, which was to say the Council needed all the evidence it could gather about the ancient tradition of sail striking, since tradition was legality.

Admiral Penn immediately began a long discourse on his experience in the fleet, the number of shots he had fired across the bows of negligent foreigners, the demands he had made upon captains hesitant to salute his flag. Batten broke in frequently to recount his own vigorous defense of the King's rights on the seas, and Sir George, when at last he got the floor, rambled on at great length about his enforcement of the ancient orders while he was Governor of Jersey.

Mr. Pepys, however, sat silent and ill at ease. These were strange and uncharted waters to him. He had not one scrap of knowledge or one hour's experience with sail salutes. He was not even quite sure which precisely were the topsails.

He was uncomfortably embarrassed as he listened to his colleagues pour out their tales of raking shots, predawn challenges, and splintered masts. He let his mind drift away from the gun smoke and the bellicose tales and considered how he might redeem himself from this awkward exhibit of ignorance. He recalled that when he was a boy in Salisbury Court he used occasionally to see Mr. John Selden, the wealthy and learned old scholar, tottering to his lodgings in Carmelite House, the dowager Countess of Kent's town house in Whitefriar's, not far from the tailoring shop. He had never said one word to the fearful-looking old man, but he had joined the other children of the neighborhood in standing in the street and gazing with rapt wonder at his long gray hair and the heavy leather folios he carried into the mysterious house. They had whispered among themselves that he was a warlock, in frightening league with the Devil, and that the books he carried in and out of the house were volumes of black magic. Samuel learned later that the old man was in reality only a very respectable old historian who enjoyed the protection of the Countess of Kent. Among his many scholarly labors, Selden had written one exhaustively learned book on the subject of the dominion of the seas. Samuel had heard someone at Magdalene say that it was the definitive work on the subject. Perhaps he could make use of Mr. Selden's impressive name.

When the meeting finally broke up, the Duke thanking them all for their trouble, Samuel slipped out quietly and waited in the Stone Gallery. When Mr. Coventry came by, Samuel fell into step and walked with him into the Privy Gardens. As they chatted, Samuel mentioned casually, as if he had just thought of it, that he had in the old days heard Mr. Selden say that King Henry VII gave firm orders to his captains to force the ships of the King of Denmark to strike sail to them in the Baltic.

"In the Baltic?" asked Mr. Coventry, with some surprise.

"So I recall," said Samuel.

"It is worth knowing, if you can find the authority," said the serious Secretary.

"I know exactly where to find it," said Samuel boldly.

On his way home through the City, Samuel stopped in St. Paul's Churchyard, among the dozens of bookstalls tucked around in the shadows of the Cathedral. For the next hour he rummaged among the stalls, quizzed the booksellers, opened a hundred dusty volumes, until at last he found it, a leather-bound folio, dated 1635, *Joannis Seldini Mare Clausum, seu de Dominio Maris.* Clasping the volume under his arm, he told the bookseller to put it to his account.

As soon as supper was over, he took his impressively weathered book over to the Navy Office. With a candle at his elbow and the large book on his lap, he began to read. The scholarly Latin gave him no great difficulty. He had mastered Latin long ago, at St. Paul's and at Cambridge; but Selden's dry legalistic style and his heavily documented scholarship made the book tedious reading. He read until midnight, until his eyes ached and his brain felt numb.

The next afternoon, while Elizabeth went to the play with the Penns, Samuel took the *Mare Clausum* up to his study and again began his search for Mr. Selden's note on King Henry's dominion of the Baltic. He read until Elizabeth came home and called him to supper, and then he went back up to his room and continued to read until midnight. He found nothing about the Baltic, but he began to see the shape of the book. The first part devoted itself to arguing, with voluminous reference to history and natural law, that the sea is no more the common property of man than is the land. As there are respected boundaries of sovereignty in adjacent tracts of land, so is there by logic and natural law, sovereignty in adjacent bodies of water. The second book argued closely, from precedent and tradition, that "the lordship of the circumambient ocean belongs to the crown of Great Britain as an indivisible and perpetual appendage."

Samuel got out his paper and began to make notes. In an hour he had reduced the heart of Selden's argument to three closely written pages. Now he had only to document, to make a list of precedents that had bearing on the Holmes incident. When he went to bed he could not sleep. He had not had this exciting pleasure of a lesson laboriously learned since the old days at Cambridge, the almost physical thrill of having facts and complex arguments lie down tamely before him.

The next afternoon he went back to St. Paul's Churchyard and located a copy of Grotius's *Mare Liberum,* a Dutch tome on the wrong side of the argument, but the question of freedom or dominion of the seas had now become a larger issue with him than merely finding a footnote for Mr. Coventry. If he could not engage with his colleagues in an exchange of battle experience, he could do what they could not do. He could bring his own talents and his own training into the office; he could use his wit, a commodity he had not seen conspicuously exhibited at the Board table. With some exertion of his energies and a discreet effort to let the powers at Whitehall know what he was doing, he could go his own way in the office, without the help or hindrance of his quarrelsome colleagues. He went to Whitehall and told Mr. Coventry that he was busy upon his report on dominion of the ocean seas. While he was in the neighborhood, he went to the Exchequer Office and asked his old friend Mr. Falconberge to search the *Domesday Book* for any reference he could find on England's oceanic dominion.

It was a happy coincidence—or perhaps more than a coincidence—that in these last months of 1661 Samuel's mind was freed for these new demands on his energies by the advent of unaccustomed serenity in his private life. In fact his most irksome personal problem, his quarrelsome family, had been solved by the benevolent hand of Providence.

The summer had been marred by one domestic crisis after another. The principal source of grief was Pall. Samuel, true to his word, brought his difficult sister to Seething Lane after the Coronation, but Pall's stay was a signal failure. Samuel made the mistake of trying to make her live up to her side of the bargain. Pall had readily agreed to enter the house as a servant. She would have agreed to anything to get away from Salisbury Court. But when Samuel took her at her word and would not let her eat or sleep abovestairs, and forced her into the company of the other servants, she quickly grew sulky and querulous. And when Samuel refused to take her to the playhouse with himself and Elizabeth, she became downright mutinous. Furthermore, the crowded household at Salisbury Court was reduced to such an uproar of dissension that it was impossible in all charity to return Pall to it.

Samuel was beginning to feel that just as some men were irrevocably cursed with a hunched back or leprosy, so he was cursed with his intolerable family. Then Uncle Robert Pepys, his father's older brother, was carried off by the hand of the Lord, and Samuel found himself the residual heir to a rich farm at Brampton. Samuel dissolved his troubles in distance. With tremendous relief he packed off his parents and Pall, and set them out to graze peacefully in the fields of Huntingdonshire. Only his improvident brother Tom was left to worry Samuel at Salisbury Court, and Tom at least made no overt nuisance of himself.

Samuel's difficulties were not over, however. The early months of autumn were made hideous by nuisance suits brought against him by disgruntled and litigious relatives who had been passed over in Uncle Robert's will. But by December most of them had gone into hibernation and left him in sudden and welcome peace.

When Samuel went to his study on New Year's eve to close his accounts for the year, he estimated that he was worth close to £500 in money and goods. But his mind thought back ruefully upon the wasted time and money of the past twelve months. He took out his diary and entered the events of the day. And then he wrote his year-end summary:

I am, he wrote, *upon writing a little treatise to present to the Duke, about our privilege in the seas, as to other nations striking their flags to us. But my greatest trouble is, that I have for this last half year been a very great spendthrift in all manner of respects, that I am afeard to cast up my accounts, though I hope I am worth what I say above. But I will cast them up very shortly. I have newly taken a solemn oath about abstaining from plays and wine, which*

I am resolved to keep according to the letter of the oath which I keep by me.

The oath he had made was very simple—but very explicit. Upon the penalty of a forfeiture of a half crown, to be given to the poor of the parish, he swore not to drink more than two glasses of wine a day, not to go to any plays except during the holidays following Easter, Whitsunday, Michaelmas, and Christmas. He would spend no money upon books and pictures, and none upon household furnishings and clothes, unless the need was great.

He copied out his new household vows, read them through, and signed his name. Now all he had to do was to get Elizabeth to agree to them.

The best time to deal with Elizabeth in matters of domestic strategy was early in the morning, while they lay side by side in bed. This was the hour of confidence and affection. When he went to bed on New Year's eve, he took his written vows with him and put them on the table beside the bed, where they would be at hand when the right moment came.

The next morning after a luxurious celebration of their conjugal happiness, Samuel told Elizabeth of his resolution for a new life. With his left arm under her head and his hand upon her breast, he talked about the strange pleasure he had had in working on his paper for the Duke. It was not, he said, that he expected this little treatise in itself to accomplish much. As a matter of fact, he knew very well what would become of it. It would be buried under a dozen other reports and papers doomed to oblivion in the dusty offices of Whitehall; but the Duke of York, at least, would know that he had written it. Up to now he had found the duties of the Clerk of the Acts a deadly dull routine of signing papers he did not understand, listening to the bickering and taking the slights of the other officers who had only one thing in common—a mutual dislike and distrust of each other. He had kept quiet and performed his routine duties perfunctorily because he did not want to enter into a fruitless engagement with the snapping Batten or the devious Penn. But now, he said, he knew what he wanted and had a very good idea of how to get it.

He would devote his full attention to keeping fresh in the Duke's memory the zeal of the Clerk of the Acts, he said thoughtfully. It would mean hard work, studying his office, learning his trade. It would also mean, he said, turning his head toward Elizabeth, less pleasure for her for a while. He would not be able to take her out to plays and dinners very often, nor would she have as much of his company—or her neighbors'—as she used to.

Elizabeth started to speak, but Samuel hurried on. There would be a compensation, he explained. In his first year with the Navy, he had accumulated nearly £500, which might seem like a lot of money, compared to what they used to have; but it was really nothing to what they would need if they were to live the kind of life he wanted—a coach of their own, a country estate, perhaps a knighthood.

Elizabeth sat up straight in bed.

For that, Samuel said, talking rapidly, they would need an estate of £2,000, and the only way to come by so great a fortune, while they were still young enough to enjoy it, was for him to devote his total energies and time to making a name for himself in the Navy Office.

He took Elizabeth by the hand. He knew his own weakness, he said, his difficulty in keeping his resolves, resisting the temptations of the playhouse and the taverns and the bookstalls and the linen shops. Between them they had spent £250 last year, a great deal more than they should have spent. In order that he might not again squander so much and that he might not relax until they had reached the goal of £2,000, he had written an oath, which would bind him to obey his vows against time-wasting, spendthrift pleasures. He reached out his hand to the table beside the bed and held up the paper for Elizabeth to see. She took it from him and read it aloud, the strictures against wine and plays and books and clothes. Only at the stipulation about clothes did her face fall, but Samuel told her to notice that there was a loophole about "necessity."

"Very well," she said, "I will sign it, too. A knighthood I won't even think of, but a coach would be heaven."

Later in the morning Samuel went up into Fenchurch Street and persuaded a pewterer to let him have a poor box, to be delivered to him on Sunday but not to be bought until Monday. He took it home with him and put it in his study. He made Elizabeth come up with him and look at it. Their oaths would be no good, he said, unless they put a half-crown in the box upon any infraction of their vows. Elizabeth said that she would wager a sixpence that he would visit the box before she did.

At the Navy Office Samuel had carpenters build a partition behind which he could work in privacy. What he had to do required freedom from the inquiring gaze of the office, which was no less than to learn his business from the ground up.

He began with the rights of his office, the traditional privileges of the Clerk of the Acts. He spent his afternoons tucked away in his cubicle reading the official *Orders and Instructions for the Principal Officers and Commanders of His Majesty's Navy*. He wrote to Mr. Barlow and had him recount at length all the functions that he had performed in the office during his tenure under King Charles I. He went back at night and with only the occasional company of Griffin, the doorkeeper, he made orderly notes in shorthand cipher in a bound volume which he set up for his own instruction.

On pleasant afternoons when his head was logy from trying to understand the mysteries of naval accounting, he went down the river to the yards at Deptford and Woolwich, rambling through the storerooms, asking questions about tar and hemp and masts. He went aboard the ships tied up at the docks and had an officer take him on a conducted tour of the vessel, from poop to forecastle, and asked him to name all the bulkheads, machines, and riggings, which he carefully wrote down in his notebook. In the midnight privacy of his study, he took out the ship models in his closet and began to study in earnest the anatomy of an English man-of-war.

On the whole Elizabeth bore up well under the new regimen. She complained only a little that Samuel was disturbing the normal sleep of the household with his early rising and late retiring, but she fretted considerably that Samuel's order to maintain a cool distance with their neighbors was depriving her of all companionship. Elizabeth was not the only one to complain. Sir William Penn came to Samuel one afternoon in the gardens and asked if there were any reason for the new stiffness that seemed to exist between their two houses. Had there been any injury that the

Penns were not aware of? Samuel told him that there was no injury; he was busy doing his service for the King and there was little time for frivolity. Sir William looked at him, perplexed, and then walked back to his own part of the garden.

Samuel held firm to his edict against socializing, with new neighbors as well as with old. The new neighbor was Sir John Minnes, who had come to replace Sir Robert Slingsby as Comptroller. In late October of the year before, Sir Robert had gone to bed of a high fever, aching in every part of his body. Samuel had gone over to the Comptroller's house in Lime Street every day to look in on his colleague, to read Latin verses to him, and to console him; but in a week Sir Robert was dead. Three days after Slingsby was committed to the earth, Sir John Minnes came to Seething Lane to take over the duties of the Comptroller.

Sir John was not only an experienced sea captain, he was also Vice Admiral of the Narrow Seas. As junior to Lord Sandwich, he contested for authority with, rather than served under, his lordship. The Earl wanted his own captains in command of the ships of the fleet, but Minnes maneuvered to gain favor at Whitehall by whispering to the Duke of York that the fleet would soon belong to the Earl of Sandwich instead of the King if the selection of captains was not checked.

Minnes, then, was a natural enemy of all the servants of Lord Sandwich, despite the new Comptroller's undoubted charm, his knowledge of medicine and chemistry, his love of old ballads and the poetry of Geoffrey Chaucer, and his fine parlor talents as a mimic and a satirist. Samuel warned Elizabeth to keep the same reserve with his family as she did with the Battens and the Penns.

At the office Samuel's new industry began to be noticed. Sir George made several sly references to the diligence of the Clerk of the Acts. Penn observed amiably that the office need not fear for thieves, for Mr. Pepys was always to be found these days in his cubbyhole guarding the office possessions. Samuel smiled at these pleasantries. Only Sir William Batten managed to get under his skin. When a piece of unfinished business would come up and Samuel, out of zeal to amend his ignorance, would ask a question about it, Sir William would snap at him that the matter had been thoroughly discussed at the previous meeting, thus implying that

Mr. Pepys had not been present. But Samuel pretended not to notice the thrust. It was better to accept the snub than to reveal his ignorance.

While he waited, he began a new project. It was a very simple project at first. He bought a large ledger and carefully ruled off the pages. Then he divided the whole book into twenty-six parts, one part for each letter of the alphabet. He told Mr. Hayter to collect from the other clerks all the contracts in the office and sort them out, the contracts for tar, for hemp, for masts, for deals, nails, tools, flag bunting, sail silk, for every supply to the fleet. Samuel then sat down to make an abstract of every contract: the name of the contractor, the material contracted, the amount, the price, the quality, the date ordered, and the date delivered. Hayter read off the facts and Samuel entered the information in its proper place in his ledger. The two men worked together on the project, quietly and steadily, for over a month, in the afternoons, at nights, on Saturdays and Sundays, whenever they could spare time from the routine of regular business.

Samuel even touched up the appearance of the valuable book by copying the headings in red ink and illuminating the first capital letters on each page.

Samuel knew that his project was full of danger. Sir William Batten had always taken it for granted that office contracts were his private domain; but in his recent study of the *Orders and Instructions,* Samuel had learned that contracts were the *mutual* responsibility of all the Principal Officers, including the Clerk of the Acts. Since he wrote out the forms and signed his name to them, Samuel had a perfect right to know the details of every one. Samuel could well understand why Sir William kept such a jealous hold on his privileges; there were dozens of ways to make a fortune that way. Such wealthy merchants as Sir Richard Ford and Mr. Wood, who profited fabulously from their Navy contracts for hemp and masts, were naturally very grateful to any officer who kept them well supplied with orders. Batten was undoubtedly getting rich by seeing to it that the proper contractors received what they considered their share of the Navy's business; and, as far as Samuel could learn from studying the contracts, there was no assurance that the King was getting his money's worth. The tedium of making the abstracts was proving to be very instructive.

It did not take Sir William Batten long to smell out the mouse at work in his cupboard. At a Board meeting one morning in late April, he complained that he had the day before wanted to put his hand on a recent contract, but his clerk had not been able to locate it. Only after a long and tiresome search had the clerk found the contract in Mr. Pepys's office. The Surveyor wanted to know what Mr. Pepys was doing with all the contracts confined to his office.

Samuel knew that some such attack was bound to come and he had prepared himself for it. He answered Sir William mildly that he was doing his duty as Clerk of the Acts. He was putting all contracts in such a condition that anybody who desired could refer to them easily. He stressed the word *anybody* ever so slightly. He went on to say that Sir William could now at a moment's notice find any contract that had become official by simply letting Mr. Hayter know what he wanted. Samuel smiled at the Surveyor and said that he hoped that was satisfactory.

By the middle of May the book of contracts was about complete. The Surveyor had kept up a steady pressure, sending his clerk every day or two to Samuel to ask for this contract or that. Samuel patiently told the clerk to speak to Mr. Hayter and he would find it for him in two minutes.

By Whitsunday the book was complete. It would be a simple matter now to keep it up to date. In the long process of compiling it, Samuel had learned several things to his advantage: that the same contractors' names appeared with suspicious regularity; that other contractors' names (Sir William Warren, for example) appeared very seldom; that there was no discernible pattern of price. But the chief thing that he learned was that he was too ignorant to assemble exact evidence that Batten was cheating the King. He did not know the difference between Holland hemp and Riga, the difference between Dram, Swinsound, and Christiana. He did not know how to measure timber, to judge the quality of hemp, or to evaluate the proper price of tar. He knew almost nothing of what he now needed desperately to know. The first thing he needed to do after the Whitsun holiday was to begin to educate himself in the affairs of the marketplace. For that, Cambridge had been of little service to him.

Two days after Whitsuntide Lord Sandwich arrived in London from Portugal. King Charles had overruled the Protestant objections of his Council, and chosen for his legal wife Princess Catherine of the Portuguese royal house of Braganza. The fact that she brought a dowry of three million *livres,* not to mention the ports of Tangier and Bombay, did much to make up the King's mind on the matter. The Earl of Sandwich was given the signal honor of escorting the Queen to England.

Samuel and Elizabeth walked to the Wardrobe to greet him and wish him joy of his return. The Earl received his cousins warmly, kissing Elizabeth and putting his arm about Samuel's shoulders. He led Samuel into his private chamber and plied him with questions about the Navy, the Court, Hinchingbrooke, Seething Lane, Sir John Minnes. Samuel reported his news in detail and then began to ask about his lordship's voyage. The Earl was full of good humor and ready to talk. The King and Queen would stay at Portsmouth a few days and then proceed to Hampton Court to spend their honeymoon. The Queen was a very agreeable though retiring sort of lady and something of a pinchpenny, a characteristic resulting probably from her rearing in a convent and a poverty-stricken court. She had given no reward to any of the captains and officers of the fleet, and she had bestowed upon the Earl only a bag of gold worth a modest £1,400 sterling. Since the voyage had cost his lordship £7,000 out of his own pocket and the King was a notoriously poor repayer, he was going to take his time in turning over to the King the £6,000 *crusados* he held in his possession from the Queen's dowry. As a matter of fact, he wanted Samuel to store the chests of coins in his cellar until they could be transferred to Mr. Backwell's goldsmith shop.

Samuel's first reaction was overflowing joy at the Earl's great trust in him and at the tingling thought of having so much money in his physical possession, but then the thought of whose money it was struck him, and what could happen to it while it was in his care. He thought of Captain Holmes who had suffered for having the King's business suddenly thrust upon him. He felt queasy in the stomach, but he told his lordship that he would be ready for the treasure when it came.

He went promptly to the ironmonger's and bought new locks for the house. He instructed the servants to keep to the house, as if a quarantine were upon it, until he told them they were free again, but he told them nothing of the reason for the great and sudden security. When the admiral's barge landed at Tower Wharf three days later with the three great chests, Samuel showed the seamen where to put them, in the darkest corner of the cellar, and then he locked the door and gave the key to Mr. Shepley, demanding that the steward give him a signed receipt that he had done so. That night he made the maids get up and light candles in the dining room to scare away any thieves who might have seen the big chests being carried to his house. There would not be an easy moment for him while the money lay in his cellar.

It was several days before Mr. Backwell's clerks came and carried away the chests, one at a time. Samuel had stayed close to the house to watch the streets to see that no suspicious loiterers were hanging about. When the last chest was gone and the clerks had given Samuel their receipt for them, he sighed deeply and felt a new comfort that he himself had only a few pounds buried in the soft earth in the cellar, which were all his and accountable to no one. He was glad that all he had to concern him now was his siege upon the stubborn walls of the Navy Office.

V

My heart rejoices to see
Mr. Coventry

SAMUEL HAD JUST finished his dinner one fine day in early May when Will Hewer announced to him that Sir George Carteret was at the garden door asking a word with Mr. Pepys. Samuel hurried out to the garden. It would be no small business that brought the Treasurer knocking at his humble gate.

Sir George was making a path up and down the grass beside Samuel's door. He was fuming and cursing softly under his breath. Samuel squared his shoulders and braced himself for the onset.

"Someone has angered you, Sir George," he offered, cautiously.

Carteret pulled up like a thwarted bull. Pointing his hand in the direction of Penn's house, he burst out in a bellowing voice, "*Guarda mi spada;* for, by God, I may chance to keep that whoreson dog in Ireland, when he is once there!"

Penn was a meddling fool, Sir George said. He had been slipping up to Whitehall, ingratiating himself with the Lord Admiral by telling all kinds of lies about the inefficiency and the corruption of the Navy Office, making recommendations to the Duke for revising the *Orders and Instructions*.

"And now," Sir George announced, getting up again from the bench and returning to his angry task of wearing a path in Mr. Pepys's lawn, "and now, the Duke of York is sending his secretary, Mr. Coventry, down to the office as an extra Commissioner, to spy upon us and to report to the Admiralty every word we say. Penn should be hanged for an impudent cur!"

Samuel moved over to the shade of a tree and stood picking at a loose thread on his sleeve. Uneasy and uncertain what to say to the startling news of Mr. Coventry's coming, he waited for Sir George to finish his tirade.

It would be a pleasure to join the Treasurer in his denunciation of Penn, who, Samuel was convinced, was an unpredictable schemer at best, affable and genial on the surface but shrewd and sharp in the dark corner. But, unfortunately, Penn was right.

In his recent zeal to fix his own name in the Duke of York's memory, Samuel had learned many things about the Navy Office that he had not known before, or cared about before. There *was* inefficiency in the office, gross carelessness, slovenliness of administration. And corruption, too, he had no doubt, although there was a very fine line between actual corruption and simply alert attention to reaping the perquisites of office. Samuel had no quarrel with the perquisites, except to see that he got his share. Corruption was only accepting perquisites without insisting that the King get *his* money's worth in goods or services.

But inefficiency was something else. Inefficiency was criminal. Among the many qualities that ruled or fought for the rule of this twenty-nine-year-old London clerk was a rage for order. A strong Puritan bias contested with a libertine sensuality; a strict conscience waged eternal war with a genius for rationalization; gross materialism contended with an almost aesthetic idealism. But to one quality in him there was no opposing enemy. In Chaos, Samuel Pepys, like the angelic Satan, would have fought for Order.

As Samuel stood in the shade of the tree and twisted the errant thread into a knot, his mind played on the dangers—and the possible advantages—of having the constant company of the Duke's secretary in the office. Coventry was a serious man; there was no nonsense in him. His enemies hated him, but his friends swore by him. In his few contacts with him, Samuel had always found the Secretary a polite, fair, and scrupulous official. One could do worse than have Mr. Coventry for a friend, Samuel thought. The *Orders and Instructions* were badly in need of revision, to clarify the areas of responsibility and if for nothing else, to establish once and for all the duties—and privileges—of the Clerk of the Acts.

It was bad, Samuel mused, that it was Penn who had instigated the invasion by the Admiralty; but he could not be sorry that something was going to be done to instill some regulation into the office.

Sir George finally wore out his anger—and the grass—concluding almost with a shout that it was very like the work of a Machiavel to cast suspicion upon the whole office and then himself run off to Ireland for the summer on the excuse that he needed to inspect his Irish estates.

Samuel answered the angry Treasurer placatingly, assuring him that there was no need for the two of *them* to fear the coming of Mr. Coventry. It was best to wait and see what became of the Whitehall invasion, but in any event Sir George could count on the loyalty of Mr. Pepys. Carteret thanked him and stalked back into the office, mopping his face with a silk handkerchief.

Samuel went into his house and spent the rest of the day tidying up his papers in the closet. After supper he took down the pumice stone he had recently bought to save the expense of the barber's weekly visit. Standing at the mirror, he ran the cool, spongy stone over his cheeks and lips, wincing a little at the sting of the abrasive but soothed and refreshed by the clean tingle of his cheeks after the whiskers were gone. He looked at his head in the glass, a matted mass of powder-caked hair. During the humid weather of May, he had had to resort to drying his hair with powder, and it had left his head matted and itching. He asked Jane to bring his comb and do what she could with his tangled hair.

As he sat in the kitchen chair, relaxing under the expert ministrations of Jane's firm hands, he let his mind wander over his condition. His health was good, except for an excess of wind that troubled him occasionally. His abstinence from wine and plays was having its good effect on his digestion and his purse. He was not much farther along on his way to the fortune of £2,000, but for the first time he was enjoying his work at the Navy Office.

The only questionable cloud on his horizon was Mr. Coventry. The Earl of Sandwich had no love for the Duke of York's secretary. His lordship had told Samuel many times that Coventry frequently stood as a barrier between him and complete accord with the Lord High Admiral. Coventry represented those courtiers who nursed their suspicions of all officers who had served under Cromwell. There was one faction at Court that either feared or held in contempt any man who had acknowledged the Protector by serving him; and another group felt that it was a man's duty to serve his country whoever ruled. The Lord Chancellor and Prince Rupert, of the Privy Council, represented the first, "loyal," group. Albermarle and Sandwich, of course, represented the latter. The King and the Heir Presumptive, the Duke of York, had so far been neutral—or tactful; but the Duke's influential secretary was a question mark. Sandwich suspected him of "loyalty."

To curry favor with a man his patron doubted was awkward, possibly dangerous for Samuel. But Samuel knew he had to follow his own judgment. It was not easy to be a protégé—even to a patron so easy as Edward Montagu. The Earl had always treated Samuel generously, acting more as a kindly uncle than a demanding master; and Samuel had always considered himself a devoted kinsman and not an obligated "creature." Mr. Coventry's coming would be awkward for his relationship with Lord Sandwich, but Samuel counted heavily on his instinct for tact to prevent any overt trouble.

When Jane had finished combing his head and his hair again fell down to his shoulders in soft curls, she brought a pan of warm water, infused with herbs, spicy and aromatic. Kneeling down, she removed Samuel's shoes and stockings and put his feet into the warm bath, laving them gently. Samuel closed his eyes and gave himself up to the sensuous luxury of his Saturday night ablutions. He would be ready for Mr. Coventry when he came.

Mr. Coventry came to the Navy Office on June 3, bearing his patent as extra Commissioner. The doorkeeper interrupted the Board meeting at midmorning to announce that one representing himself as Mr. William Coventry requested entrance. Sir George, the two Sir Williams, Mr. Pepys, and all the clerks rose from their chairs and turned toward the door. No one had intended any special ceremony for Mr. Coventry. He was, after all, just another commissioner, with no more constituted authority than any of them; but none of them could resist the impressive fact that he was also, and primarily, Secretary to the Lord High Admiral. Sir George stood stiff and alert at his place by the table, but both Batten and Penn moved quickly to the door to welcome the Whitehall officer. Samuel stayed where he was, keeping his eye closely on the tense Treasurer. He had a narrow line to walk between the hostile camps of Carteret and Sandwich versus Coventry and Penn, and he hoped that Sir George would not make it necessary for him to choose sides at once.

Mr. Coventry entered the room quietly, giving his hand to Penn and to Batten. He bowed respectfully to Sir George, tossed a cordial "Good morning" to Mr. Pepys, and then took his seat at the table.

Coventry was impressive without any apparent effort. He was tall, composed, and richly, if soberly, dressed. His mouth seemed to be fixed in a thin-lipped smile, as if he suspected the worst of the world but could stand it. His eyebrows seemed permanently raised in an expression of knowing disdain, contemptuous and amused. Samuel felt both awe and fascination as he watched the Secretary survey the room coolly and beg the gentlemen to continue with their business. He would try to catch up as he could, he said.

The Board was in the midst of a discussion of a contract for tar. As soon as Batten had finished his discourse on the advisability of accepting the contract as offered by the merchant and the Board had voted its approval, Mr. Coventry abstaining, Samuel began to write out the heads of the agreement on the office forms. Sir William Penn immediately interrupted him.

"Writing the heads of a contract," he said, "is the business of the Comptroller, not the Clerk of the Acts."

Samuel stopped with his pen in the air. "Sir John Minnes is not here," he said.

"The contract can wait for his attention," Sir William replied casually.

Samuel carefully put his pen down on the table. *It is now or never,* he thought. Penn, like a base scoundrel, is taking the opportunity of Mr. Coventry's first appearance to show his authority and his concern for the Duke's revised *Orders and Instructions.*

But even if Penn had had a hand in formulating the new *Orders,* Samuel was sure that no one had studied them more carefully than he had. He asked Mr. Hayter to bring his copy of the document. While Hayter went scurrying to the little office, Samuel asked Sir George Carteret if he had, during his tenure as Comptroller under King Charles I, ever performed the duty of drawing the heads of a contract or had ever claimed the duty. Sir George said that as far as he could remember he had not. Samuel said that that information agreed with the statement of Mr. Barlow, who had been Clerk of the Acts at the same time. He had Mr. Barlow's statement in writing and would be glad to produce it.

By that time Hayter was back with Samuel's closely marked copy of the Duke's new *Orders and Instructions.* With the Board's permission, Samuel said, he would like to read the pertinent parts of the *Orders.* Penn rubbed his forehead vigorously and said that the point did not matter that much. If the performance gave him pleasure, let Mr. Pepys draw the heads. Batten raised his hand as if to check Penn's indulgent concession, but Samuel hurried on.

"Sir William has raised the issue," he said, "and it should be settled, once and for all. There will never be clear order in the office if the simplest duty is challenged and time wasted in foolish debate. I have a documented argument and I am ready to present it."

Sir George told him to proceed with the reading of his authority.

Samuel read to them, for half an hour, never once raising his eyes or his voice, until he had come to the end. When he was quite finished, Sir George told him to continue to draw the heads of the contract. Penn had closed his eyes as if he were asleep; Batten had shredded his quill into thin, even strips; and Mr. Coventry had listened attentively, without saying a word.

When Samuel got home after the meeting, he told Elizabeth that they would have to postpone their trip to Hampton Court to see the new Queen. Now that Mr. Coventry had come to the office, he was going to have to be more careful about making little pleasure trips on the office travel expense. He had an idea that the eagle eyes of Mr. Coventry might fall sharply on the petty accounts, and he did not want his name to appear for any charge that he could not defend.

Then he went up to his study to consider the morning's engagement. He felt that he had come off rather well. It had been luck that Penn had made exactly the right move for him, but it had not been luck that he had made his preparations for that very move. That was the one advantage he had over his more experienced colleagues: they depended on being able to meet an emergency as it arose, but he, without their reservoir of experience to draw upon, had to foresee the area of battle and prepare himself accordingly. He would not always be able to depend, however, upon the luck of Penn's stumbling cooperation. He would have to force the fighting into a field where he knew he had a chance of victory.

The best battlefield at the moment was hemp. Mr. Hughes, master of the ropeyard at Woolwich, had written a letter to the Board complaining that Sir Richard Ford's Holland hemp was not standing up to tests. He begged that the Board send the Surveyor or another officer down to observe a run of tests. As Clerk of the Acts, Samuel had been instructed to inform Mr. Hughes that Sir William Batten would come down to investigate. As Samuel Pepys, he felt quite sure that Sir William would go to Woolwich primarily to see to it that a yard officer did not interfere with his own rewarding arrangements with Ford. Samuel would go along and see that Mr. Hughes was allowed to present his case.

The next morning Samuel waited until he saw Batten emerge from his house; then he went out into the garden and intercepted him. Would Sir William care for some company on his trip down the river? He had never seen yarn tested and he was curious to see how it was done. Batten told him to come along. It was a dull show. Hughes was a chronic complainer, but they would have to go through the motions of hearing him. At least the day was fine and they could enjoy the trip down the river.

They boarded a Navy barge at Tower Wharf and pushed out into the stream for the hour's ride down the curving river, past Deptford and Greenwich, up and around the long curve of Blackwall Reach and then into the straight stretch of water that carried them to His Majesty's Docks at Woolwich. A Navy barge was a much more comfortable vessel than an ordinary river wherry—soft-cushioned seats, a canopy overhead to protect the passengers from the sun and the rain, four well-trained crewmen to man the oars and help the civilian officers step on and off the vessel. Samuel always enjoyed a trip on a Navy barge and the ceremonious respect of the seamen tipping their hats to him; but he enjoyed even more the welcome he always received, as a Principal Officer, from the yardmasters who came hat in hand to greet him as he arrived at the dock. He never felt the importance of his position anywhere as much as he felt it at the river yards.

They found Mr. Hughes waiting for them in the ropeyard, his testing forms set up and his piles of hemp carefully separated and marked.

"This pile," Hughes said, "is Holland, which has been supplied by Sir Richard Ford. It is a five-thread yarn. This pile is a four-thread Riga, a much less expensive stuff."

He then put a strand of the Holland and a strand of the Riga side by side in the forms and told the workman to begin the stress. The leather-aproned workman turned the wheel of the windlass slowly and evenly. After three full turns, the Holland popped in two. The Riga stood the strain for two more full turns.

Batten told Hughes to try it again and this time he would select the samples. Again the Holland popped after three turns of the wheel and the Riga stood up to five turns.

Mr. Hughes said, "Let's try it again. Mr. Pepys, you select this time."

Samuel selected a strand at random from each pile, and this time the Holland lasted three and a half turns and the Riga still held to five. Batten wandered on away across the yard, looking at the bales of hemp, kicking at the heavy coils of rope stacked as high as his head.

Hughes touched Samuel on the elbow and said, "Wait a bit. That is not all." He picked up a rope lying on the ground and stretched it across his knee. Pulling his knife from a sheath in his belt, he began to work the blade into the strands of the rope. "This is some of Sir Richard's hemp line," he said, "and if you will notice, the inside threads are old stuff, dry and rotten, covered over with tar, and only the outside made of new hemp. Sir, this line wouldn't last an hour in a stiff gale."

Samuel hustled Mr. Hughes into the ropeyard office. He sat down at the yardmaster's table and quizzed him closely, asking him a hundred questions about the making of rope, the purchasing of hemp, the tests they had just made. He wrote down the answers as fast as the hempmaster talked. When Samuel had finally finished his inquisition, he had filled ten sheets of paper, closely packed with the minute symbols of his cipher. He thanked Mr. Hughes, assured him that his complaints would not be ignored by the Board, and went out to find his colleague for the trip back to London.

On the way home, he chatted pleasantly with Sir William about the possibility of their having an extra story built onto their houses during the good weather of the summer. He did not mention rope, or Hughes, or Woolwich once during the ride.

Mr. Coventry was back at the Navy Office for the Thursday afternoon meeting. He continued to sit silently and attentively. The old members went on with their business as if he were not there, but Samuel kept him in view, glancing at him from time to time to see how he was reacting to the discussion.

Just as the meeting was about to break up, Mr. Batten said casually that he was quite satisfied with Sir Richard's contract and that he would pass it if his colleagues were agreeable. Mr. Coventry held up his pen and asked how the tests at Woolwich had turned out. In the middle of Sir William's shrug of dismissal, Samuel spoke up. He had written a report on the tests, he said. Mr. Coventry looked at him sharply.

"And what does your report show, Mr. Pepys?" he asked.

"I will be glad to read it if the Board is interested," Samuel said.

"Well, I for one would like to hear it," said Mr. Coventry.

"Then I will read it," said Samuel.

While Sir William Penn relaxed into his favorite listening position, eyes closed, arms across his stomach, and Batten devoted his full attention to the book that lay open before him on the table, Samuel read his account of the hemp tests at Woolwich: four full pages of the most objective review, clearly and concisely abstracted. Samuel had cautiously withheld any mention of Batten's name or of Ford's name. The report dealt only with two batches of hemp, one superior and less expensive, the other costly and inferior.

When Samuel had finished reading and had placed the pages on the table, carefully lining up the edges of the sheets, Mr. Coventry said, "I think it would be in the King's interest to withhold action on the contract for hemp until further investigation is made."

From the stillness of Penn's apparent slumber came the sound of startling words. "I think so, too," said Sir William, without opening his eyes.

Samuel looked hard to see if his ears had deceived him, but the unpredictable Penn had clearly spoken; he had taken sides, Samuel's side. Sir George quickly added his assent to the tabling action. Batten continued to read his book as if he had not heard one word of the discussion; but on his way out of the room a few minutes later, after all the others had left, he stopped by Samuel's chair to say, mildly and casually, "Sir Richard is a good friend and a dangerous enemy."

Samuel said nothing.

The next morning Samuel was in his little office with Hayter, studying the hemp contracts for the past two years, when Griffin came in and announced that Mr. Coventry desired his company. The new Commissioner was in a Navy barge at Tower Wharf, ready to go down the river to Woolwich and he would be pleased to have Mr. Pepys's company. Samuel took time only to get a notebook and to give Hayter a few instructions. He rushed out of the Navy gardens by the back passageway, hurried across Tower Hill, and in ten minutes he stepped onto the barge, where Mr. Coventry sat under the canopy reading Cicero's *Orations*.

On the way down the river the two men talked about the great Roman advocate. At Oxford, Coventry said, he had been made to memorize at least a dozen of the famous orations and to deliver them in the Hall of the College before the dons. It was the most valuable experience he had had at the University. The ability to speak before men, reasonably and with eloquence, had been the greatest of his claims to a career at Whitehall. Most of the members of Parliament spoke like dolts, he said. It was no trick at all for any man who had spent some hours with Cicero to speak before the House two or three times a year and get a reputation as a great orator.

Samuel said that he had a different experience with Cicero at Cambridge. His master had made him read the orations and write papers on the rhetorical devices. It had seemed a laborious task at the time and he had come away from the University with no love for the Roman pleader. Recently, however, he had taken down the Second Oration against Catiline and had been amazed to find how good a writer Cicero was. He was sorry that he had not had the opportunity to study him as a model of spoken eloquence, for nothing frightened him more than to have to speak before men.

Mr. Coventry said that he had not noticed any fear in him the day before when he spoke out against Batten at the Board meeting.

"That," said Samuel, "was in earnest. I had no time to think of fear; and besides I had written it all out beforehand."

"Neither had Cicero time for fear," said Mr. Coventry. "He was in earnest about Catiline."

By this time the barge had reached the Woolwich dock, and the two servants of the King set out to tour the yard. They visited the storehouses, where they noticed that many perishable stores were lying about in the greatest confusion in the open air for want of space in the big sheds. They summoned the keepers and rated them soundly for their inefficient use of the space available and made a note to order new sheds built. They appeared suddenly before the clerks of the yard and Samuel spent an hour pointing out the slovenly manner of their keeping the records. They went to the ropeyard and had Mr. Hughes again run the test on the Holland and the Riga hemp. By the time they returned to the barge, Samuel's notebook was full of shorthand comments on the mismanagement at Woolwich. It was a surprise to Samuel that they had missed their dinner.

Throughout the rest of June Samuel and Mr. Coventry were up and down the Thames like scourges of the Lord. Coventry would send word to Samuel that he was awaiting him at Tower Wharf, and Samuel would throw his boat cloak around his shoulders, leave parting instructions with Hayter, and hurry across

Tower Hill to join his fellow reformer. They harried any laggard they encountered at Deptford or any self-serving workman they met at Woolwich until the yardmen began to wonder what in the world had happened at Seething Lane. They interviewed laborers as well as masters, quizzing them closely on their duties, listening to them attentively as they complained of faulty material, of arrogant overseers, and stupid decisions. They became known in the most remote corners of the yards as ubiquitous and relentless ferrets, but they also became known as quick judges of yard disputes and sympathetic listeners to any charges of local injustice. Samuel was pleased one day to hear that Mr. Pepys was considered in the yards as the best friend the poor laborers had at the Navy Office.

When Mr. Coventry in mid-July had to foresake his vigil in the Navy Yards to accompany the Duke of York on his voyage to France to bring the Queen Mother, Henrietta Maria, to England, Samuel turned his attention to another area of activity. He went into Thames Street and made the acquaintance of the tar merchants, discussed with them the different qualities of tar, the source of supply, the method of judging quality. He went regularly to the Royal Exchange in Cornhill and spent hours chatting with the great merchants, learning how they reckoned the costs of transportation, how they determined the price of goods. He sought out Sir William Warren, the great timber merchant, Sir Richard Ford's chief rival, and asked him to let him visit his deal ships and timber yards. Warren was happy to oblige the Clerk of the Acts of the Navy Board. He took Samuel aboard several of his ships anchored down the river and showed him the varieties of fir and pine boards stacked in the holds and on the decks. He took him to his yards and showed him the acres of neatly stacked lumber. He took him home to dinner and spent the afternoon telling him a number of the mysteries of the timbering profession: how a heavy snow in Norway would help to reduce the cost of deals the following year. The depth and firmness of the snow in the valleys, he explained, made it easier for the workers to drag the huge fir logs to the mills and the docks. Samuel made a note of the fact. He also made a note that Sir William Warren would be a good man for the Navy Office to take notice of, good for the Navy and, perhaps, good for Samuel.

He next went to the *Royal James,* docked at Woolwich, and located his old friend Cooper, who had been mate on the *Charles* when Samuel went to sea with his lordship. Cooper had not advanced in the service although Samuel knew him to be a good officer. Something perhaps could be done for him, and there was something that Cooper could do in return. Whatever Samuel had learned at Cambridge, he had not learned the practical uses of arithmetic. If he was to understand what the tar merchants in Thames Street were talking about, or the deal workers in Sir William Warren's yards, he had to have a surer grasp of the multiplication table and the shorter methods of division. He asked Mr. Cooper if he would be willing to come to Seething Lane to teach him arithmetic. Cooper said that he was at his service.

Through the hot days of July Samuel got up early and admitted Cooper into the house to give him his lessons. Late in the evening, after he had had his supper, he met with him again, going over and over the multiplication table or examining with him the model ship he kept in his study. Sometimes Samuel felt that this was the hardest part of the whole business, trying to master in a few weeks the intricate multiplication system.

But gradually he began to get the hang of it. He could sit down and write out the whole table from memory. He was so pleased that he decided to teach Elizabeth. She, poor wretch, had been a model of patience during the busy summer, and she deserved some of his attention. She also needed some instruction in handling her kitchen accounts. At his last reckoning, Samuel had found that the kitchen, including candles and wine, was costing 30 shillings a week; but he had learned it only after a laborious untangling of Elizabeth's muddled records. Every night after supper, therefore, on the evenings that Mr. Cooper did not come to teach him, Samuel sat down with Elizabeth in the parlor and tried to teach her to add and subtract with accuracy and to learn the multiplication table. For the first week, Elizabeth seemed to enjoy the nightly sessions with her husband; but as the lessons continued, night after night, she would sometimes think of something to tell him that had happened during the afternoon. Samuel once in his irritation threw a book at her. He thanked God that his aim had been bad.

Late in the month Elizabeth was glad to escape the increasingly stormy lessons—as well as the hot August weather—by going north to spend the month with Pall and the old people at Brampton.

With Coventry and Elizabeth both out of town, Samuel was tempted to relax his arduous attention to duty. He went up to Westminster once to see if he could find Betty Lane, the girl in the linen stall in Westminster Hall, but he missed her. One night when Jane was combing his hair, he let his head press back against her breast, and he was about to put his arm around her waist, when at the crucial moment he thought of the trouble that would come upon him if Jane should prove honest. So he desisted and preserved his celibacy, but in his dreams he toyed with the Countess of Castlemaine and awoke somewhat aghast, though pleased, that he had been so familiar with the King's mistress.

At home his life was a chaos. The workmen had come and ripped the roof off his house in preparation of adding an extra story. He and the servants worked fast to remove all his goods down to the ground floor before they were ruined by the workmen and the weather. Leaving Jane in the house to protect his possessions, he and Will Hewer moved into Penn's empty house and lived a harried hand-to-mouth existence.

He not only studied at night with Mr. Cooper; he also visited Mr. Anthony Deane, the naval architect, and persuaded him to teach him to use a slide rule. He prevailed upon the workmen in Warren's deal yards to show him how to measure timber. He went into Cornhill and talked all day with Mr. Young about flags. The bunting contracts had looked as suspicious to him as the hemp contracts, and he wanted to know all there was to know about ship flags, ensigns, and signals.

Sometimes he picked up knowledge without seeking it. He attended at Deptford an auction of three old ship hulls to be sold for salvage. He watched, fascinated, as the auctioneer placed on the table before him a little candle, exactly one inch long, and announced to the salvage merchants that the bidding would begin as soon as the wick took the flame and would end as soon as the flame died. The bidding at first was hesitant, long pauses coming between cautious bids; but as the wick burned down toward the table, the bidding became spirited and just before the flame went out there was a great shouting of hurried calls. Samuel noticed that the man who won the ships had not made a single call until the last split second before the flame went out, and had thereby won the auction with one well-timed bid.

Samuel followed the lucky merchant out of the room when the bidding was over and asked him why he had withheld his bid so late and endangered his chance of winning the ships.

"It is a little secret, Mr. Pepys," the merchant told him. "But I will tell it to you if you will not divulge it to the other salvage merchants. Just before the flame of a candle dies, the smoke always makes a sudden dip. It never fails; so when I see the smoke suddenly go downward, then I call, quick and loud. It is a little thing to notice, but I have beat my competitors many a time by this trick my father taught me."

Samuel congratulated the merchant on his sharp wisdom, and he made a note for himself that it was often only the close attention to small details that won a man a ship on the auction block— or a fight with his colleagues.

So Samuel kept his eye on small details, the petty accounts his colleagues scorned; he worked hard while the others visited their estates or slept away the hot afternoons. And gradually, by the time Mr. Coventry returned from his voyage with the Duke, the rewards began to come in, little by little—and then came the great reward.

When the Admiralty list of captains showed that there was a vacancy of a master for the fourth-rate man-of-war, the *Reserve,* Samuel sent in to Coventry the name of his loyal tutor, Mr. Cooper; and Cooper got the place, his first command in a long career of junior posts in the fleet.

Lord Sandwich sent word that Samuel's name had been proposed as a Younger Brother of Trinity House, the ancient corporation that honored the most distinguished members of the naval community by electing them, as Elder or Younger Brothers, to serve the maritime tradition of Great Britain by building its lighthouses, caring for its needy veterans, and studying all ways to improve the greatness of England as a sea-loving nation. Trinity House was a coveted honor, and for Samuel Pepys it was a beacon light on his long voyage to fortune.

But the great reward for him that summer was not a place in an honored house, although a place on a royal commission brought it about. The Crown had decided to govern and fortify the recently acquired port of Tangier by commission. Tangier gave Britain a foothold in the Mediterranean, and the Privy Council voted to spend considerable money in building a mole to protect the harbor and to fortify the area against attack. The members of the Tangier Commission were selected with the greatest care, for the Crown was investing much of its limited funds in the project. The Commission was studded with names of the great at Whitehall: the Duke of York, Prince Rupert, the Duke of Albemarle, Lord Sandwich, Lord Southampton, Mr. Coventry, Sir George Carteret.

When Lord Sandwich told his cousin that he, plain Mr. Samuel Pepys, had been appointed to serve with these great men, Samuel was beside himself.

"How did they think of me, my lord?" he asked excitedly.

"I thought of you, Samuel, and nominated you; but it was Mr. Coventry who won you your place. His speech for you convinced them all."

"What did he say, my lord?" Samuel asked breathlessly.

"Why, he said that Mr. Pepys well deserved any place that called for diligence, integrity, and ability. He said, Samuel, that you were the 'life of the Navy Office.' "

VI

Now so deadly full of jealousy

COMMISSIONER COVENTRY's testimonial to the Privy Council about Mr. Pepys's value as a Crown servant was more a shrewd estimate of Samuel's promise than a judgment of his accomplishment, but it was a link in the chain of events that was to tie the two men together more firmly as time went on. The awkwardness that resulted from the mutual suspicion that existed between Lord Sandwich and the Duke's secretary was to give Samuel many bad moments, require him to step lightly in his coming and going between them, but he was always thereafter a staunch admirer of William Coventry, his lordship to the contrary notwithstanding.

Samuel's friendship with Coventry became very quickly known in the Navy Office and at Court. Batten and Penn both tried their hands at testing the strength of the bond and promptly had their knuckles rapped for their pains. Cartaret gave Samuel some quiet advice about the danger of allying himself so closely with a man who was a potential enemy of his patron, but Samuel gave him an evasive answer and continued to put his trust in his new friend.

The next time a new contract for masts was negotiated, Sir William Warren's bid was successful; and Samuel found forty gold pieces tucked away in the fingers of a pair of gloves that Warren sent him by a porter. When Samuel delivered a victualing contract to Mr. Dennis Gauden to supply bread and meat to the garrison at Tangier for a year, the victual contractor compensated him handsomely. Warren and Gauden were both reputable merchants, men of integrity and reputation. It was a genuine service to the King to enlist them in furnishing first-rate supplies, and it was only fair that the merchants should reward the official who had the acumen to make the good bargain. By the end of the year Samuel was worth £630, and the Crown knew that the place of the Clerk of the Acts was in good condition.

The house of the Clerk of the Acts was not in good condition, however. In fact, during this period of minor triumph in the Navy Office, Samuel suffered domestic storms of steadily increasing severity. Elizabeth had come back from her visit to Brampton in a foul humor. The quarreling with Samuel's family had been as vigorous and spirited as it had always been at Salisbury Court. Furthermore, she came home to a half-finished house and a staff of badly disorganized servants.

The major operation of adding a story to the Seething Lane residences had taken several months. During the confusion, with Elizabeth out of town and Samuel abroad with his arduous work most of the day, the servants had relaxed into easy anarchy. Will Wayneman had played truant all one day and had not returned to the house until after dark. When the boy did come back, with no very convincing tale of where he had been, Samuel took him to the cellar and thrashed him with a "salt eel," a rope-end soaked in water.

Will's sister Jane protested so strongly against the severity of the punishment that Samuel told her she might leave the place if she desired. He would not have her or anyone else interfering with his rule of the house. Jane accepted the challenge, packed all her things, and before she left the premises said that if Mr. Pepys wanted to rule the house, he had better do something about Mr. Hewer, who had taken advantage of his absence by molesting the maids.

Samuel scorned to honor the girl's impudence by even listening to the charge; but as soon as she was on her way, he called Master Hewer to his closet, quizzed him closely, and told him that he would hereafter have to live out of the house. Hewer protested that he had done nothing to the girls, only teased them and kissed them to see what they would do. Samuel told him that he knew very well what the playful clerk had *hoped* they would do, and Will had better take care in playing such games in the future. In any case, Hewer had to leave Seething Lane and find lodgings with a Mrs. Mercer in nearby Fenchurch Street.

As soon as the house was finally finished, Elizabeth's pique dissolved in the absorbing effort to furnish and decorate the new rooms on the top floor—draperies for Samuel's large study, a new bed and hangings for the new bedroom. She converted the little closet on the second floor that Samuel had used for his study into a dressing room for herself. Elizabeth had so much pleasure in going out to shop for furnishings and spending her days supervising the sewing woman and the laborers who came to install the new furniture and hang the draperies that she forgot her anger with Samuel's family entirely. She invited Samuel's brother Tom to come and eat dinner with them, and she kept him all the afternoon, urging him to find a wife. She suggested the names of several girls she knew in Westminster who would make good wives, she said, for a London tailor; and she exacted the promise of Samuel to investigate their families and of Tom to find an opportunity to inspect her candidates.

But Elizabeth's plans for Tom came to nothing. Samuel either disapproved of the families or Tom vetoed the girls. The young bachelor continued on his improvident way, and Elizabeth was left in her fine house with nothing to do.

By the beginning of the new year, Elizabeth's empty-handed boredom became crucial. She complained incessantly of Samuel's indefatigable industry at the office and she rejected his attempts to entertain her by teaching her to sing or to keep her kitchen records. Samuel took her to the playhouse a few times, and whenever he could he would leave her in Charing Cross at the Unthanks, to gossip while he attended to business at Whitehall; but these occasional excursions did not content her. She was still left all day, week in and week out, with nothing to do but think of her loneliness and nurse her irritation.

Finally she came to Samuel with a suggestion. She would like to have a companion. Many ladies in Westminster kept female companions, well-bred but portionless young women who were happy to come into a good family as servant-companions. They were superior to maids. They ate with the family, slept abovestairs, went abroad with their mistresses to the shops, the playhouses, to call upon acquaintances. A companion served the function that a youthful aunt or a dowerless younger sister might perform: principally to keep the mistress company and prevent her from dying of boredom in a world in which all the social arrangements were made by and for men.

"Where would we find one?" Samuel asked her.

"Balty says that he knows of a girl. . . ."

But as soon as Elizabeth mentioned her brother Balty's name, Samuel got up in a huff and left the room. He would have nothing to do with any plan that involved Balty, he shouted as he went through the door.

Elizabeth, however, was not to be so easily put off from her desire for a companion. She entered into a siege upon her husband, using all the devices that she had used upon him for years, sulking, nagging, waking him in the middle of the night to tell him about a girl Balty had recommended, withholding her Sunday-morning favors from him. She even wrote him a letter and sent it by Will Hewer to the office, but Samuel immediately brought it back to her unread and burned it in the fireplace before her eyes.

Samuel stoutly resisted her demand upon his purse and pride. One day in February, however, after he had taken Elizabeth to Charing Cross to visit with the Unthanks and buy herself a silk waistcoat, he went on to Whitehall to meet with the Tangier Commission and told Elizabeth to take a coach and come home by herself. Elizabeth bought her waistcoat, and hailed a coach to take her through the City to Seething Lane. When the coachman stopped in Cheapside to water his horse, a man came to the open coach to ask Elizabeth if this were the right way to get to the Tower. Elizabeth told him that it was if he would turn right at Gracechurch Street and go down to Thames Street and turn left. He would not miss the Tower. Just as she had finished her instruction, another man slipped up on the other side of the coach and snatched the package from her lap that contained her afternoon purchase. Both men immediately ran off into the crowd and Elizabeth rode home in tears to tell Samuel of being robbed in broad daylight in the open street.

That did it. The streets were *not* safe for unaccompanied women. If a companion had been with Elizabeth in the coach, an alarm could have been given and the robbery prevented. He told her to summon Balty and they would see if he could find a girl suitable for the place.

The first girl that Balty brought for Samuel's inspection was a talented, attractive girl named Gosnell. She was seventeen years old, from a good family, and could sing and dance like an actress. Samuel interviewed the girl, sang a duet with her, and told her to come to Seething Lane in four days. Elizabeth bought red hangings for the bed to match the draperies in the new top-floor bedroom, installed mirrors and cabinets and chests of drawers.

Gosnell came late one evening—and she left four days later. It was not that Samuel and Elizabeth did not like her; they liked her very much. She was amusing, accommodating, and wonderfully talented. At the dinner table she entertained them with irresistible mimicries of the actresses at the Theatre Royal, and in the evening she sang them a full repertory of saucy songs with such skill that Elizabeth said Gosnell was better than going to a playhouse.

But after four days, Gosnell packed her belongings and announced that she had taken another position. Mr. St. Michel had told her that the Pepyses went every day to the theater and that a companion at Seething Lane would have complete liberty to come and go at her pleasure. What she really wanted to be, she said, was an actress; and she was afraid that she would have little chance to meet the managers living with people who went so little abroad.

Samuel was dumbfounded and Elizabeth heartbroken. After they watched the ambitious girl drive away toward Covent Garden, Elizabeth broke into tears and Samuel spent the greater part of the evening putting his opinions of Balty St. Michel into thoughtful profanity.

Balty came to Seething Lane and only laughed at Samuel's angry denunciation. The girl had mistaken him, he protested. He had only said that they *ought* to go to the playhouse every day. Samuel spluttered and cursed, but Balty calmed him down with the announcement that he knew of another girl, the very one to live quietly and companionably with the Pepyses. He would send her down for Samuel to inspect. Her name was Mary Ashwell, he said, a pretty young teacher of children in Chelsea.

At first glance Ashwell was not as impressive as Gosnell had been. She was quieter, less vivid, but pretty enough and well-spoken. She told Samuel that she could sew, read aloud, dance passably, play most of the current card games—cribbage, gleek, and loo—and could play the harpsichord. Samuel cautiously said that they would let her know their decision in a week. During the week he interviewed the girl's mother and father, making it clear what a companion could and could not expect at his house. Elizabeth went to Chelsea to see Ashwell perform in a school play and came home with glowing reports of the girl's dancing and general carriage. Samuel said that if Elizabeth was content with her, he would be.

In the middle of March, Ashwell moved to Seething Lane with her trunk and a box or two of clothing. Elizabeth took her up to the red bedroom, now to be called Ashwell's chamber, and helped her put her things away. When Samuel came home after dark, he found them sitting in the parlor before the fire, laughing and chatting like schoolgirls. He looked dubious at the quick intimacy, but he was willing to wait and see how the arrangement worked out.

Ashwell's initiation into the household in the following weeks was a gradual revelation of her quiet virtues. She was a pleasant companion at the dinner table, a willing escort for Elizabeth on her visits to the shops, and a capable servant.

Samuel himself was particularly charmed by her musical talents. He took Elizabeth and Ashwell with him to Halfway House one afternoon when he had to go to Deptford, and he was pleased with the accurate way the girl sang a roundelay as they walked through the fields. When he met them at the Wardrobe one afternoon, he found Ashwell playing the harpsichord to the whole appreciative family, Lady Sandwich, the girls, and even the Earl. Samuel immediately took the little triangle spinet he had been keeping for his patron and had it tuned. Ashwell was too good a musician to be wasted, even during Lent. Thereafter every night he would make Ashwell sit down at the spinet and play for him until bedtime. He even violated his vow about books—willingly paying his forfeit into the poor box—by buying her a book of virginal music so that she could extend her repertory.

On Easter Sunday, after going twice to church, Samuel joined his women in the parlor. Elizabeth said that now that Lent was over they could get Ashwell to teach them to play cards and they could begin their dancing. Samuel said that as far as he was concerned Lent had been over as soon as the visiting Scot preacher had finished his sermon that afternoon. Elizabeth said that Lent must have been over for him as soon as it began, since he had slept loudly through the whole sermon. Samuel retorted that a good sound sleep was the best that a lazy sermon deserved. He sent Ashwell upstairs to bring him his chest of viols. They would have a dance.

While Samuel selected a tenor viol from the case and tuned it carefully, Elizabeth and Ashwell pushed back the furniture and rolled up the carpet. Elizabeth twirled out onto the floor as soon as Samuel began to play. She had an artless grace that floated her through the music without any particular attention to the rhythms. Ashwell joined in as soon as she had finished lining the chairs against the wall. Samuel watched them. There was a difference. Elizabeth danced like a graceful child, but Ashwell danced like a trained performer. He played a *branle* and Ashwell followed the steps in perfect rhythm. He shifted to a *coranto* and she stepped it off without a bobble. He changed to a country tune and she quickly altered to the free but exacting motions. Elizabeth floated on through all the changes of rhythm. Samuel closed out his melody with a flourish, bowed deeply to the smiling Ashwell, and told Elizabeth, sprawled breathless in a chair, that she should have a dancing master at once.

After Samuel in his burst of gaiety had committed himself, Elizabeth did not let him forget his promise. She reminded him of it at the dinner table the next day, in the presence of Ashwell. Samuel started to protest that the expense would be outside the household charges their vows allowed, but he felt constrained before Ashwell. He said he intended to keep his promise.

And he did. He went across to St. Olave's to see the parish clerk. If Elizabeth was going to have dancing lessons, she was going to have them at home, from a dancing master in the neighborhood, and not go traipsing off to Covent Garden or Westminster where he could not see how she applied herself. He asked Mr. Hadley if he had any dancing masters listed in his register of the parish, and the parish clerk found the name of a Mr. Pembleton, who styled himself a dancing master. Samuel called upon Mr. Pembleton and asked what would be his charges for coming to Seething Lane once a day to teach his wife to dance.

The young man seemed strangely out of place in his miserable lodgings. He was a graceful, dark-haired fellow, who moved about the dim and cluttered room with practiced elegance. Mr. Pembleton brushed the lace at his cuffs and said that he would be happy to come every day and teach Mrs. Pepys the popular dances as they were performed at Court and in the best circles of Westminster for a pound. In a month, he said, he would have her dancing as well as Lady Castlemaine herself. Samuel said that he did not expect miracles, but that the dancing master might come the next day to begin his lessons.

Elizabeth and Ashwell set to work immediately converting the spare chamber on the top floor into a dancing room. They had the room cleared of all its boxes and trunks, put a few chairs along the wall and had the little spinet installed on a large table.

Samuel looked in on them the next afternoon to see how Elizabeth took her first lesson. Ashwell sat at the spinet, ready to play at the call of the master. Pembleton was walking slowly through the steps of the *coranto*.

"*Temps de courante*," he announced. "*Pas grave*. Bend—lift—forward glide. Bend—lift—forward glide."

Elizabeth watched for a moment, and then without waiting for him to finish the figure, she called out for Ashwell to play and began to sweep through the step.

Pembleton quickly stopped her. "I will call for the music when I am ready for it," he said. Then taking her by the hand he made her walk the pattern with him slowly. "*Pas grave*," he intoned as he walked along with Elizabeth. "*Pas grave*. Bend—lift—forward glide. Bend—lift—forward glide."

Samuel smiled as he saw the familiar creases of irritation come between Elizabeth's eyes. He went back to the office. This was probably a great waste of money, he thought. Elizabeth was too conceited to realize that she did not know how to dance, too impatient to submit herself to instruction. He was sorry that he had let himself be carried away into the foolish promise.

A few days later Samuel looked in upon the dancing lessons again. Ashwell was playing and Elizabeth was moving around the room hand in hand with Pembleton.

"*Courante simple*," he called out, and they moved forward, bending, gliding—bending, gliding.

"*Courante figurée*," he announced, and they moved into a complicated pattern, forward, backward, sideways, zigzagging across the room in graceful bends and glides. Samuel was surprised at how well Elizabeth had come along in so short a time.

When the music finally came to a stop and the couple walked back to him, he bowed happily to them and congratulated Mr. Pembleton on his fine teaching. The dancing master took him by the arm and made a motion toward Ashwell. Saying, "I will teach you, too," he brought Samuel out onto the floor and began his familiar calls, "*Temps de courante. Pas grave.* Bend—lift— forward glide. Bend—lift—forward glide."

Samuel was speechless. He had no notion of getting himself involved in the expense of dancing lessons. He had little time and less money to waste upon it; but he followed Pembleton about the room, matching his movements, listening to the rhythm of the virginal. In a moment he was lost in the music and the motions. Pembleton interspersed his calls with little words of encouragement and praise. In a quarter of an hour Samuel was bound. He was dancing better than Elizabeth; at least he was doing the basic steps better. In a week or two he would be able to outdance them all, the *branles* and the country dances as well as the *coranto*. He told the company he would join them in their lessons.

Throughout the spring of 1663 Mr. Pembleton came three times a week and taught Samuel and Elizabeth to dance. The top floor resounded with music every afternoon and until late in the evening, as the tireless Ashwell played the spinet and Elizabeth and her dancing master or Elizabeth and her husband danced. Word passed through the residences and into the parish church that the Pepyses had become courtiers, turning the quiet solemnity of the little street into the midnight gaiety of Whitehall.

One day in the middle of May Samuel came home in the afternoon to join Elizabeth at her lesson—but no sound of music came from the dancing room.

Samuel went up the steps puzzled and perplexed. He was sure that this was Pembleton's afternoon. He had told Elizabeth at dinner that he had arranged to postpone a trip to Deptford so that he could join her in her lesson, and Elizabeth had not replied. He hurried up the steps quietly, expecting to hear voices when he got to the top.

But there were no voices. He started toward the door, ready to surprise the dancers; but at the threshhold he stopped. Someone was whispering.

He moved around silently so that he could see into the room without being seen. Ashwell was not at the spinet; but in the far corner of the room, holding hands and talking in muffled voices, stood Elizabeth and Pembleton. *Ashwell was not in the room.*

Something like a blow hit Samuel in the pit of the stomach. His heart seemed to stop beating and he could not catch his breath. He tiptoed back down the steps and looked for one of the servants. He could find no one but Susan, cooking a shoulder of mutton in the kitchen. No one else was there, Susan told him. Mrs. Ashwell had gone to see her mother and Mary, the chambermaid, was out on an errand.

Samuel nodded woodenly and went out into the garden to see if he could find some air to breathe. He sat down weakly on the garden bench and tried to fathom what the evidence in the silent house meant.

This was not the first time that Samuel had fallen prey to the green-eyed monster jealousy. Once Elizabeth had come home from a shopping trip to the Exchange gaily displaying a new bracelet, which she alleged had been given to her by "an old friend," a Mr. Somerset. Samuel's smoldering suspicions were fanned into flame a few days later when an oily French footman had sidled up to Elizabeth in the crowd at Bartholomew Fair and whispered something into her ear. Samuel immediately concluded the fellow was a go-between, and his mind went into a fever of horrible imaginings of assignations, cruel deceptions, and outright cuckoldry. But his fears had so little fact to support them that he did not dare to face Elizabeth with them. Somehow she learned of them, however, and in one of their early morning periods of intimacy she had assured him of her innocence. She had only seen Mr. Somerset that once, at the Exchange, she assured him, and the sinister footman was simply a friend of her brother Balty's. Samuel had believed her, readily and with great relief.

But this was quite different. A fury rose up in him. Elizabeth had planned this rendezvous—sent Ashwell and the maid away, ordered Susan to stay in the kitchen. She had not heard him say that he was *not* going to Deptford. She had planned this chance to be alone with her dancing master. Pembleton was her lover!

A cold tremor swept over him and he got up from the bench and started toward the house, but his legs gave way and he grabbed hold of a tree to keep from falling. His head swam, and the blood seemed to desert the upper part of his body and flood his legs. He stumbled into the house and crept up the stairs.

When Elizabeth appeared on the steps from the third floor, Samuel averted his eyes and rushed past her. He locked the door and threw himself onto the bed, burying his face in the pillow and fighting the nausea that surged into his throat. He did not want to see Elizabeth or think about her. He wanted to crawl into a dark, deep pocket of oblivion and drown himself.

When Elizabeth came into the room hours later, he kept his eyes closed so that she would not speak to him. But he did, to his own horror, peep at her under his lids while she was undressing to see whether she had on her drawers. She had.

He awoke the next morning, after a miserable night of restless, fitful sleep, and slipped away from the house before Elizabeth awoke. He plunged feverishly into his work on the supply inventory with Hayter and tried to keep his mind off what might be happening in his house. But it was no good. He made a dozen foolish errors before he thought of sending Will Hewer to his third-floor study to spend the morning sorting and labeling his brother Tom's tailoring bills.

At dinner he sat speechless through the tasteless meal while Elizabeth and Ashwell chattered away as if nothing were wrong. They might at least have the decency to acknowledge their sin by looking guilty, he fumed to himself as he left the table, his dinner only half eaten, to go to the study and spend the afternoon listening for any sign of suspicious goings on. But the house was as quiet and respectable as a convent.

For a week Samuel kept a frantic guard upon his house, making excuses for not being able to attend the dancing lessons but also inventing reasons to work in his study whenever Mr. Pembleton came to Seething Lane. And it seemed to him that Pembleton was always there, intoning affectedly his French dance phrases, while Ashwell's spinet sang out its gay little melodies relentlessly. Samuel paced the floor, peeped into the room, glued his ear to the door to try to catch what the carefree dancers were saying.

Even at church Pembleton haunted his devotions. The elegant young man would sweep into the quiet little church as if it were a ballroom, throw back his head and search the Navy gallery until he found the Pepyses, and then he would smile broadly, showing his disgustingly beautiful teeth, and bow unctiously before he took his seat in his pew. Samuel would glare back at him and throughout the service shoot imaginary daggers at the back of his head. He prayed earnestly to God to give him strength to resist his jealousy and to keep him from exposing his horrid suspicions until the time should come for Elizabeth to give over her lessons and go to Brampton with Ashwell for the summer.

But Samuel could not keep up his guard upon the house all the time. He could not absent himself from Board meetings. He went over to the office one afternoon late in May to prepare a report he was to make to the Board on the history of contracts with flag merchants. He sat at his table in his little office and tried to concentrate on the facts he and Hayter had so carefully assembled. He picked up a paper, looked at it blankly, and put it down again. He walked out into the Board room and all around the large center table without remembering what he had come for. He stood at the window and stared across the garden at his house, wondering in agony what might be happening in the dancing room, the parlor, his own bedroom. . . .

He could stand it no longer. He ran out of the building, across the garden, through the gate into Seething Lane, and up to his front door. He quietly opened the door and searched the entry for any sign of a visitor; and there on a table lay a man's hat—Pembleton's hat!

Samuel sank down into the chair beside the table and gazed at the horrid hat. He knew that Pembleton was here, in his house, and the house was strangely quiet. He got up and went into the kitchen to quiz the cook. But Susan was not in the kitchen. She was not anywhere on the ground floor, nor was Mary, the maid. The ground floor was deserted.

He went back out the front door and looked up and down the street. Will Hewer was in Westminster on an errand to the Admiralty Office. The Board was to meet in ten minutes and he had no one to help him, no one to stand watch in the entry and report to him if music came from the dancing room or how long Mr. Pembleton stayed after the music stopped. He was alone and desperate.

Suddenly someone tapped him on the shoulder. Samuel whirled around and saw the master of the King's pleasure yacht standing beside him, his hat in his hand, requesting a word with the Clerk of the Acts. In a strong Dutch accent, the yacht master poured out his troubles to the distracted Samuel. One of his junior officers had struck him, he said, and he needed advice on what action to take. The yardmasters at Woolwich had told him that Mr. Pepys at the Navy Office was the man to see.

Samuel pulled the Dutchman into the entry.

"Sit here," he ordered him. "I have a meeting ready to start in the Navy building, and I must be there. But I want to hear your story. Wait for me. Do not leave this spot until I get back, and while I am gone keep your eye on that hat and tell me, when I get back, at what time its owner claimed it."

Samuel started for the door, and stopped only long enough to throw one more order to the bewildered captain. "Tell me if the music stops upstairs while I am gone." Then Samuel dashed out the door and ran back to the office.

In the Board room, Penn, Batten and Minnes waited. Samuel rushed in out of breath, panted an apology, and slipped to his place at the table. Penn announced that neither Sir George Carteret nor Mr. Coventry could be present at the meeting, but the Board had its quorum and could proceed with its business. Samuel listened stupidly to the rumble of discussion for half an hour, his mind taunting itself with images of Elizabeth laughing with Pembleton, Elizabeth kissing Pembleton, Elizabeth in Pembleton's unspeakable embrace. He got up from the table, muttered that he would have to postpone his report on the flag business, and made his way rapidly out of the room. He ran across the garden and into his house by the rear door, leaving the Dutch captain keeping innocent watch at the front, completely forgotten.

As he ran up the stairs, he made as much noise as he could. He was afraid to surprise them, afraid to know definitely, certainly, that Elizabeth had cuckolded him. He went into the bedroom and closed the door quietly. Overhead he could hear laughter and not-quite-distinct words. He could also hear the sound of feet, moving in rhythm. He went to the bed and examined the covers to see if they had been disturbed, but they were as untouched as they had been at noon after Mary had made the beds. He sat down in a chair by the fireplace and listened to the sounds that came from above.

It seemed to him that Pembleton was talking overloudly now, making an obvious effort to be heard all over the house. He was sorry, Samuel could hear him say, that Mistress Ashwell had to miss the lesson; and since she was not here to play, he had best be gone. The afternoon was lost, but there was no help for it. He bade Elizabeth a resounding *adieu,* and Samuel could hear him clacking down the stairs.

There was no further sound in the house for ten minutes; and when he heard Elizabeth go down the steps to the kitchen, he slipped out of the bedroom and tiptoed up to the third floor. He went into Ashwell's room and examined the bedclothes there, but they were as innocent as the covers on his own bed. He went into the dancing room, and there was no evidence of anything. He did not know what evidence he was looking for in that empty room, but there was none.

Finding nothing to alarm him further—or to give him any comfort either—he went into his study and locked the door. He got out his diary and confided his fears to the cryptic page:

I know not at this very minute that I now write this almost what either I write or am doing, nor how to carry myself to my wife in it, being unwilling to speak of it to her for fear of making any breach and other inconveniences, nor let it pass for fear of her continuing to offend me and the matter grow worse thereby. . . . This is my devilish jealousy, which I pray God may be false, but it makes a very hell in my mind, which the God of Heaven re-move.

Samuel stayed in his harrowing cell all afternoon. About five o'clock, he heard the maids and Ashwell return. The familiar sounds of the house floated up to him and made him feel more isolated from the flow of life than he had ever felt before, the clash of dishes in the kitchen, Ashwell singing in her room, Elizabeth calling out to the cook. But he could not make himself go out of the room. He got up and unlocked the door, but he could not go out.

Shortly after dark he heard Elizabeth's footsteps coming up the stairs and toward his door. He hurried to the table, lighted the candles, opened a book at random, and was deeply absorbed in reading when Elizabeth came in. He lifted his eyes from the page and half turned his head toward her when she spoke. Did Samuel plan to eat supper with them?

"No," he said, without looking at her. "I am not hungry."

An hour later she came back to the study and announced, as she stood in the door, that they were all ready to go to bed. Was he coming?

"No," he said, "I have work to do."

He stayed in his retreat, nursing his wounds, until midnight, until he was sure that everybody was asleep. Then he undressed quietly, tiptoed to the bedroom, and slipped into bed cautiously, so as not to awaken Elizabeth.

At three o'clock in the morning he awoke from a troubled sleep. His mind began at once to play upon the scene he had imagined in the dancing room. He thought of what he ought to say to Elizabeth to make her confess. He rehearsed the sharp eloquence of his charge, her infidelity, her shameless disregard of him. As he sought for the telling phrase that would bring her to her knees, he became aware that his bladder was uncomfortable.

He got up out of bed, noisily, and went downstairs to the privy. When he got back to the bedroom, he was sure that Elizabeth was awake. She lay on her back, but she gave no sign of being awake. He got into bed and tossed and tumbled until past four o'clock. Elizabeth continued to lie very still, breathing lightly, not her usual soft snore at all.

In a burst of irritation, Samuel sat straight up, threw back the cover, and started to swing out of bed. As his foot touched the floor, Elizabeth's hand caught his arm.

"What ails you?" she demanded.

"Nothing ails me," he said, pulling his arm free. "I can't sleep."

Elizabeth was sitting up now. "Why can't you sleep? Did missing your supper upset your stomach?"

"It's not my stomach," Samuel said fiercely. He stood beside the bed and lighted a candle. "It's not my stomach that ails me."

And then he launched into the bitterly eloquent charge that he had rehearsed over and over.

Elizabeth sat in the bed, stupefied, aghast.

"Are you out of your mind?" she cried. "Are you mad? What cause have I given you to suspect me but a little harmless dancing with Mr. Pembleton? What evidence has your suspicious mind twisted and magnified until you accuse your own wife of being a whore?"

"There is evidence to spare," Samuel shouted at her.

"You are possessed," Elizabeth screamed back at him.

For an hour they threw words and charges back and forth, until they were weary, their emotions spent, and the sun came up and lighted the room.

Elizabeth lay back in the bed, crying softly. Samuel snuffed out the flame of the candle with his fingers and stood picking at the wax on his thumb. He *had* to believe that Elizabeth had not actually betrayed him. She had flirted and played the fool, more than was wise—or kind. But surely she had committed no real sin, intended no real injury. He kissed her wet cheek and went across to his study to get his clothes and dress for the day.

He ate dinner with his lordship in Chelsea. When he got home about three o'clock in the afternoon, Elizabeth was sitting in the parlor with Ashwell, her hands in her lap and her face swollen. Samuel asked if Mr. Pembleton were not coming to give her her dancing lesson.

"He came," Elizabeth said hoarsely, "and I sent him away."

Samuel looked at Ashwell, but the discreet companion continued with her sewing as if she were in another room.

"I told him," Elizabeth went on, "that hereafter we could not dance unless my husband were present."

Samuel put his hand to his face to feel the hotness of it, and then he turned and left the room, going across the garden to the Navy Office and into the privacy of his little cubicle.

In half an hour Mary appeared to tell him that Mr. Pembleton had arrived. Mrs. Pepys wanted to know if he would be good enough to come home so they could have their lesson. Samuel squirmed in his seat. He looked at the girl. There was no expression on her face at all, as far as he could see. He told her to take word to her mistress that Mr. Pepys desired them to go ahead with their dancing; he would be along presently.

Elizabeth was taking her revenge. If he had let his jealousy make a fool of him, Elizabeth was seeing to it that his folly was published. Not only Ashwell and the maids but now Pembleton also knew that he did not trust his wife to be alone with her dancing master. Well, it was the last day of his commitment for Elizabeth's lessons. Let him see this day through and the dancing master would be gone from his house forever, whatever Elizabeth may have meant by her "hereafter" in the parlor. There would be no "hereafter" for Mr. Pembleton, if Samuel could help it.

Samuel marched up the stairs to the top floor and swept into the dancing room. He apologized to Mr. Pembleton for being late, said that he was sorry that they had come to the last of his wife's dancing lessons, and invited her master to join them in a farewell supper. He applauded Elizabeth as she danced a *gigue*. He played the spinet while Ashwell joined the couple in a country dance. He danced with Elizabeth and then with Ashwell in one last *branle*. At the supper table, he told stories of the Moors' attacks on the outworks of the fort at Tangier, he discoursed on music and plays and pictures, he teased Elizabeth about losing the keys to the house, made Ashwell sing a duet with him, proposed a farewell toast to their good teacher, and played the complete host until ten o'clock at night. Pembleton had no opportunity to open his mouth or add one *bon mot* to the evening's entertainment.

When the door finally closed on Pembleton's back, Samuel drew a breath of relief. All he had to do now was get Elizabeth ready to go to Brampton, and all he had to fear was the wagging tongue of the dancing master, who might find it amusing to relate in the taverns how he had given Mr. Pepys such a turn.

VII

My Lord is dabbling with

this wench

IN THE SUMMER of 1663 the Earl of Sandwich fell sick of a fever and came near to dying. For several weeks he lay close to death, until the fever finally broke and left him weak and exhausted but only in need of country air and rest to restore him to full health. His lordship was too spent to make the long trip to Hinchingbrooke, and there was no healthy air in London during the hot summer months. London was closely surrounded by rural seats and villages, however, country places within a half-hour's ride of St. Paul's or Whitehall. Lady Sandwich found hospice for her convalescent husband in nearby Chelsea; and then, worn out herself from her strenuous nursing, took the girls and the baby Catherine north to Hinchingbrooke to spend the rest of the summer with the boys.

She left her husband in good hands. Chelsea was a quiet village only a few miles up the river from Whitehall, a rural place of stately manor houses and modest timber-framed cottages, convenient to Westminster but secluded and peaceful in the shade of great old trees and the music of fresh-water streams. Lord Sandwich sought his convalescence in the cottage home of a retired London merchant named Becke, who was living out his comfortable retirement with his wife and his daughter, Betty, in a spacious but modest cottage only a stone's throw from the old Tudor manor built by Sir Thomas More.

Samuel, while Elizabeth was away in Brampton, went often up the river to visit his patron in Chelsea and eat Mrs. Becke's excellent cakes out of doors under the trees with the old merchant and his pretty young daughter. Samuel thought that it would be pleasant, if he ever had to undergo a sickness, to have so pretty and attentive a nurse as his lordship had in Betty Becke.

But Samuel seemed to have a true Londoner's immunity to the summer fevers that struck down so many country folk, like the Earl of Sandwich, who had to reside in the City during the hot months. Elizabeth had never been able to endure London in the summer, and Samuel had therefore had no trouble in getting her to go to Brampton for the months of July and August. With Ashwell along to keep her company and Lady Jem only a few miles away at Hinchingbrooke, Samuel hoped that Elizabeth could enjoy her summer in peace without her usual quarrels with his family.

With his time his own in the hot summer, he did not feel it essential for him to spend his whole day at the office or in the yards. He sought what pleasures the town afforded in July. He went often to Chelsea to look in on his recuperating patron, and he began to spend many of his evenings with the Pierces. Dr. Pierce had been surgeon on the old *Naseby* when Samuel went to sea with his cousin, and the able physician now had a fashionable practice in Westminster. He also had a fashionable and very pretty wife, whom Samuel found uncommonly attractive. The Pierces knew everybody and everything that happened in Westminster. They kept a good table, loved music and conversation and witty company, and made their handsome house a cheerful refuge for sociable people like Samuel Pepys.

But he also frequented less fashionable houses. The girl who kept the linen stall in Westminster Hall had long intrigued his amorous eye. Her name was Betty Lane, and Samuel had spent a good many hours chatting with her while he dawdled over the counter selecting a linen neckband he did not need or examining lace cuffs he had no intention of buying. Betty was a patient salesgirl and seemed to enjoy exchanging risqué innuendo with her more prosperous customers. Samuel was convinced that Betty was a baggage; but he was, with Elizabeth three weeks away from him, in search of an attractive baggage.

After he had selected one day a pair of neckbands and requested Betty to send them out to a laundress to be starched,

Samuel asked the girl if she had had her dinner. He would buy her a lobster and a bottle of good wine if she could leave the stall.

Betty said that even shopgirls had to eat dinner; so Samuel took her to the Rhenish Wine House in Cannon Row. While she ate, Betty chattered. She said that she no longer went out as much as she used to. She had her mind set on getting married and being freed from the confinements of the linen stall. Samuel hastened to tell her that *he* was married, but that he would be glad to help her find a husband. He met many fine-looking young fellows in the Navy, handsome seamen who would like to have a pretty wife waiting for them in London when they came home from sea. Betty said she thought that a sailor would have many attractions as a husband, and snickered suggestively.

When the sociable girl had finished her lobster and licked the grease from her fingers, Samuel asked her if she would step into the back room with him. He had a surprise for her. Without a moment's hesitation, Betty stepped.

But what Samuel had for her was no surprise. She continued to prattle while Samuel did with her what he would, and ceased talking only when Samuel stopped her mouth with an extended kiss.

And Samuel's vigorous love-making stopped only when a rock crashed through the window of the dark room and hit the opposite wall with a startling crack. Betty and Samuel clung to each other in terror while a coarse voice shouted in through the broken window, "Sir, why do you kiss the gentlewoman so?"

In a flurry of skirts and petticoats, the frightened couple scrambled out of the room and hurried back to Westminster Hall to collect Samuel's starched neckbands and calm their shattered nerves.

Betty Lane was Samuel's willing if garrulous companion the rest of the summer, meeting him whenever he summoned her to go across the river to the more secluded taverns in Southwark.

In mid-August Samuel's summer idyl was interrupted by a sudden note from Elizabeth. All pleasure was gone from her holiday at Brampton, she wrote tersely, and she was coming home the next day. Samuel met her at the Post House and saw at once that something was wrong between Elizabeth and Ashwell. They descended from the public coach like strangers and neither of them said a word to each other all the way home to Seething Lane. Ashwell went immediately to her room, and Elizabeth burst into a bitter denunciation of her companion.

Samuel could not make sense of the furious rigmarole that Elizabeth poured out. There was something about a piece of ribbon that Elizabeth accused Ashwell of appropriating, Ashwell calling Elizabeth a liar, and an exchange of blows. Whatever was the truth of the unseemly goings on at Brampton, Samuel was convinced that Ashwell's days in Seething Lane were at an end; and for that he could not be sorry. The girl knew more than was convenient for her to know about the skeletons in his cupboard, and her salary was an expense that Samuel would be happy to save. He was sure that the fracas had come about from Elizabeth's quick-triggered temper and not from any real fault in the even-tempered companion, but Elizabeth was now set against her. There was no telling what trouble would come during the winter, with Elizabeth lonely and isolated again, but it would do her no harm to consider for a while the folly of letting her temper spoil her one chance for freedom.

Trouble did not come from Elizabeth that fall, however; it came from a completely unsuspected direction—from Chelsea.

Will Howe came down to Seething Lane to bring Samuel surprising and disturbing news: the Earl of Sandwich had fallen in love with Betty Becke, his pretty young nurse in Chelsea. Samuel did not believe it. He had seen Betty Becke attending to his lordship's convalescence in the cottage garden, and he had seen no fault in the relation. The girl was kind and the Earl was grateful; it was only venomous Whitehall gossip that wanted to make something sinister of it.

His lordship had left his hospice, Howe protested, returned to his old lodgings in Whitehall to reassume his duties at Court; but every evening he drove down to Chelsea and spent the night with the Beckes—with Betty, if the report were true—and Whitehall tongues were wagging.

"Let them wag," Samuel declared. "This is only rumor to injure my Lord, and I will have nothing to do with it."

But everywhere Samuel went thereafter he heard the ugly gossip, with minute and particular details. Dr. Pierce told him that the Court was full of the talk that the Earl had deserted the King, given up all his duties at the Court to demean himself by living openly with a Chelsea wench. The Earl's status at Whitehall, Dr. Pierce warned his friend, had fallen to a low ebb. His friends or his kinsmen ought to warn him, for his own good.

Samuel changed the subject as deftly as he could without offending the solicitous doctor, but he brooded about Pierce's report for three days. If his lordship was dabbling with this wench, injuring himself at Court, and openly disgracing his devoted family, something should be done to call him to his senses; but Samuel could not think of anyone capable of undertaking so delicate a task, unless it was Lord Crewe, the Earl's father-in-law.

Samuel called upon the Crewes and managed to get invited to dinner. He hoped to pick up some clue from the Countess's attractive family. They were sophisticated people and they knew Samuel to be the Earl's loyal protégé. If they knew anything, they would give some hint, some opening for him to broach the subject of speaking to his lordship. But even after dinner, when Samuel and old Baron Crewe sat alone at the table drinking wine, the Earl's father-in-law did not mention the matter. Samuel talked about his cousin, spoke of his recovery from his summer's illness, commented upon the excellent hospitality the Beckes had given him at their modest house. But Lord Crewe still did not speak of the scandal, and Samuel went home convinced that the Crewes were not available to rescue Lord Sandwich from his ruinous infatuation.

Three days later Henry Moore called upon Samuel and put the cross squarely upon Samuel's back. Mr. Moore was the Earl's solicitor. He handled all the Earl's legal business and many of his financial affairs. Although a relatively young man, he had been a member of the Montagu and the Crewe households for a number of years. Moore was not easy to excite and he had a good lawyer's sense of caution. But he was excited now.

"Something must be done, Mr. Pepys. His lordship is ruining himself. Not only the Court and Westminster, but the Temple and the Royal Exchange as well are rife with rumors of the Earl's disgrace. I have come to persuade you to accept the responsibility of speaking to Lord Sandwich."

Samuel caught his breath. "But Lord Crewe? Certainly Lord Crewe is the one to speak. The Earl would listen to Lord Crewe."

"Lord Crewe will not touch it," the solicitor said. "He would speak as an in-law. He will not hazard coming between his daughter and her husband. You are the one to speak."

Samuel got up from his chair and wandered around the room. How could he muster the courage to face his patron and tell him to his teeth that he was playing the fool with a wench of a girl and injuring his wife and his reputation by whoring? He would be out of his mind to think of it. It would mean the end of his friendship, his relationship with his kind and generous cousin. He could not do it.

He turned to Moore. "Why me?" he asked.

The solemn lawyer looked at him steadily. "Who else?" he asked. "Who else but a kinsman, a cousin known to love him and to enjoy his general patronage? Who owes him more than you?"

Samuel could not think of an answer to Mr. Moore's blunt question. He told Mr. Moore that he would have to think about it, and he showed him to the door.

Samuel thought about it for two days and two long nights of sleepless anguish, and then he ordered a coach and rode to Whitehall. He took a coach because he was in no hurry to get there. He did not know what he would say or how he would phrase his statement, and he wanted all the time he could get to postpone the terrifying interview.

Will Howe met him at the door, almost in tears. The Earl was a changed man, he said. He did almost nothing now but play cards during the day and sleep at night with that slut in Chelsea. He was upstairs now, Howe cried, sitting alone in his room, refusing to come down to dinner. Samuel said that he would go straight up.

He knocked on the Earl's door and waited. When no answer came, he knocked again, more loudly; and a dull voice intoned for him to come in.

The Earl was sitting deep in a chair, his back to the windows, gazing steadily at the open fire in the fireplace. Without looking at him, he waved Samuel to a chair and continued to gaze. Samuel sat down and looked at the fire, too, glancing sideways now and then to try to catch the expression on his cousin's face; but there was almost no expression at all on that somber, ravaged face.

Samuel continued to sit for five full minutes in uneasy silence; then he could stand it no longer. He asked his lordship how he liked the brisk November weather. The Earl did not raise his eyes or make a sound for a moment, and then he grunted something that Samuel could not quite catch. He was not even sure that it was language. He sat for a few more minutes in the eerie room, and then he gave it up. This was no time to talk to the Earl. He left the room almost unnoticed, his cousin only raising his left hand in a kind of absent gesture.

Samuel went back downstairs and found Will Howe. He could not talk to the Earl today, he said, about anything. He was not sure that he could ever bring himself to speak to him about Chelsea face to face. He would have to write him a letter. In a letter he could think clearly without having to endure the ordeal of choosing his words in the Earl's awful presence. He gave Howe a despondent farewell and went home.

He waited until Sunday afternoon to write his letter, when the house was quiet and he could retire to his study and be undisturbed for two or three hours. He wrote all afternoon. He wrote and he scratched out. He modified a phrase, altered a sentence, changed a direct word to an indirect. By four o'clock he had made a draft. He went out into the garden for a breath of air and then came back into the room and made a fair copy in his neatest hand. He would have to stand or fall upon this. He could not make it clearer without giving sure offense, or more indirect without clouding the issue. He would get Moore to read it with his lawyer's caution.

When Moore read it the next day, he said that he could not himself have written a better letter. As a matter of fact, he said, if Samuel said the word, he would copy the letter in his own hand and put his own name to it.

"No," Samuel said, "if it is worth sending at all, it will have to come from me. I have accepted the duty now. I will take the letter to him."

He planned to take the letter to Whitehall and leave it at the Earl's lodgings or give it to Howe to deliver in Chelsea; but when he got to Whitehall the next day, the first thing he saw was the Earl's familiar gold-and-red coach, emblazoned with the Sandwich arms, standing at the door. He hurried across the yard and as his foot touched the gravel of the drive, his heart stopped. The Earl himself stepped out of the coach.

Samuel stood rooted to the ground, unable to take a step or to say a word. The Earl turned slowly and looked at his immobile cousin standing there with his mouth open, and then he beckoned to him with his forefinger. Samuel shook off his paralysis and approached, keeping his left hand firmly planted against the pocket of his coat.

The Earl looked vaguely apologetic as he stood in the drive-way with Samuel, and took some trouble to explain that he was on the way to the Palace to attend a meeting of the Admiralty with the Duke.

Samuel could think of nothing to say in reply. The Earl's explanation sounded for all the world like a child's unbidden explanation of a crash in the kitchen pantry. When Samuel continued to stand there, unable to open his mouth, the Earl gave him a light tap on the shoulder, bade him *adieu,* and walked on across the road toward the Palace. Samuel sat down for a moment on the step of the coach to let his heart slow down. He would have to let Hewer deliver the letter. He himself could never deliver it in person.

That night he wrote a short note:

My Lord,

    If this finds your Lordship either not alone, or not at leisure, I beg the suspending your opening of the enclosed till you have both, the matter very well bearing such a delay, and in all humility remain, May it please your lordship,

Your Lordship's most obedient Servant,
S. P.

November 17, 1663

    My servant hath my directions to put this into your Lordship's own hand, but not to stay for an answer.

He put the letter within the note and sealed it; then he locked the missive in his closet for the night, and next morning called Hewer into his study. He told him that the errand he had to perform was of the gravest importance. He must put this letter into the Earl's hand and his only. It must be delivered that day without fail. Take all day if necessary, but find the Earl at Whitehall, at the Wardrobe, at Chelsea. He put the letter securely into Hewer's pocket and pinned the flap with three pins.

"Now," he said, "lose your arm, your leg, or your head, but do not lose that coat. Deliver the letter to the Earl, privately if possible, but deliver it before you come home."

Hewer nodded his head slowly and thoughtfully. "The Earl will get the letter," he said firmly. "Do not worry, Mr. Pepys."

But Samuel waited and worried four days, pacing the streets, walking up and down Whitehall trying to get some glimpse of his lord and perhaps a sign that all was well. He met nervously with Moore and Howe, plied them with questions about the Earl's reaction, the expression on his face, the tone of his voice. They both assured him that the Earl must be taking the letter well, for he was now spending much time at the Wardrobe, going over his accounts with the deputy.

Samuel hurried to the Wardrobe and looked in on the Master, but the Earl was too busy with Mr. Townsend to speak to him—or even to notice that he was there.

For two more days Samuel sweated out his anxiety and then he decided to face the ordeal. Even the Earl's outspoken anger would be better than the agony of waiting. He decided to go to Whitehall on Sunday morning when everybody would be in church and ask his patron for an audience. He wanted no witnesses to his humiliation.

But as he drove into the Earl's coachyard on Sunday morning, the Sandwich coach was just getting ready to pull out. Samuel ran across the yard to the coach and, hat in hand, he asked his lordship if he could spare his morning service at the Chapel Royal to consult for an hour with his cousin. Without a word the Earl climbed down from his coach, told the coachman to put up the horses, and in a heavy silence walked with Samuel into the house.

When they came into the Earl's private chamber, the Earl

went over to his closet, unlocked a private box, took out Samuel's letter, with the seal broken, brought it back into the room, and laid it quietly on the table. Samuel watched every move carefully. There was no haste and no anger in these movements. There was only sadness and deep injury.

Samuel let his patron take the initiative. He only said, in order to open the subject, that it was about the letter that he had come.

"Yes," said the Earl, "the letter."

Lowering himself heavily into his great chair, the Earl sighed deeply and then began to talk, softly, sadly. He was aware, he said, that his cousin had written this strange letter out of love and concern for him. For this act of a loyal servant he was grateful. He knew that Samuel had not written in haste, impulsively, nor without great pain.

Samuel relaxed a little and started to relate the anxiety in which he had debated writing it, but he checked himself and let the Earl continue.

The one part of the letter that he treasured the most, Lord Sandwich said, was that in which his cousin had expressed his disbelief of the ugly rumors that he reported.

Samuel caught his breath. *He had had to say that*. He had to pretend that the rumors were untrue.

The Earl got up from his chair and walked over to the fireplace. He tapped the glowing coals with the toe of his boot and studied the leaping flames for a moment. Then he turned around and looked steadily at Samuel. Since Samuel had written the letter not as a personal reproach but only as a matter of information for his cousin to act upon as he thought wise, he said, it was necessary for Samuel now to give him the names of those who had been bandying his name about.

Samuel froze. He had not expected this. He was being asked to turn informer. He looked up at his stout cousin standing large and unmoving before the fire.

"Well," he said, "there was Dr. Pierce, who told me that the Court was buzzing with gossip of the King's displeasure. One of my former maidservants, who lives in Chelsea, reported unfavorably on the reputation of the young gentlewoman."

Samuel looked at the Earl, but his lordship waited quietly.

Samuel stumbled on. He had heard many people, all over town, he said, comment upon the Earl's present slighting of his business. Samuel wiped the palms of his hands on the skirt of his coat. Surely, he thought, Pierce and Ashwell could not be hurt by the Earl's anger. The Earl had no control over their lives. He looked again at his lordship, but the Earl avoided his eyes and sat down in his chair by the fire.

He gazed thoughtfully at the flames for a moment and then he began to talk again. What hurt him most in all of this, he said, was the damage done to the reputation of the Beckes, who were good and honest people and who had shown him the greatest kindness. It was poor pay for their care of him that their daughter should have her name abused by foul-minded gossips.

He paused for a moment to let his anger subside. It so happened, he went on, that he was leaving the Chelsea cottage in a few days, but not because of anything that had been said about the Beckes nor to please *anybody* (and he looked sharply at Samuel) but himself.

Samuel wilted under the steady anger of the Earl's glare. His mouth became dry and tears formed in his eyes and rolled down his cheeks. Without attempting to wipe them away, he stammered out his words, choking and almost sobbing as he leaned forward in his chair, clasping his hands tightly.

"Anything I have done," he cried, "has been intended only for the good of my cousin. What I have written has been seen by no one. None of the people who told me anything has ever seen the letter."

The Earl whirled quickly in his chair. He held up one stern finger and said, "You must give me leave to except one."

Samuel's stomach plunged. He thought wildly. *Which one?* Which one did he mean? He could not possibly know that he had shown the letter to Moore. Moore could not have let it slip, and there was no reason for the Earl to think that the cautious lawyer was in any way concerned in this. He must be thinking of poor Howe, but Howe had *not* seen the letter. He was safe there. Samuel cleared his throat and tried to order his words.

It was perhaps possible, he said, that somebody might know

of the *thoughts* that had been disturbing him, but no one could say that he knew what was in the letter.

Samuel watched his lordship's face as he gazed into the fire, working his lips back and forth; and then the harassed man pulled himself up out of his chair and, without a word, beckoned for Samuel to follow him.

They walked out of the house and across the road to the Palace. They went into the Matted Gallery where Peter Lely's new portraits of the royal family were on display. They spent the rest of the morning looking at the pictures, portraits of the King and Queen, the Duke of York and his Duchess, the Queen Mother. The Earl did not refer again to the letter. He talked about the pictures, stopping before each one, cocking his head sideways as he squinted at the familiar likenesses. He asked Samuel's opinion of the artist and chatted freely as if nothing else were on his mind but the abilities of Sir Peter Lely.

Samuel drove back home to an uneasy dinner. In the afternoon he listened halfheartedly to Mr. Mills' sermon, and that night he sat before the fire in the parlor, held Elizabeth's hand and told her about the interview. The Earl had been wounded, he told her. He had parted with him kindly, and his anger seemed not to be directed at the writer of the letter. But he could not be sure.

Elizabeth told him that he must not worry. He must sit quietly for a few days and she was sure it would all blow over. That, of course, said Samuel, was the only thing to do. But the trouble was that there could be no middle ground between his lordship's taking it very well or very ill. And he could not say that he had taken it well.

Samuel tried to sit as quietly as he could in the cold November days that followed. He met the Earl two or three times at meetings of the Tangier Committee, but he could not tell whether the Earl's distance was accidental or intentional. He spoke, to be sure, but he spoke much as he would speak to any member of the Committee. Samuel tried to remember the Earl's manner at these meetings before the letter, but he could not recall any detail vividly enough to make a just comparison. He decided to pay the Earl another private visit.

To provide an excuse for the visit he took the Earl a little present, a *terella,* a spherical loadstone which demonstrated the magnetic poles, which Mr. Barlow had sent him.

His lordship was fascinated with the little instrument and spent half an hour playing with it. Then he had to go abroad in the town on his business—but he said nothing of Chelsea or the letter. Samuel was encouraged.

For the next few days Samuel went about his business with improved hope, but on the last day of the month he received a jolt. Howe came down to Seething Lane in a frenzy. The Earl had called him in that morning, his face red with anger, and had charged him with reporting his most private actions to Mr. Pepys. Howe had protested tearfully that he had done no such thing, and the Earl had at least been soothed somewhat.

Samuel was disturbed. Although his lordship had not caught him in his lie, it was threatening to know that the placid man's anger had finally burst out. Lord Sandwich had always been slow to show his emotions, allowing them to well up inside him for weeks and months before they ultimately exploded or gradually were digested. It was frightening to know that the solid promontory was exhibiting alarming signs of eruption.

He sought no private interviews in the following week. He was alert to his lordship's slightest gesture at the meetings they attended. The Earl usually came in after the meeting had started and left without a word to anybody or with only the most casual nod when the meeting was over. At last Samuel was convinced that a cold blade had come between them. His lordship was either angry with him or he was deeply engrossed in his own consuming thoughts. Samuel had to know which, once and for all.

The quickest and surest test of his status with his patron would be a demand upon his favor, a request that would be a little troublesome to grant but could not be easily refused to one he valued. It must be exactly the right kind of demand. Samuel thought about it a great deal as he lay in bed at night, considering a loan of money or a recommendation for a position. But the Earl, he knew, was having his financial troubles; so money was too great a demand, and Samuel did not have time or desire for another position at the moment.

In the middle of December the right favor fell into his hand. His cousin Edward Pepys died and his sister, Jane Turner, asked Samuel to help with the funeral. Samuel did not know his cousin Edward very well, but he was deeply indebted to Mrs. Turner who had turned over her house in Salisbury Court when he was operated upon for the stone in 1658. He took over the funeral arrangements for Cousin Jane and saw to it that every detail was as decent and honorable as the family deserved. It was important that the funeral cortege look impressive as it made its way through the City. And then the resolving idea struck him: he would ask the Earl to let him have his state coach for the funeral procession.

He went straight to Whitehall and found the Earl closeted with the singers from the Chapel Royal, going over an anthem that he had arranged for them. Lord Sandwich saluted Samuel, said he was just the man he needed, and took him into the next room so they could listen to the music at a distance and get a proper judgment of it. The anthem really did sound very fine and Samuel expressed his good opinion of it, but he had the good sense not to spoil the occasion by being too extravagant in its praise. When the musicians had gone, the Earl invited Samuel to walk across the road to the Palace with him.

At the Palace gate, Samuel stopped and said that he had a favor to request. Their cousin, Edward Pepys of Broomsthorpe, had died and was to be buried within two days in London. For the honor of the family and his affection for Mrs. Turner he would like to ride in the procession in state. Would his lordship be kind enough to lend him his great coach-and-six?

The Earl walked on for a few steps before he said anything; then he asked when the funeral was to be held.

"On Wednesday," Samuel said.

The Earl blew his breath on his cold fingers and said that he was sorry to hear that their kinsman had died. "Is his family all right, well cared for?"

"Yes, they are fine," said Samuel. "Cousin Edward left a good estate."

"Well, it is too bad anyway," said the Earl, "too bad," and he started on again toward the Palace.

"And the coach?" Samuel asked anxiously.

"Oh, take it. To be sure, take it," the Earl called heartily.

So Samuel took it, and with it the best assurance he could hope for that his Lord loved him. They were still members of the same family, bound by ties stronger than the snares of gossip and envy. The Earl of Sandwich, Admiral of His Majesty's Fleet, was not just a lord to be courted and feared. He was also—and always—Edward Montagu, eldest son of Paulina Pepys and Sir Sydney Montagu, first cousin once removed to Samuel Pepys of Seething Lane.

VIII

And make the child his heir

SAMUEL HAD for some years been resigned to the fact that he and Elizabeth would likely have no children. It was an occasional prick to his manly pride, and in fact he tended to put the blame upon Elizabeth rather than suspect himself. At the same time he recognized that childlessness was even more painful a burden for Elizabeth than for him. Without children, Elizabeth simply had not enough to do. She had none of her husband's intellectual interests, and Samuel's efforts to interest her in mathematics or music or the complexities of his office produced meager rewards at best. Her circle of acquaintances was limited, nor did Samuel encourage her to go gadding about London without him, especially since the departure of the faithful Ashwell. Samuel himself was busy most of the day, and often much of the evening, with his growing responsibilities on the Navy Board. Elizabeth was left alone, and when she was left alone she became idle. When she was idle she became bored. When she was bored she became cross. And when she was cross she was unendurable.

Samuel did his best to keep her occupied. He had found that one of the best ways to divert her from mischief was to keep the house in a continuous uproar of redecoration. Elizabeth would protest and complain, but Samuel did not listen.

One afternoon in early autumn Samuel found Elizabeth sitting in the parlor reading *Cassandre* and eating an apple. He kissed her, wiped the apple juice from his lips, and while she chattered about the laziness of the cookmaid and the excellence of the new silk she had bought for her fall dress, Samuel wandered around the room pushing back the rug with the toe of his boot and getting down on his hands and knees to examine the floor boarding. When

Elizabeth stopped her monologue long enough to take a bite of apple, Samuel said that he was glad he had ordered the carpenters to come and make new floors; the old boarding was splintering badly.

Elizabeth choked on her apple. "When?" she finally gasped.

"Tomorrow," Samuel said, squatting down to look closely at the threshold of the hall door.

"Just this room?" Elizabeth loomed over him.

"The whole house," Samuel said mildly, as he got up and walked across to the sofa where she had been sitting.

Elizabeth let out a piercing scream. "You are doing this to spite me. You are doing this to keep me at home in dirt and mess for a month so you can be free of me."

"Nonsense," Samuel said, picking up her half-finished apple and taking a large bite.

While Elizabeth stormed about the room, shouting accusations, weeping in an anger of frustration and despair, calling him every name in her rich vocabulary of epithets, Samuel munched away on the apple and let her rave. At last in a burst of self-pity, she threw herself on the sofa and buried her head in his lap. He stroked her hair and rubbed her back gently. He kissed her on the top of her head and ran his hand under her arm until he found her breast. Her sobbing gradually diminished and in a little while they were at peace, relaxed and quiet in the darkening room.

It was the middle of October before the carpenters were finally through in the house. After they had finished the floors, Elizabeth and the two maids working hard to keep the furniture moved one room ahead of them, Samuel gave orders for the guest bedroom—Ashwell's old room—to be done over from ceiling to new closets. Elizabeth became interested in the daily crises that occurred, the bickering and the byplay between workmen and servants, as Samuel knew she would; and when the house was clean at last, free of the rubble and the confusion of laborers coming and going, Elizabeth actually missed them. Samuel would find her at night, peevish and short-tempered, sitting alone in the parlor, empty-handed, and bored to distraction. He had to find her a new amusement.

He took her to the New Exchange and let her spend £12 on new clothes—a velvet gown, a broad-lace petticoat, and a feathered hat. He took her with him to Westminster to visit with the Hunts in Axe Yard while he attended a committee meeting with his colleagues in the Duke's chambers. He arranged for Will Hewer to accompany her on her visits to her parents, and he sent her and her maids on an all-day journey to Chelsea to look in upon the forgiven Ashwell and eat their dinner under the trees of the rural stream that flowed through the village.

At night he took her up to his study and began to teach her the mysteries of arithmetic. He gave her problems in addition and subtraction and corrected her answers. He made a game of it, inventing problems that she might meet in the New Exchange if she had £5 to spend and three items to buy at a half crown, 1 shilling, and 16s. How much change should she have? Elizabeth became quick at computing so pleasant a negotiation, and Samuel brought out his globe to teach her to read the parallels and locate a spot on the earth when he gave her the longitude and latitude. At the expense of his time and his purse, Samuel kept her busy through the fall, and they arrived at the new year as content a couple as any in London, "pleased with one another's company," he wrote in his journal, "and in our general enjoyment of one another, better we think than most other couples do."

On New Year's Day, 1664, Samuel and Elizabeth went to St. Mary Axe to eat dinner with Uncle Wight. William Wight was old Mr. Pepys's half-brother, a cheerful simple-minded old fellow, who had made a comfortable fortune in fish and enjoyed an honorable reputation as a citizen of the parish of St. Andrew Undershaft. Samuel did not particularly like the old man or enjoy his company, but he was a wealthy and respected member of the family, an amusing if unpredictable table companion, and he had an especial fondness for Elizabeth. Samuel had given Uncle Wight a swan for a holiday present, one of a pair that Will Howe had given him, and he had accepted his uncle's invitation to come on New Year's Day to help in the eating of it.

The stuffy little parlor of the ancient house in St. Mary Axe was almost filled with Uncle Wight's holiday guests when Samuel and Elizabeth arrived. Uncle Wight greeted them at the door, bussed Elizabeth loudly, and screeched in his high piping voice for the maidservant to bring his niece and nephew a goblet of wine. The old man put his arm around Elizabeth's waist and led her away into the company, leaving Samuel to fend for himself. When dinner was announced, Uncle Wight retained his hold on Elizabeth's waist and made her sit beside him at the head of the table. He ignored his other guests and spent most of the meal pressing her to drink more wine and whispering sibilantly into her ear.

Samuel sat at the far end of the table beside his Aunt Wight. The garrulous old woman chattered endlessly, telling the company around her that the prize dish was the swan pie made from a fine fat swan given her by her favorite nephew, Samuel, sent direct to him by the Earl of Sandwich from his grand estate in Huntingdonshire. In honor of the occasion, she said, she had made the pie herself with her own hands from an old country recipe that had been in the family for years, made with sweet butter and claret and baked in an earthen pot between eight and ten hours.

Samuel took one look at his aunt's hands and blanched. Her fingers were cracked and broken open with wretched raw sores. He took a deep swallow of wine and announced that he was not going to be the sort of man who gave a gift and then consumed it himself. He would resist the swan, for the sake of the guests, and content himself with the chine of beef, although it had not had the advantage of his aunt's personal attention.

As soon as he could catch Elizabeth's eye, he nodded toward the huge dish of pie and shook his head. Elizabeth looked blankly back at him, but she did not eat any of the swan. Uncle Wight kept her hands so engaged that she hardly ate anything at all.

When the meal was over at last, Uncle Wight rose unsteadily from his chair, wavered a moment, and then began to say grace. His heavy tongue plodded slowly through the familiar words, sliding vaguely a time or two around a palatal ambush, and then without warning, came to a complete stop in midsentence. While his guests held their breath, he backed up two sentences and began again his cautious approach to the evasive passage. But when he arrived at the same spot again, his words stopped short. He took a deep rasping breath, sputtered, and then let out a blasting oath.

The whole company collapsed. They howled in helpless laughter, putting their heads down into their hands to contain their hysteria and wiping their eyes to look at their host standing at the head of the table with a foolish smile on his face.

As soon as the company returned to the parlor, Samuel captured Elizabeth and located their hostess. They could not stay, Samuel explained to his aunt. They had a previous engagement at the other end of town, an engagement made long ago and it was beyond their ability to alter it. They would have to be excused. Aunt Wight blessed them for coming, urged them to return soon, and, abandoning them, went in search of her deflated husband.

The engagement that Samuel could not alter at the other end of town was Sir William Davenant's production of Mr. Shakespeare's *Henry the Eighth,* the first play that either of them had seen in half a year. The doubtful pleasure of an afternoon in Uncle Wight's crowded parlor was not temptation enough to make Samuel forego his first play of the new year. But when the performance at Lincoln's Inn Fields was over, just before dark, Samuel felt somehow cheated—not with what he had missed in St. Mary Axe, but with what he had not received at the playhouse. The play had been overpraised and he had expected too much— his fatal failing. Aside from the costumes and the splendid pageants and processions, the production was a disappointment, a collection of scenes—not a real play at all.

When they got home, well after dark, chilled and let down, he and Elizabeth sat before the charcoal fire in the parlor and talked of the day. Elizabeth said that she believed Uncle Wight intended to do something fine for them. He had spent the whole dinner hour expressing the greatest fondness for her and showing the most intense curiosity about her being with child.

"You are not?" Samuel asked in surprise.

"No," said Elizabeth, "I am not, but if I were I believe Uncle Wight would make the child his heir."

"Then I wish you had told him that you were."

"But I am not, and he would know in time that I'm not," she protested.

"Perhaps in time you will be," Samuel suggested.

"I have not been these ten years," she answered quietly.

Samuel got up and punched the bed of coals with the toe of his shoe, and then came back and sat down beside her.

"I have had advice," he said.

And while Elizabeth sat looking at him with her mouth open, he told her of going one day to dinner at the Joyces, his mother's niece, and after dinner going off alone with the women of the house and coaxing them to give him their opinion of his childlessness. For an hour they had given him their opinion, straight and full. The fault might be his or it might be Elizabeth's, they told him, but there were some things he could do—and Elizabeth could do. Elizabeth should not lace her bodice too tight. Samuel should wear cool holland drawers and see that his stomach stayed warm and his back cool. They should frequently drink the juice of sage and they should eat no late suppers.

"Did they all agree upon these opinions?" Elizabeth asked.

"Upon these they did," Samuel said.

"I will try to remember," Elizabeth murmured, and they went up to bed without their usual late supper.

The next time that Samuel was near a linen draper's shop, he went in and bought two pairs of good holland drawers. At the office he moved his chair around at the Board table so that his stomach rather than his back faced the fire. Elizabeth brought home from the apothecary a bottle of sage water, and at night they sat in Samuel's study conning their lessons while the servants ate their supper alone in the kitchen. Samuel showed Elizabeth how to apply her problems in addition and subtraction to the kitchen accounts, 2 shillings for a pound of cherries and 6 shillings for a dozen oranges less half a crown for the basket of apples given them by Cousin Turner made the fruit for the Sunday dinner come to five and six.

On the globe Samuel showed his wife the danger spots in England's fight for trade: Tangier and Bombay, the Guinea Coast, and the islands of the East Indies, the American plantations, and the West Indian islands. The greatest danger, he told her, lay in those places where the Dutch were strong—the East Indies, Guinea, and New Amsterdam. That nation of greedy merchants was eager to monopolize the rich trade in spices, slaves, and silk. If they were allowed to monopolize them, the Royal Exchange might as well close up or become a nest of stalls for fishmongers and butchers. The wealthy merchants of London, the hard-faced men who made their fortunes in the great trading companies, had no notion of allowing their Dutch opponents such freedom. They were restless; the King was sympathetic, the Duke of York eager, and the Parliament worried. There might be war, he told her, and if there were, the Navy Office was in poor condition to do its duty.

In a few weeks, Elizabeth was able, with only a little help, to put her finger on the island of Java, the Gambia River, and the City of New Amsterdam, but she was never quite able to grasp why the English had to fight the Dutch at sea in order to bring silk into the shops at Westminster.

One afternoon when Samuel came home, he found Elizabeth in a strange state. She was in the bedroom, stretched out across the bed, sobbing, or laughing, or both—Samuel could not tell.

"What is it?" he asked, alarmed and on guard.

Elizabeth turned over and sat on the side of the bed. Her face was damp from tears and yet she was laughing, too. "It's Uncle Wight," she said. "Uncle Wight has paid me a visit and made me an offer."

Samuel looked blank. "What was the offer?"

Elizabeth threw herself back on the bed, rolled over, and shook the bed with her smothered convulsions. Samuel put his hand on her back to steady her. In a moment she turned her head and spluttered, "To be his wife."

Samuel sat down. "He has a wife," he said.

"I know. I know. But he doesn't have a child." Elizabeth sat back on the bed, her head against the headboard. "He wants a child, an heir, and he thinks I could give him one."

Elizabeth was sober now, and a mounting anger began to replace her hysterics. "He came here an hour ago, simpering and patting, as he always does. We sat in the parlor and he patted and cackled and mumbled. I have a beautiful body. My breasts were made to mother a child. He has said all that before. I should have a child. But this time he went further. He had always wanted a child, he said, but Aunt Wight had never given him one. I had always wanted a child, but you had never given me one. It was the Pepys blood, he said. It is wearing out."

Samuel sprang up from the bed and started to move away, but Elizabeth reached out and caught his arm.

"Don't get angry," she said, pulling him down beside her. "He is an old fool, and I haven't finished telling you."

Samuel sat upright on the bed. "What else did he say?"

"He said that it was up to us to continue the line, he and I, though neither of us is a Pepys. If I would go to bed with him, he said, and produce a child, he would give me £500 in money or in jewels beforehand and make the child his heir. He said that for all he knew, the thing was lawful."

Samuel considered for a moment, and then he broke out, "Lawful or not. . . ."

But Elizabeth hit him on the shoulder with her fist and went on, "He said it all with a laugh, as if it might be a joke—but it was no joke. Those patting hands were too busy."

Samuel covered his face and lay back on the bed.

"Don't worry," Elizabeth said, "I handled him. I moved out of his way and talked to him straight—at a distance. I told him that we had always loved him, and still do, but that any child I should ever have would come from you—and nobody else. He took it well enough. He stammered around a little, cackling and sniggering, but then he said that since he knew my mind, he would say no more of it. He stayed only a little longer, talking about nothing. When he left he told me again that I had a beautiful body, and he kissed me warmly. It was funny—and awful too. I didn't know what to think."

Samuel lay still, numb and perplexed. He did not know what to think either. What he felt was not jealousy; it was not like the Pembleton business. It was something more confused and complicated: anger and amazement and anxiety and also a touch of pride. Five hundred pounds for one night with his wife! But Elizabeth had handled him well. She had repulsed him without, apparently, antagonizing him. It was a touchy business. The old man was a fool, but he was a rich fool and in search of an heir. It would be well to let the matter cool a bit before he decided how to carry himself with his uncle. Samuel reached out and patted Elizabeth on the elbow. She lay back beside him and put her face into his shoulder. Samuel held her close and told her that they need not study their lessons tonight.

In the days that followed, Samuel could not free his mind of the disturbing image of Uncle Wight. At the office his mind wandered from the contract that Hayter placed before him for his signature. At the coffeehouses he looked at the buzzing ensemble of London merchants and saw a host of Uncle Wights, reputable and dignified men by day and sniggering, lascivious goats by night. He went to the new playhouse in Bridges Street, Covent Garden, to see the King's actors in their new home, but even the excitement of the actresses singing their risqué songs and switching enticingly around the stage only heightened his own lust and at the same time depressed him with the frustrating thought that he had not been able to bring Elizabeth to motherhood.

In his suddenly aroused lust he went to Westminster and searched out Betty Lane. Betty's chief virtue as a companion was that she was always willing to allow a tousle in the most cheerful good humor and yet protect the occasion from danger by her ultimate, tactful common sense. She was a ready source, if you could abide her chatter, of erotic pleasure and ultimate security.

Samuel found her at the linen shop in Westminster Hall, and she was available to go out for a bit of cheer with Mr. Pepys. They went to a little tavern, out of the way and secluded in one of the back streets, and Samuel ordered ale to be served to them in the private room. While they sipped their ale and Betty rambled on about her desire to get a good husband and leave the confinement of the linen shop, Samuel explored the softness of the girl's well-rounded body, her arms, her breasts, her legs, and at last the white fullness of her thighs.

Betty's aimless chitchat gradually became stilled; her eyes glazed; and before either of them could summon their usual caution—it must have been the ale—Samuel had done with her what he had always been sure he would not do.

On his way back home, Samuel cursed himself for his folly. A bastard would be all that he deserved. After the years of trying to get Elizabeth with child, it would now be the height of irony for him to father one on witless, garrulous Betty. He felt cheated and almost angry that she had so unexpectedly let down her guard and allowed it to happen. One thing was certain; he would not be so impetuous and trusting again—at least not until Mistress Betty had found herself a husband.

When he got home, he went directly to his office and took out his diary. The best way to get the worry out of his mind and to make firm his resolve was to embalm, in the journal, word for word, every accusing detail. He wrote for fifteen minutes, quickly, without stopping, until it was all down. When he came to the end and considered the enormity of the hazard, his mind pulled back strangely and he closed the entry in a polyglot, a confused mélange of schoolboy French and English, "My mind un peu troubled pour ce que fait today, but I hope it will be la dernier de toute ma vie." Somehow that put a double cloak of protection around the incident.

He did not see Betty again for several weeks. He was fearful of what she might have to tell him, and he was busy. The merchants at the Royal Exchange, the big men, the members of the trading companies, especially the powerful East India Company, were storming mad. The Dutch had sailed into Surat, in India, ignored the English factor, put their flag above the British standard, and had beaten every man who tried to interfere. They had proclaimed loudly that they cared nothing for what their own government had to say at home: they were Lords of the Southern Seas and they dared any man or government to cross them. The furious English merchants at the Royal Exchange beat their fists on the tables, swore themselves blue in the face, and cried that it was high time the Parliament gave the King enough money to teach the lousy Holland dogs a bloody lesson.

At Whitehall Samuel heard the Duke of York roundly curse the Dutch and say that he was ready himself to go to sea as soon as the Parliament gave them enough money to gather a fleet. Samuel went back to the Navy Office and told Mr. Hayter to be prepared to work late into the night, day in and day out, from that time onward. He went down the river and warned the yardmasters to take up all slack in their organization, keep supplies well stored and accounted for, see to it that good workmen were kept busy and lazy ones dismissed. There was trouble ahead.

He made the rounds of the principal contractors, checked the state of their supplies on hand, the disposition of their cargo ships, and their ability to fill large contracts on short notice. Back at Whitehall he conferred with the Duke of York in the Matted Gallery about the progress of the new men-of-war building at Woolwich and discovered to his happy surprise that for the first time he had felt no awe in talking with His Royal Highness.

While he was in the neighborhood he decided to go to Westminster Hall. There had been time enough for the wench to discover whether or not her carelessness had brought him the disgrace of a bastard. He dreaded even seeing the girl. There was no telling what she might do: keep him in unnecessary, taunting suspense, claim him as the parent of a child really fathered by another, or angrily demand that he support her and the child he was in reality responsible for. He cursed himself for his folly in debauching the slut, and he cursed her for permitting him to do so. He was in a wretched, fearful state when he arrived at the linen stall.

Betty was busy with a customer and, as far as he could tell, unaware that he was there. While he waited for her to discover him, he examined the linens, standing irritably first on one foot and then on the other. He selected two neckbands and four women's handkerchiefs.

When Betty was finally at liberty, she came over quickly to Samuel, grinning mockingly.

"And how is Mr. Pepys today?" she asked brightly.

Samuel handed her his purchases. "I am well," he answered her gravely. "But it is of more consequence to know how you do."

Betty laughed gleefully. "Find me a husband, Mr. Pepys, and you won't have to sweat so. I am well."

Samuel patted her hand joyfully and hurried away, almost running down the crowded Hall. As he reached the north door and stepped out into New Palace Yard, he heard his name being shouted behind him. He turned and saw Betty, her hair flying, screaming with laughter, running after him and waving a package.

He had forgotten his neckbands and the handkerchiefs for Elizabeth.

$\mathscr{I}$ had no mind to $\int ee$ him die

ONE DAY IN MARCH as Samuel walked along the hard-packed dirt road that ran from Deptford across the King's Meadow to Redriffe Stairs, he turned his mind away from the problems of preparing the supply yards for a possible war and thought about his brother Tom. The tailoring shop was not prospering, and Tom was showing no signs of settling down to the steady drudgery necessary to eke out an existence in that highly competitive trade. There was no question about Tom's abilities as a tailor. He could make a suit as acceptably as his father could; he needed only to spend more time in the cutting room and at the sewing table and less time in Southwark and Smithfield. Elizabeth was right: Tom needed a wife.

Samuel sat down on a stone under the shade of a tree to rest a bit before walking the last half mile in the hot spring weather. Down the road came three wagons, moving slowly and throwing out little clouds of dust from the creaking wheels. The wagons were festooned with bright scraps of cloth. Copper pans and tankards hung suspended from a rope that ran the length of the wagons and clanked against one another. Dark-skinned women sat on the straw of the bouncing wagon beds and wiry, hard-featured, little men walked beside the horses, as impassive and melancholy as the animals. They were gypsies, a ragtag band who came from God knows where, on their endless way to country fairs and other rural gatherings of gullible men, in slow, perpetual motion along the distant roads of an eternally foreign country. Samuel watched them creak by down the dusty road, the late afternoon sun glinting on the copper pots.

A hundred yards farther down the road, the wagons pulled to a stop under the shade of a clump of trees. The men unhitched the horses and squatted down on their heels to gaze with absorbed and solemn interest at the aimless grazing of the scraggly beasts. The women continued to sit in the straw of the wagon beds, their hands busy, working quickly and deftly at something that was too small and obscure for Samuel to see. As he came abreast the unhitched wagons, the women called out to him, jabbering and screeching. Samuel stopped. He could not understand a word they were saying, but he saw that they were making dolls and toys from string and pieces of cloth and strips of old leather. At the tail gate of the second wagon, a girl held out her hands to him, invitingly. She could not have been more than sixteen, but she had the full, rich sensuousness of a woman of twenty. While the others jabbered and laughed, the girl just smiled and held out her hands. Samuel walked toward her and all the jabbering stopped. The girl leaned down from the high wagon bed and her loose blouse looped down freely. Samuel stood transfixed.

"Tell your fortune," the girl said in clear English, holding out her hands.

Without moving his eyes, Samuel gave her his hands. The other women returned to their work, keeping their hands busy and maintaining a strict silence. The girl drew her fingers across the palm of Samuel's left hand. She looked closely at the lines on his hand and traced the length of his fingers. She turned his hand this way and that and folded his fingers into a fist. Then she began to talk in a singsong, hurried recital, like a child who has memorized a hasty lesson. The gentleman was married, she said. He had a wife he loved dearly, but he was not always faithful to her. There had been trouble in the past, quarrels and poverty and danger, but fortune was now improved. The quarrel was mended; plenty had replaced poverty; and the danger was passed. The future looked bright. There was wealth ahead and long life and much happiness. While the girl rattled on her rigmarole, Samuel kept his attention raptly fixed upon the young breasts so openly revealed inside the loose blouse, unconstricted and unblemished, and the girl made no effort to impede his gazing. She rattled on.

"Beware," she said, "of a man named Thomas and a man named John. They seek to hurt you."

Samuel looked up quickly.

"Beware this day se'nnight. The man named Thomas or the man named John will come to borrow money. You must not lend it."

Samuel looked closely into the girl's eyes and started to ask a question, but she quickly sat up in the wagon.

"That is all," she said, holding out one hand toward him. "That is all that I can tell."

Samuel took out his purse and slowly counted ninepence into her hand. "John and Thomas?" he asked, but the girl crossed her arms over her breasts, shook her head, and smiled at him.

The women in the wagon began immediately to chatter, jabbering and caterwauling, drowning Samuel out in a flood of sound. He walked on down the road, thoughtful and perplexed, and a shrill cackle of laughter followed him.

There was something uncanny about the girl's prophecy, her hitting upon the two names that were in his mind. They were common enough names, appearing regularly on any roll of English families, but so were Edward and William and George—and Samuel, for that matter. There was some lucky—or unlucky—chance involved in the girl's hitting upon the names of Samuel's two brothers just at the moment when he was concerned about them.

As Samuel rode up and across the river from Redriffe to Tower Wharf, he thought about John. John was staying at Seething Lane during the Lenten holidays. Samuel had invited the boy to come to London instead of going to Brampton, so that he could test his scholar's progress at Magdalene. Samuel had assumed the expense of keeping his brother at the University. John had always shown a kind of brightness in books—not brilliance, but enough aptness to justify Samuel's hope that the boy could make a career either in the Church or in some clerkly office, perhaps in the Navy if he applied himself. But John had not been distinguishing himself in his studies, as far as Samuel could learn. He was inclined toward laziness and he showed much more interest in the newfangled, superficial, modern books than he did in the solid, classical writers. But up to the moment John had shown no tendency toward being spendthrift. It was not John's finances that worried Samuel, as Tom's did. Why, Samuel wondered, had the gypsy included John in her prophetic warning about borrowing? He shrugged and dismissed the foolish augury.

On the last night of the week, John was late to dinner. Samuel sent Will Hewer out to inquire if his truant brother had been seen in the neighborhood during the afternoon, and ordered the maid to serve supper without awaiting Master John. When Hewer returned with the information that no one in the neighborhood had seen anything of Mr. Pepys's brother since noon, Samuel returned to the study. He would wait up for the young man.

It was nine o'clock before John put in his appearance at Seething Lane. He ran up the steps, burst into the study without knocking, and poured out his excuses before Samuel could collect himself for an attack. He had spent the afternoon with Tom, John explained hurriedly, helping in the shop and delivering clothes for him. It was supper time before he returned to the tailoring shop from his last errand and Tom had urged him to stay and eat with him, for Tom had a letter he wanted to write to Samuel. John put a letter into Samuel's hand and sat down, his excuses made and his errand performed.

Samuel looked at his brother and then he looked at the letter. "What is it?" Samuel asked, but John only wiped his brow and waited for Samuel to make the next move.

Samuel broke the seal with his finger and opened the letter. He read it through quickly, paused, and looked at John, but John's attention was riveted on the books that lay upon the table. Samuel got up and walked to the window. He came back to the candlelight and read the letter again. Without a word he dropped the missive, face open, in front of John and walked back into the dark shadows of the room.

"Do you know what brother Tom writes me for?" Samuel asked from the dark.

"Yes," said John, without raising his head.

"He asks to borrow twenty pounds," Samuel informed him.

"I know," John said.

"Why does he need twenty pounds? Why does he need any money?" Samuel kept his position in the dark edge of the room.

"He needs to buy cloth. He needs to pay his servants, to buy food, to pay his debts." John's voice began to rise in petulance. "I don't know why he needs the money," he cried out, "but he needs it, and he turns to you, the only member of the family who has any money, just the way all the rest of us have to turn to you. We don't enjoy it. We wish we didn't have to, but you are the eldest and all benefit has fallen to you. We can't help that we are younger and impoverished and dependent on you."

John's voice broke and he dropped his head into his arms on the table.

Samuel came over quietly and sat down beside him. "Do you believe in prophecy?" he asked after a moment.

John shook his head in his arms and mumbled "No."

"Neither do I," Samuel said. "But a week ago today a gypsy wench told me that Tom and John would come that day se'nnight to borrow money. Somehow she was right. You did come. Right on time."

John raised his head. "It is Tom that wants the money."

"Of course," Samuel said, getting up to leave the room.

"Will you send him the money?" John asked quickly.

Samuel stopped in the doorway. "No," he said, smiling benignly. "The gypsy told me not to."

Samuel sent Tom no money, but he did send word to his father to come down to London to stay for a week in the shop and see why Tom needed to borrow money for cloth. The old man came promptly and refused Samuel's invitation to stay in Seething Lane. He would need to live in Salisbury Court the few days he would be in London, he explained, in order to understand Tom's accounts and business. John also said that he would go to Salisbury Court and live while his father was in town. He made some reference to a slight that Elizabeth had made of him, but Samuel suspected that John was more interested in escaping his nightly lessons than in avoiding Elizabeth's slights.

On the first afternoon that Samuel had free from his work, he went to Salisbury Court to learn what his father had discovered in Tom's accounts. He discovered as soon as he walked into the parlor that he had entered a hostile camp. Tom and John sat together on one side of the room and his father sat at the table by the window. Samuel seated himself at the center table and asked his father what he had found in Tom's books to account for the fact that he did not have the money to buy cloth.

Nothing very much, the old man said. Tom was just temporarily behindhand in his collections. He would stay in the shop with the boy until the accounts were balanced, until all of Tom's affairs were straight. He just needed a little help from an old retired tailor.

Samuel said that he was very glad to hear it.

"However," the old man continued, "since I am here, I think I ought to tell you that Elizabeth. . . ."

"I have not come to discuss Elizabeth," Samuel broke in quickly.

"But I have a right. . . ."

"I am the only one who has any rights with Elizabeth," Samuel retorted before his father could finish his sentence.

A tense stillness suddenly enveloped the room. Samuel glared at the three men, his father and his two brothers, and stood firm, daring them to insert one word into his private life. Young John mistook the moment, thinking that at last he was with the strong majority outfacing the cornered tyrant.

"Elizabeth as much as told me to leave your house. Do you let your wife order your family out of your house?"

Samuel stood for a moment looking at his frightened, angry brother. Clasping his hands behind his back to hide their trembling, Samuel slowly arose from the table, and surveyed his antagonists. Tom was looking out the window as if he were no part of the proceedings. John, having fired his bolt, clung rigidly to the arms of his chair. Their father looked at John in blank surprise, caught between awe and shock at his youngest son's foolhardiness.

When he got to the side of the room where John and Tom were sitting, Samuel pulled back a chair and sat down slowly. He addressed himself solely to John but pitched his voice loud enough for the others to know that they were included. The house was Elizabeth's home, he told John. It was the only place in the world she had where she could do as she pleased, command her servants, go about dressed or undressed, order her own meals, or fling a fit if she felt like it. Elizabeth's only obligation in that house was to her husband, and the details of that obligation were a matter of debate only between them. If Elizabeth, within the limitations of her nature, satisfied him, then she would have to satisfy anyone who came into that house.

He would not discuss, he said, even with his own brother, his wife's faults. He knew Elizabeth's faults better than anyone else, and on the whole he had learned to live with them. He had learned well enough to be able to enjoy a certain success in his profession and a certain prosperity in his affairs. His family, his parents, and his brothers and sister had reason to love his prosperity and would in the future continue to have reason, but neither he nor they could hope to reap the rewards of industry and diligence if his life at home with his wife were made a hell of faction and discord.

"It is to your interest," he said turning to his father and then to John and Tom, "to see that my life with Elizabeth is not made difficult. You have nothing to fear of her but her occasionally foolish tongue, which for love of me you can bear, but you might well fear the injury that would be done to me if you magnify her faults and make me discontent with my only place of refuge in this troubled world."

Samuel stopped and watched his audience. He was aware that he had warmed to his subject and had begun to enjoy his own words. He waited for their reaction very much as he would wait after playing to a new audience on his violin. The stress of the occasion had given way to the excitement of the performance itself. Tom and John kept their eyes on the floor, looking neither from him nor directly at him, but his father cleared his throat, wiped the back of his hand across one eye, and pushed himself up from his chair. He eased across the floor to Samuel's side and patted him on the shoulder.

"Come," he said, "let us see what we can do to help Tom with his business."

After John and his father had left London, John returning to Cambridge and his father to Brampton, Samuel kept his distance from Tom's troubles at Salisbury Court. If Tom wanted to be free to ruin himself, Samuel was resolved to give him all the freedom he wanted; but when he received word a week later that Tom was ill, he went at once to the tailoring shop and looked in on him. Tom lay in bed, the covers pulled up to his chin, shivering and looking miserable. It was the old consumption that had bothered him during the winter, Tom said weakly. He would be up again in a day or two.

Samuel told him severely to see to it that he stayed in; a sick tailor was no tailor at all. But before he left the house he instructed the maid that kept Tom's house for him to see that her master did stay in bed. The weather was too tricky in March for his brother to take chances. If he got no better or needed anything, she was to send to Seething Lane.

Sunday morning was foul and blustery. Rain came down in sheets, beating against the windows and turning the office gardens into a lake. Samuel looked out at the soaked streets and gave up his intention of going to Westminster to visit Mr. Coventry. The weather was too bad even for going across the street to church.

After dinner the rain held up, and he ran across to the office to work a while, but as soon as he was settled the heavens opened up again and he was caught. It did not matter; he had work to do, and he was safe from interruption for the afternoon.

It was almost dark and his eyes were stinging from reading in the bad light, when he was stopped by a knock on the door. It was the cookmaid, soaking wet from her dash across the garden, panting breathlessly that two men were at the house saying it was urgent to see Mr. Pepys. Samuel closed up his work, draped a small tarpaulin over his head, and followed Bess back to the house.

Anthony and Will Joyce, the loud-voiced tallow sellers who had married his mother's nieces, Kate and Mary Fenner, stood dripping on the Turkey carpet in the parlor. Samuel took them down to the kitchen, where their dripping would be less destructive, and gave them a round of ale. What they had come for, Anthony said, was to advise with him about getting someone to look after Tom. Tom was getting worse and the maid only worked till dark; he needed somebody to stay with him at night.

Samuel sat down and looked at the pouring rain outside the window. "Can your wives find somebody for tonight?" he asked. "Someone in the neighborhood?"

Anthony Joyce finished his ale, wiped his mouth, and said that he thought the girls could handle it—for one night. Samuel said that one night was all he was asking for. He would himself come the next morning and take charge. The two brothers bade Cousin Samuel goodnight and plodded out the door into the rain.

As Samuel stood in the door watching the Joyces disappear into the heavy night, a young boy came panting up to him from the opposite direction, winded and wet. He handed Samuel a sodden note and said that he had run all the way from Mrs. Turner's house in Salisbury Court. Samuel took the boy into the kitchen and put him near the fire to dry while he read the note. It was brief, a few lines of Cousin Jane's awkward scrawl. Samuel had better come, she had written. Tom was not likely to last the night. Samuel sent the boy running toward Tower Street to find the Joyces, get a coach, and come back for him.

As they rode, three-quarters of an hour later, through the wet and running streets, Will Joyce said that it was for the purpose of telling Samuel how sick Tom was that they had come, but their courage had failed them and they had spoken only of the need for a nurse.

"How sick is he?" Samuel asked, restraining his impatience with the Joyces' weak-kneed stupidity.

"Out of his head," Anthony said, "and near destroyed with the pox."

Samuel caught his breath. "How do you know?" he demanded.

"Tom told the doctor and the doctor found an ulcer in his mouth."

Samuel beat his knee with his fist, but he said nothing more until they got to the tailoring shop.

The parlor was full of cousins and neighbors—the Joyces, the Fenners, Jane Turner, her son Will, and her daughter Theophila. Uncle Fenner grabbed Samuel immediately and began to blab about what a Dr. Powell had told him about the ulcer in Tom's mouth, but Samuel cut him short and went into the bedroom. Tom lay on the bed, turning his head back and forth on the pillow and muttering. Cousin Jane Turner sat beside him mopping his brow with a damp cloth. Samuel sat down on the bed for a moment and listened to the gibberish that Tom was muttering. Then he took his brother by the arms and held him firmly.

"Who is this?" he asked, loudly.

Tom stopped moving his head, looked hard, and said feebly, "Samuel."

Then he began moving his head back and forth again and mouthing incomprehensible words. Jane Turner shook her head sadly. Samuel got up and left the room. He was sure Tom did not have syphilis.

He went back into the parlor and beckoned for Will Turner to join him. Together they went into the kitchen in search of the maid. She was sitting by the fire, solemn and stolid, like a guest at a wake. Samuel said that they would like to discuss Master Tom's household affairs; he was very sick and they needed to know about his possessions.

The phlegmatic woman looked at him without expression. "I am ready for you," she said. "I know that death is in this house—it has been for two days—and I got everything ready. All his books and papers and money are locked in his office and here is the key. Nobody has been in there but me, and you will just have to take my word for it that it's all there."

She unpinned a key from the inside of her dress and gave it to Samuel.

"Now, you're responsible," she said flatly.

Samuel twiddled the key a moment and then returned it to her. "You are a good servant," he said. "Keep the key. My brother is fortunate to have you here."

"Then it is the only thing he *is* fortunate in," she said darkly.

Mrs. Holden, the hatmaker's wife, who lived in the neighborhood, had arranged for a nurse to come and spend the night by Tom's bedside. Samuel thanked her for her kindness and walked home through the wet streets, his mind numb at the thought of Tom dying.

When he returned to Salisbury Court the next morning, only the nurse, a stupid, slow-witted old woman, was with Tom. Samuel dismissed her and sat down on the bed.

"Who am I?" he asked, but Tom only muttered sleepily and moved his head from side to side.

Samuel sat in the dark, ill-smelling room for an hour, watching his brother toss and moan until the maid came in with a tankard of beer. While Samuel drank his morning draught by the bed, the maid sat near him in a chair and answered his questions. Master Tom had paid little attention to his business of late, allowing his apprentice to operate the cutting room unsupervised while he was gone all day in the City. She had turned away a dozen creditors who claimed that he owed them money. There had been mysterious meetings behind locked doors with a sorry-looking old man and his slattern wife, pensioners of the parish, but whether that was about money or something worse she did not know.

When Mrs. Holden and the Joyce sisters came at midmorning, Samuel left Tom in their charge and went out to tell his clerks that he would not be available at the office unless something of urgency required him.

For the rest of that day and all of the next, Samuel did what he could to trace down the rumor of the pox, as syphilis was referred to in those times. He could not find the doctor who had claimed he had seen the ulcer, but he told Uncle Fenner sharply that he was not to say anything further about it until they had proof. Cousin Jane Turner offered the services of her doctor, Mr. Wiverly, to go with Samuel to Tom and examine him. Samuel told her to fetch him, and they would learn the truth at once.

Wiverly came the next afternoon. He cleared the sickroom of the women and, with Samuel by his side, he examined Tom's mouth. He pulled back the covers and looked closely over his whole body.

"Whatever this boy is dying of," he said at last, "it is not the pox. I will lay my life on it. He is as clean as the day he was born."

"Well, that at least is a comfort," Samuel said, "but he is still deathly sick."

"He is indeed," Mr. Wiverly sighed. "We can only hope for the fever to break."

But the fever did not break—that day or the next. When Uncle Fenner's physician came to call on his patient, Samuel handled him roughly, denouncing him for a quack and a rumor-monger, and packed him off, unpaid, and with a threat to have him charged if he said another word about the pox.

There was nothing left to do but wait. Samuel sat by the bed through the long afternoon. Elizabeth came to the house and stayed in the parlor helping Cousin Jane and Theophila and Mrs.

Holden receive the visitors who came to console and take the family's light refreshments. It was an endless afternoon. Samuel sat quietly in the room and listened to Tom's labored breathing. For long spells Tom lay still, as if in a coma, and then he would stir and begin to jabber, broken phrases, senseless words, sometimes a whole clear sentence related to nothing. Once, after Samuel held up his brother's head and poured a sip of wine into his mouth, Tom sat straight up and in clear French said, "*Quand un homme boit, quand il n'a point d'inclination à boire, il ne lui fait jamais de bien.*"

But the drink did do him some good, for his head seemed to clear and for half an hour he was as lucid as he had ever been in his life. He took Samuel's hand and in a clear calm voice asked, "Am I dying?"

The threshold of death did not seem to Samuel a worthy place to bandy words of futile hope.

"Yes, Tom, you are dying," he said.

Tom looked at him steadily for a moment and nodded his head. Samuel felt his insides begin to melt and flow downward, but he managed to keep his face steady. There was one more thing.

"And whither do you think to go, Tom?"

Tom looked thoughtful for a minute and then he began to speak. "Why, whither should I go? There are but two ways. If I go the bad way, I must give God thanks for it; and if I go the other way, I must give God the more thanks for it. I hope I have not been so undutiful and unthankful in my life, but I hope I shall go that way."

The long speech seemed to tire him; he put his head back upon the pillow wearily; his eyes closed as if in sleep, and then the restless tossing and the idle words began again.

Samuel suddenly surrendered to his grief, weeping openly in the dark room as his brother muttered away his life on the torn bed. In a little while the foolish words stopped. Samuel looked at him quickly. Tom's mouth kept working and a rattle of phlegm came from his throat. Samuel hurriedly sat down beside him and urged him to try to clear his throat of the spittle. Tom gasped until the breath finally broke through and discharged a flood of phlegm into the basin that Samuel held for him. Then he lay back and the agonizing fight for breath started again.

Samuel could stand no more. He gave the pan to the nurse and fled from the room. Elizabeth met him in the hall and caught him. She held him fast while he trembled and muttered, "I have no mind to see him die."

In a few minutes the panic was over. Elizabeth took him to a chair in the hall and brought him a glass of wine. She held his hand while he sipped the wine and regained his composure. When he went back into the room, Tom lay strangely still, his chops fallen and his hands relaxed. The nurse was standing beside his head, holding his eyes shut.

Samuel summoned Mrs. Holden and Cousin Jane and stayed in the room while they stripped off Tom's clothing and laid him out, pale as a stone and as foreign as a Turk. Mrs. Holden turned once from her work and said to Samuel, "This man's body is clean," but he seemed neither to hear her nor understand what she had said.

When their work was done, the women departed and Samuel took one last look at his brother. He did not recognize him. He went to the little office in the shop and gathered all the papers the careful maid had stored there—Tom's accounts, his letters, his unfilled orders, and the bag of money. When he got home, he put them all into his closet, and then sat down to write the bitter news to his father.

They buried Tom three days later in the middle aisle of St. Bride's Church. Samuel called upon the grave-maker and with him surveyed the small plot in the churchyard where his eight brothers and sisters who had died in infancy were buried. There would not be room there for Tom, Samuel decided, and it would be a comfort to his mother to know that Tom was buried as near as possible to her own pew in the church. So they went back inside the church, and the grave-maker said that for an extra pound he could find room for Tom somehow. "The middle aisle is pretty full," he said, "but for a sixpence I will justle them together. Though the corpses are not all full rotten yet, I will make room for Tom Pepys."

Samuel winced at the thought of a man's tomb being at the

mercy of such a cheerfully callous arranger of the dead; but there were few details of death that were not harrowing.

At the tailoring shop he found Mrs. Holden supervising a group of maids in cleaning the house, and Mr. Honeywood's clerk was busy making an inventory of all Tom's goods. There was a satisfying consolation in the quiet efficiency of these good, shop-keeping neighbors, who thought of the needful thing to do and did it without pretense or show.

In the afternoon the carpenters brought the pine board coffin, nailed it up, and set it upon trestles in the parlor. Samuel sat in a chair and watched them, lulled by the quiet movements of the workmen, fascinated, as he always was, by the easy adroitness of men who lived by the skill of their hands. His mood was suddenly broken, however, when Will Joyce burst into the house, half drunk and maudlin, to pay his respects to his dead kinsman. He stood by the coffin, his hand on the lid, and shouted his eulogy. "Tom Pepys was a good man," he cried. "He was a good tailor, a good speaker, and a loyal citizen. The world will be less without Tom Pepys in it." Then he put his head on the coffin and bawled.

Samuel left the room quickly and went down the street to Cousin Jane Turner's house. He found Theophila busy making sweetmeats for the funeral. He drew her out of the kitchen and led her to the harpsichord in the parlor. He needed to hear some music. Theophila did not play very well, but even her faltering melodies were enough to take the sound of Will Joyce's outlandish grief out of his ears.

On the morning of the funeral, Samuel took his best pair of boots to Mr. Wotton and had him black the soles. He looked in at the tailoring shop to see that all was in readiness. The invaluable Mrs. Holden was supervising the arranging of the 120 chairs borrowed to seat the guests. Cousin Jane and Theophila were busy in the kitchen pouring up wine and counting biscuits. The Joyces and the Fenners came in and out upon sundry errands. The tailoring shop was ready for its funeral.

Samuel went home to put on his mourning clothes and to get Elizabeth. It was a relief to him that his father and mother and Pall and John would not get to London in time for the burial. They would only present another problem in the tense affairs of the day, and it was best that the old people were spared the grief of seeing Tom lowered into his grave. It would be grief enough for them in the days ahead to realize that their twelve children had now been reduced to three.

When Samuel and Elizabeth arrived in Salisbury Court at one o'clock, only the family attendants were present: the Turners and the Joyces; Cousin Joyce Norton, who was to dispense the refreshments; the girls in white gloves who were to serve the biscuit and burnt claret; and Mrs. Holden. A hundred and twenty guests had been invited to come between one and two o'clock, but none had yet arrived.

And none had arrived by two o'clock. Samuel went to the church to see that the grave and the vicar were ready. Both were.

At three o'clock the 120 chairs were still empty. Samuel wandered around the stilted rooms, counted the chairs, sampled the claret, and chatted with the girls who were to serve the wine.

It was four o'clock when the first guests arrived. Mrs. Holden showed the women into one room and the men into another. The girls passed the biscuits and Samuel watched the street.

The guests came steadily after that, City people, dressed in sturdy woolens and somber worsted, neighbors and relatives and acquaintances, who took it as their duty to pay their last respects to John Pepys's unhappy boy, who were willing to close their shops an hour early to go to a funeral but who would not, even for death itself, close them for the whole afternoon.

By four-thirty the rooms were almost filled, the men in the parlor and the women in the dining room; and the guests still came. Mrs. Holden sent out for more chairs, and Cousin Norton reduced the serving of biscuits to four for each person. By five o'clock a hundred and fifty men and women were sitting close but decently in the crowded little house.

When all the wine had been drunk and the biscuits eaten, Samuel gave the word and the bearers took up the coffin and bore it out of the house into the narrow street. The procession of guests followed on foot up Salisbury Court into Fleet Street and through the north gate of the churchyard. The vicar met the coffin at the door of the church and led the procession to the open grave in the middle aisle. Raising his arm, he began to read the ancient

Order for the Burial of the Dead: *I am the resurrection and the life, saith the Lord: he that believeth in me, though he were dead, yet shall he live.* ...

The solemn words poured out around Samuel, enveloping him in familiar sound, rising and falling, isolating him from the reality of the late March afternoon. *Man, that is born of a woman, hath but a short time to live, and is full of misery. He cometh up, and is cut down, like a flower; he fleeth as it were a shadow, and never continueth.* ...

The words seemed to have little to do with Tom; only Tom in this whole company was now insensate to anxieties of the moment, the perplexity of the future, and the sudden realization of shocking mortality. No longer would Tom have to endure the pain of trying to catch his breath, or worry about the solvency of a little tailoring shop. Tom was at least free from pain, but Samuel had before him the ordeal of consoling his parents and ordering his brother's tangled affairs, while he fought his own battles at the office, at Whitehall, at Seething Lane. And there was now the threat of war. War was uncertain and freighted with hazard. There was no telling. ...

O Lord God most holy, O Lord most mighty, O holy and most merciful Saviour, deliver us not into the bitter pains. ... Samuel closed his eyes and tried to keep his mind from the troubles that lay ahead.

X

This year of public wonder and mischief

ON CHRISTMAS EVE, 1664, Samuel sat in his study working late on his accounts and transcribing his journal. It was a fine cold night, frosty and bright with moonlight. Elizabeth was long since in bed, and Samuel's new boy servant, Tom Edwards, was asleep in the entry, waiting for the bellman to wake him and tell him that the comet had appeared. The comet had been visible on the eastern horizon of London for several weeks, but Samuel had not had time or opportunity to see it. Lord Sandwich on his flagship at Portsmouth had seen the bright object with its long ten-degree tail spread out across the dark sky. Mr. John Evelyn, of Greenwich, had reported that he had seen the phenomenon clearly from his gardens at Sayes Court. But Samuel had not seen it. He had heard about it, however; a great deal about it. The gentlemen of the newly chartered Royal Society had gone up at night to the high ground at Hampstead and observed it. Dr. Robert Hooke, the professor of geometry at Gresham College, had lectured the Society, estimating that this was a return of the great comet of 1618. Other citizens, less objective than the scientists of the Royal Society, discussed the heavenly wonder over their pots of ale in the taverns and speculated fearfully what it meant. Some said it was just a star broken loose from its moorings, plummeting to its own death. Others said that it was a sign, a warning of famine, plague, and war, a portent of God's wrath for the sins of those who ruled England in the name of the Antichrist.

While awaiting the bellman's summons, Samuel checked his

accounts and reviewed the events of the year. Now by the grace of God he was worth £1,349, an improvement of over £500 since the same time last year, although he had had heavy charges. He had spent over £400 in the twelvemonth. He had employed a young woman, Mary Mercer, the daughter of Will Hewer's landlady in Fenchurch Street, as a companion for Elizabeth. He had obtained his own new servant, Tom Edwards, from the school for choir boys at the Chapel Royal. Additional servants, especially of the caliber of Mercer and Tom, cost a pretty penny in extra food, new livery, and increased entertainment.

But there had been compensating profits. His share of the victual contract for Tangier was bringing him £300 a year. Sir William Warren had received an order for 1,000 masts and the grateful merchant had given Samuel a present of £100; and there were always driblets from other equally grateful or equally hopeful contractors. In the early summer the opportunities had taken a sudden spurt. A small English fleet under Captain Robert Holmes attacked the Guinea coast, destroyed the Dutch strongholds there, and turned the profitable slave trade over to the English Royal African Company. In a fury of revenge the Dutch began to assemble a battle fleet. To add to the Dutch anger, Colonel Richard Nicholl sailed into the harbor of New Amsterdam and claimed all of the New Netherlands for his patron, the Duke of York. There was no question in anybody's mind that war with the Dutch was at hand.

In expectation of Dutch retaliation, the King ordered all ships of the line to prepare for duty, and made his plea to the Parliament for funds to conduct a three-year war with the United Provinces. Lord Sandwich went into the narrow seas with a small fleet of twenty ships to keep a summer guard. The Duke of York ordered the Navy Office to begin at once to lay up an ample supply of stores and ship materials. If the Dutch could be kept at bay until the spring of 1665, the new fleet would be ready and a war chest provided.

Samuel inspected the yards, conferred with Ordnance and Victual, and fretted about the inability of the press gangs to muster enough good hands to man the ships.

When cool weather came in October the Navy yards were well

stocked with supplies. Lord Sandwich was ordered to keep his fleet out on winter guard, and Samuel continued to confer profitably with the naval contractors. In order to facilitate the increased work of the Office in preparing the battle fleet, the Lord Admiral appointed William, second Viscount Brouncker, to come on the Navy Board as an extra Commissioner. Lord Brouncker was a distinguished scholar, a mathematician; he had had the honor of being the first President of the Royal Society when it was chartered by the King in 1662.

Samuel was pleased to have so famous a scholar join the company in Seething Lane, but he was skeptical of the wisdom of cluttering the Office with uninitiated and untested officers in times of approaching trouble. Brouncker, he felt, was a mixed and doubtful blessing.

Despite the fear of what the future had in store, Samuel felt that his position was improved in the world. He was in good condition at the office; he had a reasonable fortune buried in the cellar of his house; and his domestic life was as pleasant as he could expect. There was much to be thankful for.

It was two o'clock in the morning when the gatekeeper tapped on Samuel's door and woke Tom Edwards. The comet was visible now on Tower Hill, Griffin reported. Tom closed the door quietly and tiptoed up the steps to the study. "The comet is out," he said sleepily. Samuel closed his books, blew out the candles, and telling the boy to wrap himself up warmly, he and Tom stepped out of the chilly house into the painfully cold night. Swathed in heavy cloaks, their hats pulled down low to their eyes, and their faces half-covered in thick scarves, they made their way through the dark gardens. As soon as they were beyond the gate, they broke into a trot, jogging through the shadows of Moscovy Court and on up the moon-bright incline of Tower Hill.

On the top of the Hill, standing by a gaunt tree on Postern Row, a knot of huddled figures stood looking eastward over the tops of the houses of East Smithfield—a bellman, two citizens, and a soldier from the Tower. They hardly noticed Samuel and his boy when they joined them. The bellman made an inarticulate sound when Samuel thanked him for sending word, but the others stood quiet, blowing vapor from their nostrils and staring toward the east. Arms crossed and hands cupped in the warmth of his arm-pits, Samuel stood with them in the freezing cold and looked at the comet. It was almost like a star, he thought, only larger and duller than any others in the sky. It was not what he had thought a comet would look like. There was no tail. His lordship, in his letter from Portsmouth, had spoken of a tail, a long tail that swept away from the body of the star. But there was no tail here, only a huge, glowing body, looming low on the horizon.

Samuel heard a muffled sound from the boy. Huddled in his heavy cloak, the boy was visibly shaking. "What is it?" Samuel asked.

"I am frightened," Tom whispered, very close to tears.

Samuel put his arm around the boy's shoulders and held him close. "You are cold," Samuel reassured him. "There is nothing to be frightened of. It is only a large star. There can be no harm in that."

But inside his own cloak Samuel shivered a little, too, because it was cold and also because one could not be absolutely certain. The little knot of men stood under the tree on the cold hilltop, isolated and silent, while the great comet moved slowly through its low arc and disappeared behind the houses of Whitechapel.

Extreme cold weather lasted throughout the winter. Great frosts were followed by heavy snows and then a sudden thaw that turned the streets into quagmires. Before the snow disappeared, there came another hard frost and a repetition of the bitter cycle. Twice during the winter ice blocked the Thames and brought all river traffic to a halt. It was the coldest winter that Samuel could remember. He had to order an extra chaldron of coal and summon the glaziers to come and make his windows tighter. He also pro-cured a new rabbit's foot, one with a joint in it, to help ward off the colic.

Elizabeth took more frivolous measures against the weather. Having been confined to the house for over two months with the coal dust and the smoke, she began to feel umcomfortably grimy. Mercer told her of a hothouse where they could go with propriety and clean the grime from their skins. Samuel hooted at the vanity of the notion, but Elizabeth and her companion, on a fairly mild day, bundled up warmly and set out to take a bath.

When Samuel came home late in the afternoon, he found his two gentlewomen sitting before the fire in the parlor, limp, cleansed, and somewhat self-conscious. He sat across the room from them, vowing that he was afraid to come any closer for fear of contaminating their purity. Elizabeth and Mercer joined in the joke. They said that they doubted they would be able to eat supper at the same table with him, and he had best make his meal in the kitchen with the maids. But that night Samuel learned that Elizabeth's new fastidiousness was more than a joke. When it was time to go to bed, she told Samuel that Mercer was to sleep with her and he was to go to bed in Mercer's room. He said that was carrying things too far, but Elizabeth held firm and for the next three nights Samuel slept in Mercer's bed and Mercer slept with Elizabeth. She also insisted that Samuel wash himself with warm water before he set out for the day and not just dabble his hands and face in the cold-water basin. Samuel groused about the antic fancy that had taken possession of her and blamed the foolishness on Mercer's sophisticated influence. After three days of inviolate purity, however, Elizabeth relented and invited Samuel to return to his accustomed place in their bed. A few days later Samuel found Elizabeth down in the cellar with the servants, helping to hold her little bitch while it was being bred to one of Lady Batten's house dogs. Samuel rebuked her sharply for having no more dignity than to perform such an office before the servants, but he was relieved that Elizabeth's fad of cleanliness was over.

The cold weather did not stop the preparations for war. De Ruyter, on his way home from the Indies, struck at the Guinea coast and returned its bastions to the Dutch merchants. He also hit an English merchant convoy in the Atlantic, sinking one of the ships with Warren's masts, and captured a fleet of English colliers in the north. The Dutch admiral was a wily fox. He was now apparently on his way home around the backside of Scotland, and no one had been able to sight or touch him.

In March Lord Sandwich brought his winter guard into the Downs for repair and provisions. The Duke of York ordered him to Whitehall for discussions about the ordering of the battle fleet for the summer campaign. Samuel waited at his lordship's house hour after hour to confer with him, but the Earl stayed at Whitehall closeted with the Duke. Lady Sandwich said that she had not seen him more than twice in the week he had been at home. Great affairs were brewing at the Admiralty.

Eventually Lord Sandwich came in, weary from Whitehall, and asked his lady, "How do you, sweetheart? How have you done all this week?"

The Earl insisted that Samuel stay for dinner. He had news, secret as yet, but news of interest for the Clerk of the Acts. The Parliament had voted two and a half million pounds to finance the war for three years, and after hours of debate and discussion, the battle fleet was at last organized. The Duke of York himself would go to sea as Commander-in-Chief and Admiral of the Red Squadron. Prince Rupert would command the White and the Earl of Sandwich would have the Blue. Ayscue and Teddiman would be his vice and rear admirals. Rupert would have Myngs and Sansum, and the Duke would have Lawson and Sir William Berkeley, as well as Penn as Captain of the Fleet. These were the best naval names in England. Nothing was to be slighted in the effort to overwhelm the Dutch as quickly as possible. A hundred ships, men-of-war, auxiliary merchantmen, fire ships, and ketches would sail to the Dutch coast as soon as war was declared and the fleet provisioned.

The Earl was happy to have Ayscue and Teddiman with him and relieved to be free of Penn. It had been decided to leave the Admiralty Office in the sole command of the Duke of Albemarle. A wise decision, Samuel said. He had no love for bluff old General Monck, but it was better to have to deal with one known personality than to try to appease a commission of three or four jealous and ignorant lords.

Admiral Sandwich agreed and told Samuel to work as hard for Albemarle as he had for York, and his value to the service would not be overlooked. "He is a tough man but a fair one," the Earl concluded.

A few days later while Samuel was at the Royal Exchange negotiating for a better price on sailcloth, he saw a troop of the Horse Guard clatter up to the entrance of the Exchange. The scarlet-coated soldiers on their shining black horses lined up across the open way, and nine trumpeters in royal livery stepped forward and sounded a fanfare. Three City Aldermen in scarlet gowns emerged from the building and stood before the quickly gathering crowd. Samuel pushed forward to get a place near the officials. Two heralds in the royal coat of arms accompanied by four mace-bearers approached the City officers and presented their scrolls. The trumpeters sounded another fanfare, the Guardsmen drew their swords and rattled them in time to the notes rhythmically, and then the herald began to read. Amid the stiff and courtly words one sure fact was clear. His Majesty took this solemn occasion to announce to his loyal subjects, the citizens of London, that Great Britain had declared war on the United Provinces of Holland. Samuel slipped out from the crowd before the herald had finished reading and found a coach to take him to Whitehall and to work.

With what seemed like providential grace, the cold, bleak weather suddenly broke. The heavy dark clouds that had hung over the City all winter gave way to clear blue skies and bright sunshine. London put away its woolens, opened its windows, and basked in the suddenly warm air. Samuel beat a steady path between Whitehall and Seething Lane and between Seething Lane and the river yards. He made a vow to pay a forfeit into the poor box if he lay in bed more than fifteen minutes after waking. He went early to the office and worked hard until dinner. His tailor came to the house and took his order for light clothing for the summer. He placed an order with the periwig maker and had the barber cut off his hair.

By the end of the month the fleet was ready. Samuel made his farewells to the Duke of York, the Earl of Sandwich, and Sir William Coventry. The King had finally recognized the Secretary's worth by granting him a knighthood. They in turn thanked Samuel for his service and requested his prayers for their success. He watched them go down the river in canopied barges. Upon their shoulders rested the safety and the security of England. If disaster came to them, there was no telling what would come for Samuel Pepys. He thought of the great fleet riding at anchor, the bright sun glinting on the elaborate, gilded scrollwork on the square sterns, the huge poop lanterns, large enough to hold ten men, swinging slowly with the roll of the ships, the silken sails embroidered in bold designs furled neatly to the yardarms, waiting for the admirals to come aboard. The full strength of England's naval power, concentrated into one great fleet, would soon be away to station itself off the Dutch coast to wait for De Ruyter slipping home the back way, or Admiral Opdam mustering Holland's new fleet in the reaches of the Texel. Samuel bade them Godspeed and and took a coach to Whitehall to meet with Albemarle and consider the cost.

At the Duke's lodgings in the warren of buildings across from the Palace called the Cockpit, Sir George Carteret reported that the expense of getting the fleet out had come to half a million pounds. The estimated cost of keeping the ships provisioned and repaired during the next seven months would easily amount to a million pounds more.

"So three-fifths of the King's whole treasury for war will have been spent in the first year," Albemarle said quietly.

"If all goes well," Sir George replied.

"You cannot count on all going well. Not in war. But we will do the best we can with what we have. In the meantime, keep the yards supplied and the victual ships ready. Mr. Pepys, I look to you to keep the contractors busy."

"I will do my best," said Samuel.

The Duke looked at him sharply. "That ought to serve," he said. "I hear you know your way on the river and in the yards. Keep them busy."

Samuel kept them busy. He visited Sir William Warren and urged him to fill the storage docks with masts. He talked to the contractors for anchors and sailcloth and cordage and flags and pitch. Supplies must be furnished, he insisted. The money would come.

He kept in close touch with the Duke of Albemarle, reporting success in hemp and anchors and failure in tar. The Duke ordered him to try again with the tar merchants. The ships would need calking if they had a serious brush with the enemy.

As the April days continued, hot and dry and still, Samuel trudged to the Exchange and sat in the cool retreat of the coffee-shops, talking to the tar merchants and listening for rumors of action in the fleet. He rode up the river in a wherry, hoping for a fresh breeze on the water. In St. James's Park, he noticed that the new leaves were beginning to curl and that the whole Park was dusty and dry. In London the cart horses moved more slowly along the tight, narrow lanes. The vendors sang their street cries less lustily, and the apprentices sagged idly against the shops, content to rest in a spot of shade and let the street girls go by unmolested and unchallenged. The whole City seemed to droop in a kind of unnatural late-summer lethargy.

In the outparish of St. Giles to the west of the City, the overflow and outcasts of the City, the whores, pimps, ne'er-do-wells, and unemployed servants moved sluggishly along the dark ways and sunless alleys. Lank dogs picked at the offal that befouled the cobbles, and small black rats grew fat and sleek on the garbage that festered in the streets. In Vinegar Yard a man sank to the ground, exhausted and sick, his neck and chest covered with hard spots encircled by a crimson ring. Two loungers picked him up and dragged him into the shade. As they put his head upon a stone to ease his fever, they saw the spots. Backing away slowly, they looked at each other and turned white. "The token," they said together, and then they ran out of the filthy alley as fast as they could.

The "token" was a hard core encircled with a scarlet ring: the certain sign of plague. The early signs might disappear, and the ignorant but fortunate man might go his way with no more danger than if he had suffered a summer rash. Even the buboes that developed under the arms or in the groin might be lanced at a certain stage and fatality averted. But the fatal token could not be treated—or hidden. A man with a token was a dead man; and a city beset with bubonic plague was a threatened—perhaps a doomed—city.

London had long known the plague, and learned to fear it. There was an old saying in the City that the pestilence visited the kingdom every twenty years; and some of the more rabid fanatics found an odd, apocalyptic pleasure in pointing out that a disastrous visitation of the plague had accompanied every Stuart to the throne, except—so far—King Charles II.

The man who was left to die alone in Vinegar Alley was not the first to frighten the parish of St. Giles with the exposure of his scarlet encircled blemish. A prostitute in Whetstone Park, an un-employed footman in Stable Yard, an ironmonger's apprentice at the Seven Dials, all were said to have borne the stigma on their dead bodies before they were quickly and secretly buried at night in the potter's field. The rumors spread, whispers ran from tavern to shop, from court to alley, from High Holborn to Long Acre.

One day the parish officers came to a house in the New Build-ings, at the sign of the Ship, and marked in red ocher the cross of the plague on the door. Neighbors quickly gathered in the street and watched in sullen silence as the watchman affixed, under the fearful cross, the official quarantine paper signed by the magis-trates of Westminster and Middlesex. As soon as the watchman's back was turned, the neighbors stormed the marked door, tore down the paper, obliterated the still wet cross, broke open the lock, and freed the infected inmates.

The magistrates had fixed on quarantine as the only known guard against the spread of the plague. Apothecaries might sell their pills and potions, quacks their cordial waters and elixirs; but only isolation of the afflicted had official approval. Whenever a new victim was betrayed by the awful token, either he would be sent to sure death in one of the noisome pesthouses, or, if he were taken at home, his whole household would be immured for forty days, as in a prison. It was worse than any prison, for the almost inevitable result was the infection and agonized, untended death of everyone in the house. Consequently the official red cross, chalked on the doors, was a sight more dreadful in its implications than the symptoms of the disease itself.

The contagion spread and the authorities took stronger measures. They offered a reward for the bodies of all cats and dogs that were slaughtered. Cats and dogs disappeared from the parish but blotches and tokens continued to mar the flesh of the dwellers in the crowded lanes of St. Giles. When four persons died in the house of Jonas Charles in Newton Street, the justices of Middlesex gave permission to James Angier (who claimed to have stopped the plague in Lyons, Paris, and Toulouse) to try his remedy of fumigation. Stopping all the window cracks with heavy burlap, he lighted his fuming pots of brimstone, saltpetre, and amber. For four hours the rank odors of the disinfectant rolled through the house, nearly suffocating the remaining eight members of Mr. Charles's family. After the house was aired again the next day, M. Angier declared the fumigation a complete success, but the prostrate inhabitants saw no marked improvement in their condition except that their cellar was free of the black rats that had infested it.

Fumigation, however, did not keep pace with the epidemic. Although the weekly Bills of Mortality failed to show any deaths by plague, the gravediggers in St. Giles' Churchyard were kept busy finding room for new graves; and word passed into the City that St. Giles-in-the-Fields was a cesspool of contagion. The justices ordered a quarantine of the whole parish, setting up guards at all the streets that led into the neighboring parishes; but even the most vigilant watch of the constables failed to stop the infection. Tokens began to appear in Covent Garden, Drury Lane, Lincoln's Inn Fields, closer and closer to the City itself. The Lord Mayor looked at the cloudless sky that had withheld its rain for six weeks and issued a proclamation requiring every shop owner to wash down his part of the street with water every night.

On May 15 the English fleet sailed back into Harwich. De Ruyter had not appeared, but scouts reported that Opdam's new fleet of over a hundred sails was expected to appear. The Duke of York had decided it was wise to come in for provisions before getting set to meet its thrust. The vast fleet filled the ports and docks and rode at anchor off the Gunfleet Sands. The Duke of Albemarle hastily sent Samuel to call a guard of soldiers to man the docks and keep the impressed seamen aboard. The admirals and the captains complained loudly that the victualing ships were not getting the food and the beer to them. Samuel spent his days down the river cursing the victualing officers, pleading with the shipmasters, coaxing the contractors. Finally by the end of the month, the Duke felt that he could wait no longer, and the fleet sailed up the coast to Southwold Bay, half-provisioned and undermanned. The Dutch were out and they must be met.

For a week nothing was heard of the fleet. Sir William Batten at Harwich sent daily letters to the Navy Office, reporting the gossip and the rumors, but Samuel set little store by them. On June 3 the watermen and the workers down the Thames swore that they could hear the guns of the fleet quite distinctly. Samuel in his office heard a distant rumble in the east. It might have been thunder, but it also might have been gunfire.

In the next few days rumors were thick at the Royal Exchange. The Dutch were in retreat. The English were in pursuit. The Dutch had been routed with hundreds killed or captured. Samuel listened skeptically. People were believing what they wanted to believe. He would wait until there was an official communication at Whitehall. He called upon Lady Sandwich and found her in surprisingly good temper, neither confident nor troubled with fear. If the wife of the Admiral could show such courage, so could he. He went into Pater Noster Row and bought silk for a new suit.

June 7 was the hottest day of the summer. The unclouded blue sky arched clear and serene over the sharp spires of the City churches. Even early in the morning, the City sweltered in a dense, inescapable stupor. Elizabeth and Mercer hired a boat and went down the river, under the protection of Will Hewer, to find a breeze if they could on the waters at Gravesend. Samuel put on his new silk suit in an effort to outface the hostile day.

That afternoon, driven nearly wild by distorted rumors at the office and at the Exchange, he took a coach to Whitehall. As the hackney ambled through Covent Garden, almost empty and lifeless in the afternoon sun, Samuel looked idly at the shady walks of the Piazza. Under the overhanging roof, he saw an odd marking, almost indiscernible from the distance of his coach. Putting his head out the window, he looked more closely, and then ordered the coachman to stop. In a moment his eyes adjusted, and he saw that the marking was a crudely painted cross, the red paint dribbled, and under it a paper sheet scrawled in ink, "Lord have mercy upon us!"

Samuel quickly ordered the coachman to whip up his horses and get out of Covent Garden as fast as he could. The plague crosses were on three doors in the south Piazza.

At Westminster Hall he bought a roll of tobacco and stuffed a leaf into his mouth, for it was a belief of the times that tobacco, chewed or sniffed, gave protection against contagion. He went back toward the Cockpit sniffing and chewing until his nostrils were free of the suddenly revolting odor of his own body.

He found Mr. Creed, the Earl's secretary, at the Cockpit and the two men hired a boat to take them across the river to the Spring Garden at Vauxhall. Creed said that he had heard a rumor that Lord Sandwich had been killed in the fighting, but it was only a rumor. The fearful thought, however, depressed their spirits, and they went into a booth and made their supper on six pennyworth of whey.

They stayed in the Gardens until nightfall. About nine o'-clock they took a boat back across the river and inquired at the Cockpit for news, but there was none. Samuel went home by water, depressed and weary. Sheet lightning flashed vaguely in the northern sky and a light breeze blew over the Thames. When he got home, the house was empty. Elizabeth had not returned. He undressed, and, leaving a candle burning, got into bed. The lightning grew brighter and about midnight there was a shower of rain. It did not last long, but it cooled the air, and Samuel fell asleep.

It was five o'clock in the morning before Elizabeth came in, wet and exhausted. She lay down on the bed in her clothes, too tired to answer Samuel's angry questions. She would tell him about it later, she said sleepily. It was a good day. The rain had held them up. That was all.

Samuel got up at seven and dressed. Before leaving the house, he woke Elizabeth long enough to tell her that she must not by any means go near the western outparishes. Crosses were on the doors in Covent Garden and she must stay away from that whole neighborhood.

That afternoon there was a meeting with the goldsmiths at the office of the Lord Treasurer. Ready money was needed and the whole Navy Office was present to urge the goldsmiths to make an advance on the King's credit. The goldsmiths were respectful but wary. The King was already heavily in debt to them, they pointed out, and they had some reason to fear for their security even if the fleet had not already met disaster. While the gold-smiths were explaining their position tactfully but firmly and answering the Lord Treasurer's assurances with cold, hard facts, a messenger suddenly burst into the room. A dispatch had come from the Duke of York, he announced excitedly. The meeting hastily broke up and they all rushed over to the Cockpit.

Mr. Baptist May of the Duke's household was in the antechamber, breathless and happy. He had just arrived from the fleet. "It is a victory," he shouted, waving his arms wildly. The gentlemen of the antechamber swept him up onto a table and pressed spilling tankards of claret into his hands, shouting and cheering for joy. Samuel left the ecstatic courtiers and went into the Duke of Albemarle's chamber, where a small knot of officials were clustered around the Duke, reading a letter over his shoulder. Samul slipped into an opening between Lords Arlington and Peterborough and joined them in the silent perusal of the news.

The fleet, the letter said (it was in Coventry's writing), had first sighted the Dutch at noon on June 1 some seven leagues off Southwold. For two days the two fleets had maneuvered in sail-sight of each other, playing for the advantage of the wind. On the morning of June 3, with the sea smooth and a steady, fresh breeze from the southwest, the Duke of York decided to strike. With the White Squadron of Prince Rupert in the van, the Red Squadron of the Duke in the center, and Lord Sandwich's Blue in the rear, the English fleet moved toward the long line of Dutch sails stretched out 15 or 20 miles across the gray sea. As soon as the English started to move in, the Dutch quickly tacked and the two lines made their first pass east and west in the hazy light of predawn. The ships blazed with broadsides, flashing orange and crimson, as the two lines slid slowly past each other.

After the first orderly pass, with little damage done on either side, both fleets immediately tacked to come about again and at each other, but the Dutch now had the advantage of the wind and tried to capitalize on it. The Duke immediately ordered a new tack, the bright little signal flags running up and down the riggings. The original line of battle was thus altered, the Duke now being in the van, Sandwich in the center, and Rupert in the rear. The quick maneuver immediately paid off. The Dutch were prevented from weathering the English fleet and an attempt to break the English line was prevented before it started. The sun was now well up and the ships were banging away at each other through clouds of gun smoke. The firm lines of the battle order began to break up as visibility improved and the fighting in some parts of the line became a general melee. Admiral Opdam brought his whole battle group of four ships to bear directly upon *The Prince,* the Earl of Sandwich's flagship, and raked her heavily. The Earl received a slight wound when a chain shot tore through the quarterdeck.

Albemarle stopped reading and looked solemnly at Samuel, but Samuel only wiped his brow, and said he hoped the wound was minor. The Duke continued to read.

The Duke of York, Coventry's report stated, fortunately was close at hand with his battle group, the *Royal Charles,* the *Norwich,* the *Mermaid,* and the *Drake.* The Duke tacked quickly and stretched out ahead of Opdam, drawing him off from the outgunned and hapless *Prince.* The two admiral groups, grappling and locked together, poured chain shot and musket fire into each other at pointblank range, one shot from the *Eendracht* killing three noble volunteers standing beside the Duke on the quarterdeck and splattering His Grace with their blood.

Lord Sandwich, freed suddenly from his antagonists, ordered his mainsail lowered and the blue flag run up on the mizzen. This was his signal to the squadron: "Follow me!" Veering his ship sharply, he led the Blues straight through the disordered Dutch line of battle, smashing and firing as he went.

In a moment the enemy's fleet was divided. The fire ships ran among the floundering Dutch vessels setting sails and rigging ablaze. The heavy shot fired at close range tore great holes in the timbered hulls of the men-of-war, and boarding parties armed with muskets and swords jumped across the rails and disarmed or slaughtered the bewildered Dutchmen.

By dusk the fleet of Admiral Opdam was scattered, burning hulks ablaze on the dark water, wounded seamen calling for help from the floating debris, and the remnants of the battle line flying in disorder toward Holland.

While the English captains secured their own ships, tended their dead and wounded, and salvaged distressed Dutch seamen from the water, the Duke of York set out in hot pursuit of the fleeing Dutch. During the night, however, by a mistake of orders while the Duke slept, the chase was broken off. By daylight the low-draught vessels of the Dutch were upon their own shallow coast, and it was too late to catch them.

Nevertheless, Coventry's letter concluded, the Battle of Lowestoft was a great victory. The Dutch had lost a fourth of their fleet; 4,000 of their men were dead and at least 2,000 were captured. The English had lost only one ship, 1,000 men, Rear Admiral Sansum, four volunteer earls, and Captain Lawson's leg. The *Prince,* with thirty holes in her hull, was the most badly battered ship in the fleet, but the Earl of Sandwich was alive and well, except for a superficial wound on his arm.

Samuel let out a deep sigh and sank back into a chair. The Earl and the fleet were still above water. The Duke of Albemarle turned to Samuel and told him to notify the yards at once. Repair crews must be ready and provision had to be made for the wounded. Muster the yards at Deptford, Woolwich, and Chatham, and tell Mr. Evelyn at Greenwich that hundreds of wounded men were on the way.

Samuel stopped by Lincoln's Inn Fields to tell Lady Sandwich the great news, called in at Seething Lane to tell the Penn household that Sir William was safe, and then hurried on down to Tower Wharf to get a barge for Greenwich.

XI

ℐ kissed the bride in bed

THE VICTORIOUS FLEET returned to the English coast three days later. The flagships and most of the second-rates anchored in the Nore; the lesser vessels scattered in harbors convenient to the supply ships. Nine Dutch ships were herded down the Medway for the Commissioner of Prizes to evaluate. Twenty Dutch ships of the line had been left burning or sunk and the Duke of York's fleet had lost only one small vessel, the ketch *Charity*.

A flotilla of welcoming boats flocked down the Thames from London to greet the triumphant seamen. Samuel boarded the *Prince* and found his lordship. The *Prince* was badly battered; not one mast or yardarm was whole; and at least thirty shots in her hull made her look more like a collander than a ship, as Mr. Evelyn told Samuel. But his lordship was undamaged, except for the slight wound on his arm, looking "fat and lusty, and ruddy by being in the sun."

The chief officers were escorted in honor back up the river to the City where church bells pealed, bonfires blazed, and the citizens of London shouted their joy.

There was little time for Samuel to enjoy the victory. The fleet had to be repaired and made ready for another onslaught, for the angry Dutch were sure to come out again, and this time under the more skillful command of De Ruyter. Sir William Warren's large supply of masts was nearly depleted in replacing the shattered spars and mainmasts. Caulkers had to be pressed into service to reseal the damage done by the Dutch guns to at least twenty hulls. New sails and rigging had to be installed, fresh supplies of powder and victual loaded. The docks at Chatham and Woolwich worked around the clock, and a host of workmen and stevedores swarmed the ships anchored at Hollesley Bay, the Rolling Grounds, and the Nore, repairing yardarms, rigging sail, and loading beer and salt beef.

Samuel tried to be everywhere at once, at Deptford spurring on the hemp workers, at Woolwich checking the movement of supplies to the Nore, at the Royal Exchange cajoling the sailcloth contractors into furnishing another thousand yards of silk on credit. The contractors were reluctant; they had not been paid for the silk they had furnished the first fleet. Samuel promised to go personally to see the Lord Treasurer to obtain a firm commitment that they would receive the money due them if they would only go ahead and provide silk available now. The contractors hesitantly agreed, and Samuel went to Southampton House in Bloomsbury Square. But a footman informed him that the Earl of Southampton was not in London; his lordship had taken his family to the country to escape the growing danger of the plague.

"So," Samuel fumed as he walked down toward Holborn, "the exodus has begun." England was in a pickle when the chief officers of the government fled their posts at the very moment they were engaged in a war with the most dangerous naval power in the world. The Dutch were already out, the scouting ships had reported, gone northward to meet De Ruyter and bring the rich East India merchant fleet home. They would have to be intercepted—and quickly.

At the Watchhouse Samuel flagged a hackney coach headed toward St. Paul's. He settled back into the hard leather seat and brooded on the precarious state of affairs the King was in, when his officers either shirked or fled their duties. As the coach jogged on down Holborn Hill toward Newgate Street, Samuel gradually became aware that they were going slower and slower. In Cheapside the coach finally came to a complete stop. The coachman crept down from his seat and staggered over to the shop wall. His fingers slid down the boards slowly and the man crumpled into an awkward, cross-legged sitting position. Samuel got out of the coach and stepped to his side.

"What is it?" he asked.

The man gasped weakly. "I don't know. I am sick. I can't see."

Samuel dropped a half-crown into the coachman's lap and

hurried away. He could have flogged himself for not having noticed that the coach had come to him from the direction of St. Giles. The coachman probably had the plague. Samuel hurried on down Cheapside until he found another who swore that he had not been out of the City that summer. As he rode home, Samuel resolved that he would hereafter stick to the river. Coaches were too dangerous. He thought of the poor fellow crumpled against the wall, his horse standing idle beside him in the open street. Elizabeth must be gotten out of town. The plague was coming too close.

When the fleet was ready to sail in July, the Earl of Sandwich was placed in command. The King had refused to allow the Duke of York to submit himself again to the danger of the Dutch guns, and Prince Rupert had declined the honor of sharing the command with an earl. Lord Sandwich was left alone with the responsibility of intercepting the elusive De Ruyter.

A week before his lordship sailed, he took Samuel aside at Whitehall into the robe chamber and closed the door. There were one or two matters he had to discuss, the Earl said, before he left. This command of the fleet was not to be taken as an honor by default. The Earl of Sandwich now enjoyed the greatest love and respect he had ever had from the royal family, despite the endeavors of some of his enemies to discount his services in the late fighting. He suspected, he said, the fine hand of Coventry, who was now puffed up by his recent knighthood and who never missed an opportunity to injure anyone who stood between him and the Duke of York.

Samuel cleared his throat and looked thoughtful. It was hard to believe, he said, that Sir William Coventry had attempted an injury to his lordship in this case, for he had himself seen the Secretary's letter to the Duke of Albemarle, and Sir William had given the Earl full credit for breaking the Dutch line.

"Well, at any rate," said the Earl, "I am glad to be free of joint command with Prince Rupert. The Prince enjoyed Lowestoft from a safe distance and is now swaggering around the Court as if he had won the battle single-handed. The Prince will be of greater service to the country with his bottle and his mistresses safe in London."

"Nobody is safe in London now," Samuel said.

"That is true," his lordship conceded. "Lady Sandwich and the girls are going to Dagenhams, Lady Wright's estate in Essex, until the danger is over. And that brings us to the matter at hand. Lady Sandwich and I have decided that the best provision for Jemimah is a match with Carteret's oldest boy. We think it should be contracted and consummated as soon as possible. You can never tell about wars. Since I shall be away, I shall need your help."

"You will have it," Samuel promptly volunteered.

"I felt sure of it. I think the negotiations should begin and the contract be made before I leave at the end of the week. It will not do for me to make the suggestion to Carteret. I want you to speak to him about it as an interested party. Or better still, find someone of good reputation with both families, but not too closely connected with either, to broach the matter to Sir George as a suggestion from you and felt by you not to be inimical to us. Do you know the man?"

"Dr. Pierce has a good reputation in Westminster, and is a friend of mine who would love to play Cupid."

"He is the man. Do not tell him, but I will tell you that I am prepared to give £5,000 with Jem and I shall expect an £800 *per annum* jointure from Carteret. He should be able to stand at least that, but my greatest concern is that the match should go through with dispatch, good feeling, and mutual approval. I think I can count on the King's consent."

"I will speak to Dr. Pierce at once and report to you in the morning."

Samuel went home by water and immediately sent Hewer to Pierce with a carefully written letter.

At seven the next morning Samuel was back in Westminster. Although it was early, large wagons were standing at the doors of several great houses, being loaded with household goods. Plague had encroached into the neighborhood of Whitehall, arriving by the backway of the little alleys and cul-de-sacs that surrounded the royal village. Red crosses now stained the doors of a dozen hovels of Long Ditch, Bell Alley, and Petty France. Plague was in the air of Whitehall, and the nobles were packing their goods and their families off to country manors. Samuel took his roll of tobacco from his pocket and holding it close to his nose hurried to Dr. Pierce.

The sociable doctor was overjoyed, he told Samuel, at the prospect of a marriage between two such noble families. He had taken the liberty, he said, of going at once last night to Sir George as soon as he received the letter, and put the notion before him. Sir George had seemed genuinely pleased. He had said that he would be glad to discuss the matter further with a representative of the Montagus, especially Mr. Pepys.

Samuel found Sir George at home and, as Pierce had said, beaming at the prospect of a happy arrangement for his heir. But Samuel was not to be rushed. As official agent, he insisted that his premeditated, cautious discussion be listened to. He sat down soberly and started at the beginning, commenting upon his own pleasure at the thought of a match between Lady Jemimah and Mr. Philip, the joining together of the two families he loved above all others in the kingdom, both related already in their high service to the Navy and in their just esteem at Court. He talked at length of his personal feelings for the Lady Jemimah, of his care for her in her childhood, his delight in seeing her develop into a charming and virtuous young woman. He spoke of his respect for young Master Philip, whom he had seen upon several occasions conducting himself like a sensible and intelligent young gentleman. He had no doubt, he said, that this could be a perfect mating of noble houses and worthy persons. Nor did he doubt, he concluded, that his lordship, the Earl of Sandwich, might be persuaded to the same opinion.

Sir George listened attentively to Samuel's carefully worded speech. When Samuel had finished, the baronet quietly thanked his colleague for his kindness in taking this interest in the welfare and happiness of his son. As for the marriage, he could see nothing against it. He would, of course, have to break the subject to Lady Carteret, and he would do that immediately. In the meantime, Mr. Pepys could rest assured that if the match was agreeable to Lady Carteret, he would do all in his power to render his son fit for his lordship's daughter.

Samuel hurried to report to his patron. Lord Sandwich tapped Samuel approvingly on the shoulder and said that he might now tell Sir George that the Earl of Sandwich would be willing to enter into discourse the next day. Without waiting for his dinner, Samuel ran back to the Carteret's house and delivered his message. Sir George smiled and said that Mr. Pepys was as swift as Venus's own son, and it was well. He had himself also acted with speed. Lady Carteret had given her approval. Time was important now, he said. The Earl was going to sea shortly and he himself was moving his family down to Deptford to get them out of the pestilential air of London. He would call upon the Earl at once.

His part of the marriage negotiations at an end, Samuel turned to the needs of his own family. The Mortality Bill for the week showed 267 persons listed as dead by plague. Only four of the number were reported as inhabitants of the City, but the Bills were not to be trusted. It was true that no one in St. Olave's parish had yet been touched, but it was now impossible to walk through the outparishes without seeing the fearful signs, the shuttered shops, the watchmen on guard before the quarantined doors, searchers ambling along with their white staves. In the shops that remained open, stood bowls of vinegar to receive the purchaser's coins. Through the half-empty streets the official bearers, armed with red staves, drove their carts and intoned their awful cry, "Bring out your dead. Bring out your dead." Occasionally one of the doctors who had not fled with his patrons tapped on a door with his gold-headed cane and disappeared into the fearful recesses of an afflicted house. On the outskirts of the City, in the open fields beyond the wall, huge pits had been dug to receive the naked bodies now too numerous to find Christian burial in the consecrated ground of the churchyards.

Although the plague had so far in its eastward movement spared St. Olave's parish, it had crept near. Dr. Burnett's house in Fenchurch Street bore a red cross. Samuel's doctor had discovered an inflamed bubo on the groin of one of his servants. He had at once reported the symptom to the College of Physicians, ordered a quarantine established on his own house, and locked himself in to nurse his stricken servant and to wait either for death or providential release after the forty days. Samuel was amazed that his doctor could set so good an example to the panicky citizens. He was not sure that he could himself have mustered so much courage, but in any event he had a duty to get Elizabeth out of town. As for himself, he would have to stay, at least until the Navy Office was ordered away.

He went down to Woolwich and found a place for Elizabeth down the river, large enough for Elizabeth, Mary Mercer, Tom Edwards, and one of the maids. Samuel shipped their bedding and clothes in a Navy barge, bought Elizabeth some painting materials, and found her a drawing master to occupy her time. Elizabeth always got along better when she had something to keep her busy.

With Elizabeth safely established down the river, Samuel made what arrangements he could to insure his own safety in London. He stayed close to Seething Lane, and made it a point to conclude all his business at the office before nightfall. The Court had moved to Hampton, leaving the Duke of Albemarle at Whitehall to represent the Crown. Whenever occasion demanded that he make the trip to the Cockpit, Samuel went by water, being willing to wait an hour if necessary to obtain one of the few wherries left on the river.

The Earl joined the fleet on July 6 and set off hurriedly to catch Penn's squadron, which had sailed impetuously without waiting for the Admiral. Lady Sandwich took the girls into Essex and the Carterets moved to Deptford. There was not a great deal to attract Samuel to Westminster now.

As often as he could, Samuel found occasion to go down the river, stopping in at Woolwich to see how Elizabeth progressed with her painting, visiting with Mr. Evelyn at Greenwich to discuss his new gardens, or calling at the Carterets in Deptford to hear the wedding plans. He met the bridegroom, a modest, quiet young man, who walked with a slight limp in one leg. Sir George was in continual good humor and began to call Samuel "cousin." Lady Carteret was busy collecting bedclothes and jewels and tableware as gifts for the bride, asking Samuel's advice about Jemimah's taste.

The wedding date was set for August 3. In the middle of July, Lady Carteret called Samuel aside and said that they had a special favor to ask of him. Lady Sandwich now thought it was time for the two young people to meet each other and begin their amour.

It would help to take the strangeness and the surprise off the wedding day itself. It had been arranged for Philip to go to Dagenhams on Saturday and stay the weekend as a guest of Lady Wright. Since Philip had never met any of the Montagus and would be a stranger among them, Lady Carteret would appreciate it greatly if Samuel would go with him as his guide and sponsor. Samuel said that nothing would give him greater pleasure than to introduce the bridegroom into his new family.

Next afternoon, on the long bumpy journey through the Essex countryside, Samuel tried to engage the young man in a conversation of gallantry. He told of some of the sights he had seen at the Court and in the Royal Box at the Theatre Royal—the King's little trick of tickling Lady Castlemaine's knee while he gazed impassively at the stage. He told Philip of a mild little escapade he had had with an unknown girl at a country inn, decorous but very amusing. He mentioned one or two ladies at the Court who were known to be good wives and good mistresses at the same time. But it was a one-sided conversation. Philip either was not listening or he was too embarrassed to respond.

It was eight o'clock when the coach finally arrived at Dagenhams. Lady Wright and Lord Crewe met them at the door and welcomed them. Lord Crewe took the young man into the parlor and chatted with him about his recent travels in Europe. At supper Lady Jem sat at her place at table with her eyes lowered, concentrating on the food which she barely touched. Philip devoted his whole attention to Lord Crewe, never once even so much as looking at his fiancée.

After supper Lord Crewe drew Samuel aside and suggested that it might be a good idea to leave the young people together, but Samuel objected. The girl, he said, was frightened half out of her wits. There was no telling what damage might be done by submitting her so suddenly to the onslaught of love.

So they all sat in the parlor until bedtime, listening to Lady Wright play the harpsichord and making a bold effort to keep conversation going, while Jem sat on the sofa and studied her fingers and Philip sat in a chair with his eyes fixed on a portrait of the Earl of Sandwich. Finally at a nod from Lady Wright, Samuel made their excuses and took the young man up to bed.

In the privacy of the bedroom, Samuel asked Philip how he liked his intended bride, but the boy only blushed and hung his head and stammered out that he liked her well enough.

"Pish," said Samuel.

As soon as he was up the next morning, Samuel took Philip into the gallery where portraits of brooding Crewes, Wrights, and Montagus hung darkly on the high, weathered walls. Samuel told him the plans for the day. They were all going to church, in three coaches. Philip would ride with the Lady Jemimah, and Samuel would ride with them. At the church in Romford, they would be the center of many curious eyes, and Philip must conduct himself like a man in love. He must give the lady his hand when she descended from the coach and continue to hold her by the hand as he led her into church and to their pew. Samuel rehearsed the boy, taking him by the hand and leading him down the gallery, and then he made Philip take him by the hand and show him to a chair. When he was satisfied that Philip knew how to perform the little ceremony, he sat him down and lectured him about conversation. During the ride to Romford, there would be ample opportunity for the bridegroom to talk to his bride. He must pay her compliments—on her dress, her jewels, her hair, anything—but he must say something to her and say it easily and pleasantly. Be neither lumpish nor too forward, Samuel cautioned. These public courtesies were all a part of getting married.

The boy sighed and said he would try to do as Mr. Pepys bade him.

But he did not. During the whole ride, he did not say one word to Jem; and when he got to the church, he hung behind so awkwardly that Samuel had to hand Jem down from the coach and lead her into church, the confused boy following along behind like a calf on the way to the altar.

After the stiff, cheerless dinner at noon, Samuel took Philip up to his bedroom and talked to him straight. This was nonsense, he told him. There was no need to be so bashful and backward. The boy surely knew what a woman was, how she was made, what she was capable of. He could not have arrived at his years without having at least once known a woman. That was different, Philip protested vigorously. Not at all, Samuel went on. Jem was a woman. She was flesh and blood. She was capable of feelings and desires, but it was up to the boy to bring her out. Jem could not make the advances. Philip had to do it, for her sake and for their families' sake. If this sort of thing continued, Samuel warned, people would talk, and Sir George would feel that he had been disgraced by his son.

Philip wiped his hand. He had meant no slight, he said. He did not want his father disgraced and he did not want to hurt the lady. Philip came across the room and took Samuel's hand vigorously. "And neither would I offend you, Mr. Pepys, who have been so kind to me. I will bear my part like a man from now on. Just wait and see."

Samuel disengaged himself from the boy and looked at him closely. There was a new light in his eye. He hoped, for Jem's sake, he had not goaded the boy too far.

Late in the afternoon when they were all seated in the long gallery, Lady Wright caught Samuel's eye. He arose and walked out into the garden. Lady Wright followed him, and in a moment Lord Crewe strolled out. They took a seat on a bench near the gallery door and sat there, the three of them, like conspirators. After a decent interval Lady Crewe came out. Now only a child, Lady Wright's ten-year-old daughter, kept the lovers company. The child was too young and inexperienced to read her mother's glances, but perhaps Philip and Jem would not mind her innocent presence. Indeed, perhaps they would be able under her simple influence to start a conversation and gradually proceed to amour.

Lady Wright looked at Samuel, and Samuel shrugged. Lord Crewe got up from the bench and paced down the path toward the flower garden. Lady Crewe patted her lips with a handkerchief. It was stifling hot and still in the late afternoon sun.

Just as Lord Crewe arrived back at the bench from his nervous little journey, the child appeared at the gallery door, looked backward into the room, and then carefully shut the door. Samuel gasped. Lord Crewe let out a roar, and in a moment the four grown people were howling with laughter, holding each other to keep from falling off the bench, while the child looked at them in blank amazement.

That night, after he had shown Philip to his room, Samuel went into Jem's chamber. How did she like this gentleman, Samuel asked her. Jem blushed and hid her face in the pillow. Samuel sat down beside her and made her uncover her face. "Tell me," he said. "Tell me how you like him?"

Jemimah pinched her lips together. "I can readily obey my father and mother," she said primly.

Next day Sir George was at Deptford to greet them when they got home late in the afternoon. He asked Samuel to spend the night to discuss advancing the date of the wedding. The sickness had grown so alarmingly that they were afraid to stay much longer so close to London. If it were agreeable with Lady Sandwich, they would like to move the wedding date up three days. Samuel said that he would speak to her ladyship and he was sure that the whole family would do all they could to get ready by the last day of July. But, asked Samuel, was the boy himself willing to hurry the wedding night? He had not said two words about Jem the whole day.

Sir George winked. "He has talked to me," he said.

Samuel returned to London the next morning, armed with a bottle of plague water given him by Lady Carteret. The streets were almost deserted. An occasional wanderer slipped cautiously along the wall, crossing the street hurriedly when he came to a marked door or met another person coming in the opposite direction. Above the ominously silent City, there was an intermittent tolling of the parish bells, hollow and reverberant in the still air. The relentless sun continued to bake the parched City.

Samuel stayed away from the streets. He hurried down to the Thames and hired a boat for his trip to Westminster. He ran all the way from the stairs to the Cockpit, his roll of tobacco clasped firmly to his nose. The Duke of Albemarle had some news of the fleet. Lord Sandwich had finally overtaken the impetuous Penn, restored him to his proper place in the fleet, and taken a stand about latitude 55.5, just north of Texel. There had been no sign of De Ruyter, and the Admiral was patiently waiting while Sir Gilbert Talbot, the King's envoy to Copenhagen, completed his negotiations with King Frederick to insure the neutrality of the Danes in case De Ruyter slipped into the narrow harbor of Bergen.

At Westminster Hall Samuel bought a copy of the week's Bill. Seventeen hundred people were reported dead of the plague within the week, and God only knew how many had really died. He waited until dark to make the trip back down the river. It was hard to know what to do to avoid the danger. Some doctors said the infection was in the air and that no place was safe, not even a boat upon the water. Others said that the disease was in the ground and that contact with the very earth was dangerous. There were almost as many opinions as there were doctors, and the harried City fathers did anything that promised an ounce of hope. They killed the dogs. They sluiced the streets. They shut the infected houses. They buried the dead in quicklime. But the plague continued to grow and to spread like fire.

At the Swan stairs Samuel left his boat and started up the narrow passageway that led into Thames Street. As he turned the corner, he ran full into a little group of men. As he recovered his balance he saw first their red staves and then in the flare of the link he saw that they carried a naked body, gaunt and white in the flicker of the yellow light. He threw his cloak about his face and ran down the pitch blackness of Thames Street.

Samuel stayed close at home the next day, spending most of the time at the office, writing letters and receipting completed contracts. In the afternoon he met Mr. Hadley, the parish clerk, walking in the Navy gardens. "Thank God for this spot," said Samuel, "where men may sit and breathe a while free of the contagion."

"No longer are we so fortunate," said Mr. Hadley. "Plague has finally come into St. Olave's. There are nine dead."

"But the Bill showed none," protested Samuel.

Mr. Hadley shrugged and waved his hand vaguely. "Panic is worse than plague." He sounded both apologetic and officious.

Samuel started to speak and then stopped himself. Nodding to the clerk curtly, Samuel left him and went into his house. As soon as he got to his study there was a tap at the street door, and Samuel went down to see who had business at this empty house. Standing at the door was Dr. Burnett. Samuel looked at him, speechless for a moment, and then he opened the door for him to enter. But the doctor said that he would not come in. There was no need to take chances. He had only come to tell Mr. Pepys that he had outlived his forty days and was abroad again, sound in body, as far as he knew, but full of distress at an ugly rumor that was going around. Some evil gossip was abroad that the doctor had killed his servant and had used the self-imposed quarantine as a cover for the murder. Since the poor fellow was now dead of the plague and lost beyond all recovery in the anonymity of the lime pit, there was no way of proving his innocence. He had to depend upon the good offices of friends to uphold his reputation.

It was a damned cruel charge, Samuel expostulated, and he would not fail to give the lie to any gossip who dared so much as to whisper the calumny in his presence. More than death had taken possession of London, Samuel fumed, as he closed the door and went back to his study to get off his letter to Lady Sandwich.

On July 27 the Court made its exodus from the plague. It had moved to Hampton Court as soon as the death rate in Westminster became alarming, but by the end of July the King found even the environs of London too dangerous. Samuel rode up the river to Hampton on the day of their departure for Salisbury, and got there in time to see the long train of coaches and carts assemble in the courtyard. He bade the Duke of York farewell, wished him a safe return in happier, healthier days, and kissed the fat, white hand of the Duchess.

A score of devil-may-care courtiers on horseback raced up and down the line of coaches emblazoned with the royal arms and filled with dazzling ladies, laughing and singing, dressed like men, in velvet coats, laced bands at their throats, and brightly colored caps flowing with ribbons. They were retreating from the stricken capital like cavaliers on a spree.

"God have mercy upon us," Samuel prayed, as he watched the royal household disappear down the road toward Salisbury.

On his way home down the dark river, Samuel watched the shoreline to see if there were any signs of life in the silent City. Occasionally there was the brief glint of a link or the vague glow of a smudge pot. The bearers were out upon their dreadful rounds and a few aldermen were trying the experiment of fumigating the air. But there were no other signs of life. As they approached the Swan, Samuel told the waterman to shoot the bridge.

"The tide is running," the waterman warned.

"Shoot it anyway, and land me at the Tower," Samuel ordered, taking a firm hold on the gunwales and closing his eyes.

When he got home, wet and tousled, he found Will Hewer stretched out across his bed, holding his head and moaning.

"What is the matter?" Samuel asked.

"My head," Will moaned. "It hurts."

"Have you been into the outparishes?" Samued demanded.

Will held his hands to his temples. "Not once," he groaned.

Samuel looked at his suffering clerk in silence. Violent headache was frequently the first symptom of the plague. There was nothing to do but inspect the boy and find out.

While Will groaned and moaned, Samuel stripped off his clothing, shirt, breeches, and stockings, down to his skin, and then examined him. He looked behind Will's ears, under his arms, and in the groin, but there was no sign of a spot anywhere, no blister, no ring, no hard blemish, except for a brown mole on his hip, which Samuel had seen before.

Samuel stood by the bed and looked down at him. "Perhaps you should go to your family," he suggested. "They could care for you."

Will covered his eyes with his hands and said that he thought he would die if he had to move from the bed.

Samuel covered him up and left the room. He locked the door. If Will were not better tomorrow, he would have to find some way of getting him out of the house. He could not face the thought of quarantine, locked up alive in a house with a dying man, imprisoned for forty days, cut off from every contact with family or friends. He did not feel that he had Dr. Burnett's courage.

But the next morning Will was recovered. He came into Samuel's room, fully dressed and smiling sheepishly. The headache was gone, he said, and he felt as well as he ever had in his life.

"See that you stay that way," Samuel charged him. "Drink some of my plague water and carry a roll of tobacco with you. Avoid the streets and stay away from strangers."

Will backed out of the room gratefully, bowing and bobbing his head, and Samuel got up to spend the day catching up on his accounts, recopying his will, and listening to the bell in St. Olave's tower toll out the passing of another member of the parish. It tolled five times that day.

Samuel was up before daylight the next morning—the morning of the wedding. He put on his new blue silk suit, the coat trimmed with gold buttons and the cuffs rich with broad gold lace. His hired waterman was waiting for him at Tower Wharf, ready to take him to Deptford on the first leg of his journey to Dagenhams and Jemimah's wedding.

To get to Dagenhams from Deptford, it was necessary to go to Greenwich and take the ferry that connected the south shore with the Isle of Dogs. The coach and horses had to come across on the horse boat and pick up its passengers on the far side. The drive through the Essex countryside was only about ten miles to Romford, but the roads were winding and in poor repair. Lady Wright's estate was about four miles beyond Romford.

Sir George and Lady Carteret were waiting for him at the dock when he got to Deptford at six o'clock. The waterman took them on to the ferry landing at Greenwich, but when they were finally across the river in the Isle of Dogs, there was delay. The tide was ebbing fast and the horse boat, loaded with the Carteret's coach-and-six, was grounded fast on the south shore, unable to move an inch until the tide turned.

Samuel pulled his boat cloak around his shoulders and kept a nervous eye on Sir George, who was not noted for patience. But the baronet, after only three trips to the landing, came back to his wife and his guest and sat down on a large stone. This was a stop in nature, he announced. It could not be helped.

After an hour of forced conversation and long periods of heavy silence, Sir George said that something would have to be done about the ring and the license. The wedding was to take place at eleven and the ring and license would have to be in Romford even if the parents of the bridegroom were not. Samuel found a boy who was willing, for a crown, to ride hard to Romford. Samuel paid him his fee, gave him his package, and sped him off to the church. And then he came back to the river bank and joined Sir George in the silent task of looking across the river at the grounded ferry.

It was close to ten o'clock when the tide came in and floated the horse boat. It took only ten minutes for the flat-bottomed craft to make its way across the river, and the coachman was in his seat with his whip ready as soon as the boat touched shore. The Carterets and Samuel clambered into the coach and the driver brought his whip down across the flank of the near horse. The coach rocked and swayed as the coachman kept the six sleek animals at full speed along the winding road. No one said a word during the tumultuous ride; they held to their seats and tried to keep from tumbling over each other.

When they pulled up in front of the church at Romford, the horses wet and foaming, the churchyard was empty and not a sound issued from the church. Then just as they stepped out of the coach, the bell began to ring and the married couple came out the door, followed by Lady Sandwich, the girls, the Crewes, the Wrights, and the whole roll of the county gentry. Sir George let out a mighty oath.

While Lady Carteret subdued her angry husband, Samuel left the coach and hurried to Jemimah, pale and wan in the heavy burden of her elaborate wedding dress. Samuel took her by the shoulders and shook her gently. "This is not your funeral, Jem," he said. "This is your marriage day. This is the good way of dying."

Jemimah looked at him as if he were a stranger. Samuel kissed her. "You will see," he said. "You will see."

At dinner the young couple sat side by side, speechless, while the gentlemen offered decorous toasts and the ladies reviewed the past. Philip and Jemimah sat in the parlor all the afternoon watching the card players and listening to the music of the harpsichord. It was the soberest wedding, Samuel thought, that he had ever seen. It was not at all like weddings he had witnessed in Westminster; and yet, in a way, it was better. It was reassuring to know that such decency and decorum could still exist in noble houses. This wedding was as innocent and simple as a City marriage. It was hard to believe that both these houses held high position and respectful place at Whitehall, where marriage was frequently a kind of open joke or a callous arrangement. Samuel thought of the laughing girls riding away from Hampton Court in their masculine clothes, ribald and wanton, and he looked at Jem, sitting beside her young husband, her hands in her lap, white-faced and frightened. There is a great distance, he thought, between Whitehall and the rest of England.

Supper was as quietly decorous a meal as dinner had been, only the immediate families of both houses sitting with the bride and bridegroom at the long table, eating broiled pullets and drinking well-aged claret. Philip picked at his fowl diffidently, but he downed his glass of wine every time the servant refilled it. Jemimah touched neither one nor the other.

At ten o'clock the wedding day was over. Lord Crewe took Sir George into the study to discuss the last details of the settlement; Lady Wright took Lady Carteret into her sitting room to show the gifts that Jem had received. Lady Sandwich went up with Jem to prepare her for the night, and Samuel accompanied Philip to his bedroom. While the young man took off his wedding suit and put on his night clothes, Samuel talked. He told Philip of his own wedding night, his awkwardness, his fear, until the bed curtains were closed, and then the feeling of dark security that had come over him, isolated and set apart with a girl he had really never known before yet had known always, since the moment he had been born into this world of pain. It was a kind of return to something vaguely remembered, warm and enclosed and secure.

Philip listened gravely to Samuel's description of his wedding night. When the maid tapped on the door at 10:30 and announced that Lady Jemimah was ready, Philip got up and walked through the door quietly.

In Jemimah's room the whole family was gathered around the bed, which was thickly draped with heavy curtains. Lady Sandwich and Lord Crewe together held back the curtains, and Samuel could see the silent Jem, swathed in yards of white linen and lace, sitting upright in the high bed. Philip climbed into the bed and sat beside her, erect and formal. One by one the party leaned into the dark bower and kissed Jem good night. Samuel, too, stepped beside the bed and kissed the bride. With his lips he formed the words, "You will see," and the Lady Jemimah managed a sudden smile before the curtains dropped and the party tiptoed out of the room and closed the door upon the consummation.

Samuel lay long in bed the next morning. This would probably be his last chance to play the slug-a-bed for a long time; so he dozed and yawned and encouraged the faint border dreams that played through his mind. It was nearly nine o'clock before he dressed and went downstairs. Sir George and Lord Crewe, the servants told him, had gone abroad and the ladies were not up yet. Samuel tiptoed up to the wedding chamber and tapped on the door. Immediately he heard Jem's voice telling him to come in. When he opened the door, he saw that Jem, still in her nightdress, was alone in the room.

"And has your husband deserted you so soon?" Samuel asked.

Jemimah made a quick protest. "He has gone to dress," she said. And then she blushed and ran to Samuel and put her head into his shoulder.

Samuel patted her gently and held her until Philip came back into the room, dressed for the day. The three of them sat in the bridal chamber and chattered for half an hour about the plans to drive into Kent and to spend the honeymoon at Scott's Hall. The now loquacious couple urged Samuel to come with them and enjoy the holiday in Kent, but Samuel told them that he could not. His holiday was over and he must go back to London.

"Then take Elizabeth and go to Hinchingbrooke," Jemimah urged. "Get out of London by all means."

"Your father is this minute waiting for the Dutch guns to open fire," Samuel said quietly.

"But take care, Samuel. For all our sakes, take care."

"I always take care," Samuel assured her loftily, and then he kissed her and left the room.

XII

Great spoil, I hear, there hath been

SAMUEL NEEDED MORE than Jem's stern warning to protect him from the raging death that was sweeping London. The hot August sun blazed relentlessly all day in the cloudless skies, and the rats scampered free in the foul, almost deserted streets. Before the rows of cross-marked houses, silent "watchers," armed with halberds, sat motionless on their wooden boxes, seeing that no man broke the seal on the doomed, quarantined houses. From time to time the unnatural silence was broken by the crash of an upper-story window being thrown back, followed by an agonizing scream of despair. But the "watchers" sat unmoved, and the streets remained deserted, while inside the stricken houses whole families died, one by one, the father's last hours agonized by the screams of his wife, children, and servants.

Despite the quarantine the plague spread westward through the outparishes, the Liberties, and into the City itself. Three thousand died in a single week—four thousand—five thousand. The bells of the 109 parish churches kept up a constant peal, tolling their dead. The churchyards were soon filled up, grave on top of grave of uncoffined corpses, fresh earth brought hurriedly to cover the topmost bodies and quicklime scattered liberally to hasten decomposition and to abate the noisome odor of death.

To relieve the congestion in the parish cemeteries, the magistrates ordered public pits opened in the fields on the outskirts of the City—Moorfields, Shoreditch, St. John's Wood. The death carts that went through the streets at night gathering the naked bodies of the day's victims drove out to the pits, when the carts were filled, and dumped their load into the common hole. By the light of flares the gaunt white bodies were tumbled grotesquely on top of other naked, token-marked bodies; and then the workmen threw over them a layer of quicklime and a layer of dirt to ready the pit for the next gruesome load.

In desperation the magistrates ordered the trial of a last noxious remedy. Before every sixth house of an infected street the plague officers placed a fire pot, a large drum filled with wood, coal, and tar. The fires were lighted and great clouds of black smoke filled the air and hung over the street, acrid and suffocating. The watchmen ran out to the pots, choking and spluttering, to feed the flames and renew the dense cloud, and then they ran back again to the partial protection of their tavern stalls. The distrait authorities knew of only two remedies against the plague, quarantine and fumigation. They were determined to enforce both upon the suffering people, even if the remedies proved almost as grievous as the disease.

This was the London to which Samuel returned—a London filled with disease, smoke, and panic. He came back to the dangerous ground with considerably less courage than he had tried to exhibit to his anxious friends in the country. That was bravado —also vanity. They must not think him craven. He had played the role of wise counselor to the very end, to the moment their shouts of "God be with you" diminished in his ears, and he was aware that before him lay the ghastly threat of death in the plague-ridden streets of London. But as soon as he was alone with his thoughts on the bleak river, the terror began to grow. The prospect of having to live and do his business in the midst of unstoppable, incurable infection was almost more than he could face.

It was night when the waterman eased the wherry into the slip at the Tower. There was no sign of distress or trouble at the wharf. It was murky, quiet, with a strong odor of burning tar in the air, but the riverside usually smelled strongly of tar. Samuel paid his waterman and hurried up Tower Hill to the Navy Office. The building was quite dark, but he could see light in several windows of the residences. He let himself into his own house and bolted the door after him. Bolts and doors would not keep out the plague, but Samuel was a bolt-and-key man by instinct. There was always for him an illusion of security when the door was securely locked and the key in his pocket. He crept up the stairs to his bedroom without disturbing the servants. He was back in Seething Lane, alone with his fear, helpless to defend himself, unless the King in his gracious mercy ordered the Board to move its office out of danger.

When daylight came the next morning his courage returned. In the light of day he could see what was before him: his familiar furniture, his pictures, his books, his servants. With his possessions he could be at ease—and busy. Business topped the disorders of imagination, and he could always find chores readily at hand when he was at home with his things and there was daylight enough to command them. He called his servants together and instructed them not to go out of the house unless he gave them permission. Under no circumstances should they go outside the parish. They would live as normally as they could within the house, but they would all take the greatest precaution. And if one of them became ill. . . .

Samuel let the possibility hang in the air. He did not know what he would do if one of them became ill. He knew he could not send them out to die in the pesthouses or in the streets, and he could not, he *could* not, keep them here and have the plague officers come and seal him inside his own house with the dying, waiting through forty days for certain death. He went to his study and spent the day working on his long-neglected accounts, keeping his mind free of the horrors of imagination by concentrating on the complex figures. By nightfall he had made his balance. He was worth over two thousand pounds. The thought gave him little comfort.

For two weeks Samuel stayed close to the house. He could slip over to the Office through the garden without running much chance of meeting anyone, and he made the doorkeeper maintain a firm watch at the entry gate. No one without necessary business was to be admitted. He did not go into London and he stayed away from Whitehall.

It was both a satisfaction and a bit of a jolt for him to see that Elizabeth was living a serene and even gay life in her Woolwich lodgings. Her drawing master was taking her out on daily sketching trips. Their old friends the Pierces had joined the community of London *émigrés* and the nights were usually devoted to parties or dances where Elizabeth was made much of. She was finding more pleasure in living at the center of a small and merry social group in exile than she had in living in a kind of splendid isolation in Seething Lane. Samuel was jealous, not of the drawing master or any of the men who helped to make her Woolwich days so gay, but of the fact that Elizabeth and they could sing and dance and dine together as if the plague were not within a thousand miles, while he had to keep to his office in London within constant sight of the death carts, and the sound of the bells eternally tolling out their doleful news. He invented excuses for finding work in the Deptford yards, and he spent most of his days thereafter down the river at the hemp house and the tar sheds. At night he could stay with the Carterets and talk over the happy details of the wedding, or he could go up to Woolwich and spend the night with Elizabeth. He kept his mind off the work he needed to do at the Office. Just as he felt that he had worked out a way to compromise with living in the plague, he had a summons to Whitehall.

Samuel had hardly dared to look westward during the dreadful weeks of August; it had not occurred to him to go in that fearful direction. No one was now in Whitehall—no one of importance—except the Duke of Albemarle. It was worth his life to make that journey and, as like as not, the Duke only wanted company to help him break the dullness of deserted Whitehall. Samuel raged and swore and kicked the furniture, but—had to go.

He wrapped himself in a boat cloak, keeping his face covered. He held the swatch of tobacco leaves to his nose. The waterman, without instruction, kept the boat close to the Southwark bank, and they sped up the river as fast as the waterman could row. When the heavy odor of the burning tar reached out and assailed them, Samuel turned his face away and tried to hold his breath until they were around the south turn. He had the same feeling he had once had as a child when he hurried past a graveyard at night.

At the Palace the Duke of Albemarle sat at a table in his

chambers conducting his business with his usual phlegmatic thoroughness. Samuel had to wait in the anteroom while His Grace conferred with a committee of magistrates about the opening of new pits for the plague dead. Samuel had an uneasy feeling, as he waited, that it was not just for the sake of breaking boredom that the Duke had summoned him. Messengers were coming in and going out, bringing the daily count of the dead, taking orders for supplies for the pesthouses, reporting a violence of citizens at the quarantining of a house in a new neighborhood. The Duke was in touch with the plague and it was upon his strength and authority that the City fathers were drawing to keep order in the despairing town.

When he was finally summoned into the Duke's presence, Samuel had given up trying to guess what the Duke had in mind for him. The Duke, in his own good lethargic time, would tell him.

The tough, weather-beaten old man let Samuel stand for a few minutes while he put away the papers he had received from the last messenger. He glanced briefly at his visitor, giving no evidence that he had ever seen him before or had even the slightest notion what he was standing there for. He fumbled around among the disorder of papers and documents on the table, took time to peer closely at a letter, put it away with a noncommittal grunt, and then leaned back in his chair and looked out the window.

"Well, Mr. Pepys," he said at length, "we're upon hard times. Four thousand dead this week. No place to put 'em. It's easier at sea. The ocean holds a lot of dead, but the land is awkward. Pits. Quicklime. Very awkward. And people get panicky. Lose their heads. Have you lost your head, Mr. Pepys?" The old man turned from the window and peered at Samuel.

"I think not, your Grace," Samuel said as convincingly as he could.

"Of course not," the Duke blurted. "You're not the kind to lose your head. You're too sharp. Batten might lose his, and Pett, and the others, but not you. Not you and Penn. You're too sharp. It might cost you." The Duke chuckled. "There are two kinds of men who don't panic, men with strong wills, like you; and men without imagination, like Penn. Penn is good for a battle. It doesn't occur to him that a bullet will hit him. Men like that make the best soldiers. You wouldn't be a good soldier. You're afraid, but you don't let fear get in your way of what you want. You are good for running things, like a war." The Duke stopped and looked again out the window. Samuel stood silent and perplexed. He could think of nothing to say to this blunt analysis of his character. It was neither flattering nor derogatory, and yet it was both; it had the ambiguous sting of truth, and he did not know where all this truth-saying was leading.

"Have you seen the death carts in St. Olave's parish?" The question was asked in mild curiosity, the Duke continuing to look out the window.

"Not yet," Samuel answered tersely, committing himself to nothing.

The Duke turned back to his table, pulled out a document bearing the royal seal from a mass of papers, and without looking at it nodded to Samuel with what looked like grim satisfaction. "You will," he said emphatically. "You will." He touched the document. "The King has ordered you down the river. 'His Majesty's Principal Officers and Commissioners are instructed to establish their office at Greenwich and to conduct all their business from that place until ordered to return.'" The Duke flipped the parchment with his finger and stared hard at Samuel, waiting for his reaction.

Samuel held his face immobile. While his heart pumped hard at the news, he simply narrowed his eyes and made himself wait. He was not going to give the Duke the pleasure of seeing his relief.

The contest of wills lasted only a moment, and then the Duke smiled ruefully. "Enjoy your escape, Mr. Pepys. I enjoy it for you. You are of more use to us safe at Greenwich than dead in Seething Lane. The fleet cannot wait on the vagaries of the plague. Sandwich is back at Solebay, short of provisions and angry with the Norwegians for frustrating him at Bergen by protecting the Dutch India fleet. He needs supplies. Take your office to Greenwich and get Lord Sandwich back out to sea."

Samuel went back down the river elated. The Duke had said *your* office. It was *not* his—yet; but even the Duke of Albemarle thought of it as his. His feeling for the crusty old Duke soared. When the crises came, the kingdom had to call in the tough old dogs like Albemarle, the men who did not scare. The Duke seemed slow-witted and dull in the gaiety and dash of the Court, but in the pinch he was formidable. Despite the established enmity that existed between Lord Sandwich and the Duke of Albemarle, Samuel felt that it was to his interest to stand well with the Duke.

And so the Navy Office moved down the Thames to Greenwich, away from the horrors of the Black Death, which swept on into St. Olave's parish as they moved out. While the death toll mounted to 6,000 in a week, making a total of 17,000 for the month, the officers of the Navy Board scurried around getting Sandwich's fleet ready for sea before De Ruyter could slip his treasure ships down the coast to Holland. By the end of August the Earl's fleet was ready, repaired, and augmented to an imposing 100 sail, but very ill provisioned. The fleet could not wait. They sailed away on the last day of the month, the bright flags of the admirals standing out straight from all masts of the flagships. By dusk they were over the horizon and on course for Holland.

Early in September a great rain blew in from the coast and drenched the countryside. Samuel walked back to Greenwich from his Sunday at Woolwich through the downpour, past Coome Farm and its yelping dogs, past the parish church of St. Alphange. He arrived at the office soaking wet. As soon as he had removed his sodden coat and wiped his face dry, he called Mr. Hayter and asked him what business had accumulated in his absence.

"Nothing," the clerk said, "except a dispatch just delivered from Whitehall. The courier has just gone."

Samuel sat down by the roaring office fire and broke the seal. He read the dispatch through and then called out for Hayter. "Where are the other officers?"

"At my Lord Brouncker's lodgings, dining with Mr. Evelyn."

"Fetch me a dry coat," Samuel ordered and stuffed the dispatch into his pocket. He ran all the way to Brouncker's house and interrupted their dinner to read them his news. Lord Sandwich had hit the Dutch East India fleet!

On the morning of September 3, the scouting ships had sighted the East Indiamen under heavy convoy slipping along the coast from their snug haven in Bergen harbor, heading for the final security of the Texel. Lord Sandwich, feeling that this was the time to hazard his luck in the shallows of this coast, ordered immediate pursuit. By afternoon he was in sail-sight of the rear division of the merchantmen. Ordering all sail spread, the Earl charged in. It was risky and overbold, but only boldness could surprise the Dutch, who had depended on the shoal coastal waters to protect them. Skillful navigation and sheer good luck paid off, however. By dark Sandwich had captured two East Indiamen and four men-of-war with 1,300 prisoners. That night the fleet moved out to safer water, but at dawn it returned to the attack. The Earl broke his fleet into divisions and ordered them to chop the convoy into pieces, one division keeping the fighting ships busy while another herded the merchants into the fold. The strategy worked. From one group of eighteen sail, the English captured four more men-of-war and two rich merchantmen, a Straitsman and a Malagaman, loaded with spices. The weather became increasingly rough, the wind rising to hurricane force. Sandwich ordered his divisions to disperse and attack at will. For two days the storm tore at De Ruyter's convoy, breaking his line and scattering his treasure ships over a large expanse of the North Sea. The English simply stood off, keeping the best order they could, and sent their fast little frigates out to gather in the helpless India merchants.

The danger was weather now and not De Ruyter's guns. When the wind finally fell, a great fog rolled in and shut off all possibility of another contact with the Dutch. Sandwich, with the advice of his flag officers, decided to forego the possibility of a decisive meeting with the battle fleet. They would hold onto the prizes they had won and count their blessings in spoil. The ships returned to sailing formation, the thirteen prize ships carefully herded on the starboard, and headed for the English coast. At sunset on September 13 they dropped anchor at the Buoy of the Nore and sent off messengers with the news.

The Principal Officers in Lord Brouncker's lodgings in Greenwich let their dinners go cold as they listened to Samuel's recital of the great capture of prizes. A victory at sea was a usual cause for celebration, but even a victory at sea meant strenuous work for the civilian officers, repairing the inju. d ships, handling the endless detail of furnishing fresh supplies. Even a victory meant little else but back-breaking work. But a wholesale capture of prize ships! *That* was glorious news. It took a little while for the realization to sink in. Then Brouncker demanded, "How many Indiamen?"

"Thirteen," Samuel reported, his eyes shining.

"Cargoes intact?" Minnes asked hopefully.

"Cargoes intact," Samuel answered.

The men sat still for another minute, trying to think about it calmly. This was a considerable part of the year's supply of essential commerce for central Europe, the spices and silk and copper for the great markets of Vienna, Prague, Dresden. It was impossible for them even to guess the value of the spices stored in the holds and between decks of these thirteen Dutch merchantmen.

Lord Brouncker suddenly broke the paralyzed silence. "We must go at once to the Nore and greet Lord Sandwich."

It was still dark and a misty rain was hanging in the air when Samuel boarded the yacht *Bezan* early the next morning. Brouncker and Minnes were already aboard, taking the chill out of their bones with mulled claret down in the cabin. With them was "Captain" George Cocke, the King's steward for sick and wounded seamen. There would be sick and wounded seamen aplenty in the fleet, English and Dutch, and disposition would have to be made of them; but it was not his duty with the casualties that attracted Captain Cocke to the Nore. The enterprising Cocke was first and last a merchant—a prosperous tanner—and prize goods on this grand scale needed the attention of merchants. Brouncker and Minnes, not being sure what lay ahead for them, had been happy to include a man of his talent in the party.

Samuel accepted his cup of claret and felt the good warm stir of well-being in his vitals as the yacht caught the morning ebb of the tide and moved out into the river. His conviviality mounted with each cup. In the snug cabin the talk became happier and happier as Cocke made his knowing speculations about the content of the cargo and rattled off the laws of prizes. The seamen, he told them, were traditionally entitled to all cargo between decks. The holds were always sealed for the inspection of the Commissioners of the Prize, but the cargo between decks belonged to the poor seamen. Captain George smacked his lips over the wine and talked of twenty-pound bags of nutmegs, hampers of cloves and cinnamon. The seamen would want help in disposing of their goods. They would want cash.

Samuel lolled back on the cushions. The spiced wine, assisted by thoughts of cinnamon and cloves and pungent mace, relaxed him into blissful reverie, until the little ship, entering the open water beyond Gravesend, began to roll and pitch with the swelling sea. Then the very thought of spices turned traitor to him, and he was gripped with his old curse of seasickness. When the cold sweat popped out on his brow and his stomach began to surge toward his throat, he curled up on the cushions, miserable and angry. It was maddening to have this old weakness attack him at the moment of great hope. It was also humiliating to have to make this abject show of unseaworthiness before his naval colleagues. He lay on the cabin bench fighting his nausea and hating the imperious, smug well-being of his colleagues, until the *Bezan* arrived at the Buoy and hailed the *Prince,* Lord Sandwich's flagship.

Samuel's experience on his journey down the Thames in the *Bezan*—beginning in warm elation and ending in *mal-de-mer*—marked a pattern that was to begin again as soon as he stepped aboard the *Prince*. It was one of the ironies of his life that in the midst of a general catastrophe like the plague, Fortune should throw him the temptation of sudden and incredible wealth; and then as he had it almost in his grasp, the unpredictable Lady should snatch it from him. The prize goods were to be of little profit to Samuel, and were to be the undoing of the Earl of Sandwich.

The Principal Officers found the admirals closeted with the Earl when they arrived on board. While Cocke went off to survey the prizes, they were immediately summoned into the council, for there was much that had to be pressed upon them: the care of the wounded, the repair of storm-beaten sails and riggings, the immediate replenishment of wet and dry victuals—the usual business. In addition to the toll of battle, the fleet had taken a fierce beating in the heavy storms. Samuel took notes and promised that the Board would do all in its power to relieve the fleet. All the vice admirals and rear admirals were there: Allin, Ayscue,

Berkeley, Harman, Jordan, Myngs, Penn, Teddiman. Three of the commanders were also present: Cuttance, Jeremy Smith, and Spragge. Samuel was surprised at the full attendance. It did not need the whole staff of flag officers to agree about these routine matters, and he could not account at all for the presence of three of the ship commanders. Something more than matters of supply and repair was in the wind, and he had a good idea that the prize ships were occupying some portion of their thoughts. His wretched stomach now back in its normal place, Samuel was himself eager to hear some mention of that delightful subject. But the Earl of Sandwich was full of troubled complaints about the short supply of victuals in the fleet, "No beer at all and but few days' dry provisions."

Sir William Penn finally brought the prizes into the discussion. Some of his commanders, he said, were very uneasy about discipline in their ships. The seamen were clamoring for their rights to break out the cargo between decks.

"There are no such rights specified in the regulations covering prize goods," Lord Sandwich said. "According to regulations, the holds of all the prize ships will have to be spiked up and the ships delivered to the Commissioners of the Prize."

"Those are, of course, the regulations, my lord," Penn replied shortly, "but the seamen know, and we know, that since the reign of Elizabeth, the Crown has allowed seamen the right to all cargo stowed between decks. They are yelling to heaven now for their 'rights.'" Penn looked more eager than his usual concern for the "rights" of common seamen could account for.

Admiral Harman quickly reminded the meeting that he already had his lordship's orders to spike the holds and deliver the ships to the Commissioners at Ipswich and Harwich.

"We are now closer to Chatham and Erith," Penn pointed out. "You should have carried out your orders before we came into the Nore. The merchants from the river ports are already on board the ships negotiating with the men. They will be hard to hold, and I can't blame them. They are unpaid for over a year. They want their money one way or another."

Harman started to answer the insinuation that he had failed to carry out an order; but Sandwich, bored with the whole pettish discussion, waved him down. "Let the men have their prizes. They will get it later anyway. Let them have it."

Discussions of money always bored his lordship. He never had enough himself, because he was a lavish spender and a careless husbandman and also because the King was a tardy paymaster. But things always worked out. The money always came in the end, and it was a sordid business to haggle about a few pounds of spices.

"Send the men in parties to the prize ships. Set guards to see that the holds are not breached. They may stuff their wallets with whatever they find between decks before the ships are consigned to the Commissioners. Does that satisfy your conscience about the seamen, Admiral Penn?"

"Not entirely, my lord," Penn retorted. "His Majesty is unhappily six thousand pounds in arrears of good money that he owes me for past and present service. Before we sailed he gave me his generous promise that I should quit him of his debt from the first fruits of whatever we managed to snatch from the Dutch. We have snatched a good deal, my lord. I would like to accept the King's promise before the Commissioners consign it all to the bottomless pits of the Treasury. I am sure my Lord Sandwich will be sympathetic with this mark of prudence."

Samuel knew that Penn had struck a telling blow. It was common knowledge that the Earl of Sandwich would be a wealthy man if the King had paid him all that he was by royal promise entitled to. Samuel was aghast that Penn could be such a fool as to bait the Earl like this in open meeting, but he was also aware that his cousin would think twice before he would dismiss the practical suggestion of collecting their debts first and seeking permission afterward. The King was as easy of dispense as he was laggard in fulfillment. He would agree to this sharp arrangement. Samuel knew this. Penn knew it. Everybody in the room knew it, including the Earl of Sandwich.

"What do the gentlemen value the captured cargoes?" the Earl asked quietly.

"A half-million sterling," Harman answered tersely.

The Earl tapped his fingers on the table and looked glumly at his staff. Samuel knew it was a bad moment for him. He did not like this kind of decision. The flag officers were entitled to something from His Majesty for their service. They ran as much danger as the men, and as superior officers their expenses were considerable, much more than their precarious salaries could ever cover. This chance for repayment did not come often in the course of a long career. It would be niggling to deprive them of it. And the Sandwich fortunes would be appreciably helped by a tithe of what was due him.

The Earl turned his solemn gaze upon Penn. "You wish me to give a warrant for a specified amount of captured goods, in anticipation of the King's approval?"

"Yes, my lord. A warrant to each of us here, a signed warrant for each of us to command goods to a certain value in proportion of rank. I suggest a thousand for the commanders, two for the flag officers, and four each for the admirals. This is only a pittance of £27,000 out of the King's half-million. It is money not only deserved but owed. The King would despise us for troubling our consciences about it."

The Earl blew a blast of air through his lips that was half a sigh and half a hiss. Samuel could not tell whether the hiss was for Penn, for the Earl himself, or for the whole distasteful issue. At any rate, his lordship got up from his chair and ambled slowly toward the door of his own cabin. He stopped there and paused for a moment as if trying to think of something he might have forgotten. Some of the officers watched him eagerly, intent upon a decision that had to come before he left the room. A few others—Spragge, Ayscue, Berkeley—looked down at the deck, embarrassed and unhappy.

Sandwich opened the door abruptly. As he passed out of the room, he muttered over his shoulder, "Make the warrants. I will sign them."

Penn and Cuttance and Allin and Jordan fell into a close huddle of joyful congratulation. Myngs and Teddiman and Harman drew to one side and talked in excited whispers. But two of the captains, Smith and Spragge, and two of the flag officers, Ayscue and Berkeley, got up without a word and left the room. Samuel picked up his notebook and followed Lord Sandwich into his cabin. He wished that he could have stayed with the now wealthy officers and listened to their plans for securing their goods. He looked jealously at his colleagues who were already busy paying them court but he would have to wait to get at them. His first duty was with his patron.

It did not take long for Lord Sandwich's decision—reluctantly and imprudently given—to start the chain of action that was to lead to the great scandal of the year. The seamen boarded the prize ships like berserk pirates, ripping open bales of silk, breaking crates of expensive copperwork, throwing huge sacks of pepper and nutmegs and cinnamon onto the decks and scattering the precious stuff underfoot in a bedlam of confusion. They ransacked whatever was at hand, greedy to get their share before a stronger hand could snatch the bags from them. They fought each other with belaying pins and attacked the guards who defended the sealed holds. Only by shooting a few seamen point-blank were the guards able to keep the holds intact for the flag officers and, ultimately, His Majesty. The half-wild seamen dropped bales and boxes and bags of spices over the sides into the small boats that waited to haul their goods for them into Erith. Sometimes a heavy box would crash through the bottom of a boat and send goods and men floundering into the water. The sea seethed in costly jetsam, dyed dark with black pepper and nutmegs, the wasted harvest of the Orient.

When the frantic seamen had stripped the decks, Vice Admiral Jordan took command and shepherded the half-ravaged ships into Chatham and Erith. The ships now rode five feet higher in the water, but they still contained a major treasure. Lord Sandwich ordered Brouncker and Minnes to go with the prize ships and see that the holds remained inviolate until the Commissioners could arrange for storage room in adequate warehouses. He specified that the flag officers should obtain their rewards from the two largest Indiamen, the *Phoenix* and the *Slothony*. Admiral Jordan and Captain Kempthorn were delegated to see that the operation was conducted without dishonor to the King or to the Admiral of the Fleet.

As soon as Samuel had paid his personal respects to his lordship, given him all the news of his family, and listened again to the unhappy story of the scanty victuals, he hurried on deck to catch what tardy news he could of the disappearing prizes. He cursed his luck that duty had deprived him of an equal start in the race. He ran to the leeward side of the ship to see if any boat was putting off toward Erith, and ran headlong into Captain Cocke. The busy merchant had just returned to the *Prince* from his personal survey of the prize ships. He held fast to the toppling Clerk of the Acts and guided him to a secluded place under the quarterdeck.

"We are well met, Mr. Pepys," he jovially assured Samuel. "I need you, and you need me. Where can we get five hundred pounds for the asking?"

Samuel straightened his rumpled clothes and looked sharply at his blunt companion. "Why do we need five hundred pounds, Mr. Cocke?" Samuel did not bother to give merchants their honorary titles.

"We need five hundred to make five hundred, Mr. Pepys. Money is in the air, Mr. Pepys. It is underfoot. It is floating on the water. One needs only a little wit to salvage it. Are you interested in the prizes, Mr. Pepys?"

Samuel pursed his lips and looked thoughtful. He did not know a great deal about Cocke. He was not sure how far he could trust him. The man had frequently been in and out of the office, looking for opportunities, flaunting his semiofficial connection with the Navy.

"I have thought of them," he admitted. "I have thought that I might be able to make a little bargain or two with the seamen."

"Don't bother with the seamen," Cocke trumpeted. "Don't bother with the crumbs. You may sweep them in at any time. Take a few pounds into the taverns at Erith any time in the next week and you can make your journey worth the trouble. But that is pence-and-shilling business. How would you like to share a thousand pounds for an hour's work? How would you like that?"

Samuel felt his heart jump. Five hundred pounds was a little fortune, a golden egg for security against the precarious future.

"How would five hundred get five hundred, Mr. Cocke?" he asked, as composedly as he could; and before Cocke could answer, he hastened to add, "I do not have five hundred myself, you understand."

"Of course, you don't, Mr. Pepys," Cocke shouted joyfully. "The more fool you if you did. A sharp man never hazards his own money on a speculation. I would not have selected you for a partner if I thought you a fool. But you have better than ready money. You have connections."

Samuel admitted the honor and asked how that might serve them.

"Lord Sandwich is your patron, Mr. Pepys. Lord Sandwich is the Admiral of this fleet. The prize goods at the moment belong to him. I. . . ."

"Lord Sandwich is my cousin," Samuel broke in, "and neither he nor I would consider for a moment the violation of his trust."

"Of course, you would not," Mr. Cocke went on unperturbed. "And I would not join you if you did. My little scheme is the soul of honor and simplicity. The flag officers are eager to realize their money on their share of the goods. I know one that is willing to let us have over a thousand pounds' worth of spices for five hundred pounds in ready cash. I have just had a little talk with Captain Cuttance and he will assign his spices to the first man that brings him five hundred pounds.

"Cuttance is not a flag officer," Samuel protested. "He is only a ship commander and a rogue at that."

"But Cuttance managed to be included in the bounty, although the other captains refused it."

"Why did the others refuse it?" Samuel demanded, his sense of caution on the alert.

"I don't know. It is not our affair. He has his warrant, and that is all we need—except five hundred pounds and a *transire* from the Admiral to insure that we can pass our goods through the customs. How say you, Mr. Pepys?"

Samuel walked to the side of the ship and looked down at the water moving in erratic swells along the wooden hull. The rhythm of it made his head swim, and he fixed his attention on the hemp line tied away on the belaying pin under his hand. He felt its texture and dug his thumbnail into the taut strands. His subconscious mind automatically recorded "Riga" while his conscious mind turned Mr. Cocke's proposal this way and that. The scheme did have simplicity and it was perfectly legal. His lordship would certainly give him a *transire* and there would be no trouble at all in having five hundred pounds transferred from the fleet account to his own account for a few days. That kind of transaction was almost routine in the casual economics of the seventeenth century navy. It was only the handling of the goods themselves that would be difficult, getting them off the ship at Chatham and having them carted to Greenwich for quick sale to the London merchants, who did not let anything, not even plague, interfere with opportunity.

Without turning his head, Samuel asked, "You will take care of the sale of the goods?"

"Easily," Mr. Cocke answered brightly. "No trouble to you at all. You just get us the *transire* and the money."

Samuel walked back to the underhousing of the quarterdeck. "I will speak to his lordship," he said. "Locate Captain Cuttance."

While Cocke hurried off to close his deal with Cuttance, Samuel ran back to Lord Sandwich's cabin; and after fifteen minutes of comforting assurances, he came out with an order for £500 to be transferred from the fleet purse to Mr. Samuel Pepys and a *transire* inscribed by the Earl of Sandwich, directing all who might be concerned that the goods in Mr. Pepys's possession were rightfully his and not to be molested without order from His Majesty, King Charles II.

With a gleam in his eye and the fine spicy scent of quick profit in his nostrils, Samuel plunged into the task of collecting the harvest. He ordered the *Bezan* to take Captain Cocke down the Medway into Chatham to arrange for collecting their goods from the holds of the *Phoenix* and the *Slothony*. As soon as the yacht returned to the flagship in the Nore, Samuel commandeered it again for his personal use. Lord Brouncker and Minnes were busy with the prize ships; they had no need of the yacht. He ordered it to take him back up the Thames to Greenwich and to wait for him while he slipped into London for an afternoon's business. His business was to visit his iron chest in the cellar of his house in Seething Lane. Captain Cocke might loftily refer to the seamen's prizes as "crumbs," but Mr. Pepys had not yet arrived at a point of fortune that permitted him to overlook trifles. He needed some of his ready cash to take to Erith to bargain a bit with the seamen. The chance to fill his pockets with shillings and pence was worth to him the danger of an hour in the plague-ridden city.

The plague had reached its peak in the devastating heat of mid-September. The dead lay piled in casual heaps at the street corners and at the edges of the desolate fields. The death carts rumbled by, unable to add another corpse to their load. The magistrates had felt some encouragement about the effectiveness of the street fires until the heavy rain of the hurricane came and drowned them in a hissing cloud of steam. The cloudburst drenched the streets and swept a month's accumulation of sordid debris down the kennels, and a blessed coolness followed for a few days. The Bills of Mortality showed a hopeful decrease of 500 deaths in the week; but the hope was only a hope. The sun came back with renewed strength and London again sweltered in a thick humidity. The death rate soared at once to a staggering total of over a thousand dead a day. The Bills recorded over 7,000 dead by plague in the week, but Albemarle made his official estimate at 14,000. The dead were too numerous either to bury or to count.

That was the worst week, that third week of September. In the pit of their misery the helpless citizens snatched at straws of comfort. The clapper fell out of the Great Bell of Westminster, and excited rumor swept the town. The same clapper had fallen in '25 when the last great plague had come to an end. It was a sign, an omen of promise. Men talked of the bell clapper for a week, and others caught sight of another hopeful symbol—the daws were returning to the Palace and to the Abbey in great numbers. Everyone knew that the daws had departed in April when the plague first began to appear, and now they could be seen any day soaring about the chimneys of the Palace or sweeping down to roost in the trees of St. James's Park. Perhaps the fury of God was spent and London's sin—whatever it was—expiated in agony and grief.

The odd thing was that the plague *was* over—almost. The clapper and the daws were right; but the skeptical and the profane and the enlightened, like Mr. Pepys, did not believe in signs—not quite.

When Samuel slipped into London to visit his chest, he hurried up Tower Hill, past the shuttered door and windows of the alehouse at Tower Stairs, and hurried into the Navy Office grounds by the back way, avoiding any chance of meeting his contaminated neighbors. He let himself into his house and with a tallow candle lighted his way down into the cellar. He opened his chest and took out his two bags of gold, £180 in guineas, half-guineas, and double guineas. He distributed the coins in the pockets of the belt he wore next to his skin, blew out the candle, and hurried back to Tower Wharf. He had been in London less than an hour.

Next morning Erith was a confusion of frantic men and crowded taverns. The usually peaceful little river port was bursting at the seams with sudden wealth. The few taverns and ale-shops which normally fought for the custom of a hundred or so dock workers were now packed to overflowing with the sailors, who had suddenly appeared loaded with sacks of precious spices and yelling their heads off to find purchasers. The narrow streets became market fairs of indigo, cinnamon, and nutmegs. The wretched men did not haggle or bargain for their profits; they were too eager to change their bulky goods into ready cash and their cash into ale and good landside victuals. The village merchants preyed upon the simple sailors as ruthlessly as the sailors themselves had ransacked the carefully stored goods on the prize ships.

By the time Samuel arrived on the scene, the pillage of the seamen was just about complete. There were still a few merchants' carts loaded down with pungent sacks rolling out of town toward the inland markets. The streets still bore evidence of strange merchandise, torn sacks, and spilled pepper. But the impromptu markets were deserted. Samuel circulated the taverns and walked the streets from one end to the other, but he saw only drunken seamen or exultant merchants. Down by the docks he met a London waterman, a wherry owner, who had deserted the City to escape the plague and was now trying to eke out an existence carrying passengers between the down-river ports. Samuel knew his face, and the waterman knew Mr. Pepys's name.

"Looking for spices, Mr. Pepys?" he asked his former customer. "I know where you can find a sack or two if you have ready money."

"Where?" Samuel demanded.

"Come, I'll show you, for old time's sake, Mr. Pepys."

"What will you want for your trouble?" Samuel knew the ways of the watermen, and he wanted his bargain clear before he committed himself.

"Two shillings, a tankard of ale, and the trip back up the river," the waterman specified.

"I will give you one shilling now, the ale when you have shown me the sacks, and the second shilling when we are back in Greenwich." Samuel was Londoner enough always to make a bargain sound like his own arrangement.

"Done," said the waterman; and they set off through the winding little streets to the far end of the town, where in a dark alehouse the waterman pointed out two ragged seamen sitting at a table in a dark corner of the room. While the waterman drank his promised ale, Samuel started his negotiations with the seamen.

He asked them if they had any spices they wanted to sell; they said they had some, but they were not giving them away for nothing to greedy merchants.

"I am not a merchant," Samuel said, "and I will pay you your price. What have you got?"

"Cloves and nutmegs," one of them replied, "and you will pay us five and six a pound for the cloves and four shillings a pound for the nutmegs. Not a penny less."

"How much have you got?" Samuel wanted to know.

"Weigh them and see," they said.

On scales borrowed from the tavernkeeper, Samuel weighed the sacks. There were 37 pounds of cloves and 10 pounds of nutmegs. He paid the men in gold guineas, stood them a round of ale, and happily received their joint judgment that he was an honest man—no merchant. Since there had been something rather dark and *sub rosa* about the whole negotiation, he was pleased with the assurance that he was an honest man.

When he arrived back at the dock, the waterman carrying his spice sacks for him, he dismissed the yacht *Bezan*. He did not need the elegant little ship any more, and he was glad that he did not have to take his prize goods on board. Although everything he had done was perfectly legal, he somehow was relieved that he was not having to use His Majesty's ship for conducting his private business, at least the tangible part of it. Mr. Pepys prided himself on these delicate shades of honor.

And when he got back to Greenwich with his little hoard of spices, he voluntarily gave the waterman an extra shilling—for being his porter, he said—but the generosity of the gesture gave a fillip to his pleasure in the whole adventure. Cocke could sneer at crumbs, but Samuel had now not only realized a nice £12 profit for himself, he had also had the safe excitement of the adventure. He had himself touched the prize goods with his own hands, made actual contact with the great sea fight, the fabulous De Ruyter, and the distant and exotic Indies.

That was the last of Samuel's pleasure in the prize goods. Thereafter the spices became a burden; the adventure, a series of harrying episodes filled with ill omen.

While the seamen at Erith and the flag officers at Chatham were digging into the rich spoil of the prize ships, the Court at Oxford was congratulating itself on the timely windfall that had come to the Government in its moment of dire necessity. The Duke of Albemarle wrote Lord Sandwich a long letter of thanksgiving and praise, urging him to take every precaution against embezzlement, since the Court was put to great shifts for money. Lord Arlington, the Secretary of State, chortled to the Council, "If we must have war, may the next be as prosperous." The Duke of York added his public thanks to God for His goodness in supplying the Crown with this great treasure and to the Earl of Sandwich for his "care in this action." The cold stone courts of the several colleges that housed His Majesty's Government during its exile from the plague rang with new cheer as the Council and the courtiers drank their toasts of congratulation and speculated about the price of cinnamon.

And then admirals Myngs and Ayscue arrived with their story of the flag officers—the *other* flag officers—breaking cargo with the permission of Lord Sandwich. The anger was instant. The furious courtiers ran back and forth from Balliol to Trinity with fire in their eyes. The Council met in a stormy session and prophesied how ill the Parliament would take this bilking of the public treasure. Lord Albemarle, already in the midst of a negotiation with the East India Company to take the whole Dutch spoil for conversion to sorely needed gold, immediately sent off an order to the Commissioners of the Prize to instruct the Custom to stop all entry of goods from the prize ships.

Samuel was quietly at work in his office at Greenwich when Captain Cocke's servant burst into the room in a sweat to tell him that four wagonloads of the prize from Chatham had just come into town and had been impounded by the Custom officers. Samuel snatched his *transire* from his file and rushed out into the street. A crowd of two or three hundred jabbering people surrounded four wagons, their freight hidden by tightly stretched tarpaulins which ballooned above the wagon beds twice as high as a man's head. Samuel shouldered his way through the crowd and confronted the officious-looking rogue who held the drivers at bay. Samuel put on his best official front and demanded to know what right the gentleman had to stop these goods. The Customs man, who introduced himself as Captain Fisher, showed Mr. Pepys his orders from the Commissioners. Samuel in turn showed him his *transire* from the Earl of Sandwich. Captain Fisher pointed out the fact that his document bore the later date and said that his orders were to lock the goods in a convenient warehouse and to seal it until the Commissioners gave a release. Samuel was on the verge of resorting to angry words in an effort to overbear the fellow, but he thought better of it and went back to his office to get off a letter to the Earl. He told his patron what had happened and asked his advice about how to conduct himself in the face of this frightening development. He also cursed himself for having become involved with Captain Cocke and the whole dubious business in the first place.

The Earl immediately sent him a comforting reply. Samuel need not worry. The King had confirmed the distribution of the goods to the officers and his official order would be along presently. In the meantime Samuel could own his goods with confidence. "Carry it high," his lordship advised him, "and own nothing of baseness or dishonor, but rather intimate that I shall know who have done me indignities."

Although the Earl's letter of assurance was comforting to Samuel, it was not impressive to Captain Fisher. That gentleman kept a close watch on the sealed warehouse and informed Mr. Pepys that he would release the goods only when he had something official in writing.

So Samuel, despite the Earl's advice, worried. In a few days he was given something else to worry about. He received notice from the Duke of Albemarle that a fleet of eighty Dutch sails had been sighted off the coast and that the Navy Office must make every effort to prepare a fleet to meet them.

Samuel threw up his hands in despair. There was no way to get a fleet ready. Not more than four ships were still fit for service. It would take all winter to repair the damage done by the high winds of the last engagement. At least half the seamen were injured or sick. There were not enough men available to man twenty ships, even if twenty ships could be fitted. And as for supply—the whole system of victualing had broken down in the panic of the plague. The last fleet had had to go to its work without enough food or drink to last two weeks of an extended campaign. Now there was almost no beer available and only a scant supply of bread and salt pork. Samuel hurried down the river to the Earl.

Lord Sandwich had just come out of a conference with his flag officers when Samuel arrived. He was as composed as usual, but he told Samuel that he, too, had had a letter from Albemarle, demanding that a fleet be put in readiness to repulse the Dutch. It was understandable, he informed his cousin, that the Duke of Albemarle, bothered as he was by trying to hold London together during the plague, should get excited and impractical about sending out a fleet when the Dutch were only trying to save face by making a show of force. But the Duke did not understand the realities of campaigning at sea. The weather would soon drive the Dutch away. Even if it did not, it was suicidal to send out a poorly equipped squadron to meet a force of eighty sail. The flag officers were in complete agreement, and the Earl was now on his way to Oxford to explain the situation to the Duke of York and the King. He told Samuel to quit worrying. The King would listen to reason.

The King did. But there were others who would not. The

Council was still angry at the Earl's presumption in allowing the prize cargo to be broached, and the Duke of York was worried about the threat to the prestige of the Navy. It was bad enough to have a noisy Commons yelling about violation of the public trust, but now with the Dutch sailing unchallenged off the coast, public opinion demanded, however unwisely, that the Navy should also make a show of force. Lord Sandwich explained his position as calmly and clearly as he could, but tempers in Oxford grew short. The Duke of Albemarle in London was rattling the sword with threats that if my Lord Sandwich did not see fit to put to sea, he was resolved to go with the fleet himself. Lord Sandwich smiled at the Duke's gusty belligerence and ignored the common people's whispers of cowardice; but he could neither smile at nor ignore the Council's lack of understanding. The King might generously pat him and promise him protection, but the King ruled his factious courtiers no more firmly than he ruled his mistresses. Lord Sandwich could be ruined while he waited for the King's indolent benevolence. He left Oxford and returned, like a sullen Achilles, to his flagship in the Nore.

Samuel in Greenwich worked hard at getting the supply of stores assembled and loaded. He kept a close eye on the weather. A good autumnal tempest would forestall the need of getting out an ill-equipped token force. It was high time for a good blow. But the Duke of Albemarle kept him busy with orders to get the ships ready.

When Samuel was just about convinced that the Navy and the Earl of Sandwich were going to have to stake their lives on half a dozen ships of the line and a flotilla of frigates, the weather suddenly took a violent turn and began to blow the tops out of all the trees along the river. Samuel watched the raging wind tear up the scenery and prayed to God that the Dutch were getting their share of it.

They were. With the first heavy gust, De Ruyter tacked northward and fled for the security of the Dutch coast. The threat upon the English Navy was over for the year. Only a convoy for the Hamburg merchantmen had now to be arranged. They had the whole winter to restore the fleet. Samuel sighed in relief. He also took steps to clear his own decks for the future. He sold his share of the prize goods to Captain Cocke for a clear £500. He felt that he was probably losing a hundred or two hundred pounds of ultimate profit, but he was anxious to free himself from the stigma that rightly or wrongly had attached itself to the unhappy treasure.

The peace that came to him as soon as he had transferred all his papers to Captain Cocke was suddenly disrupted by a terse command from the Duke of Albemarle to present himself immediately at the Tower of London. Samuel was frightened. It was not the idea of a conference with the Duke that frightened him. He had had many during the long exile and he had learned how to face the blunt old soldier. Nor was it the danger of going into London. The plague had definitely broken. He knew in all reason that the Duke had selected the Tower for the convenience of it, and he was glad not to have to make the longer trip up the Thames to Whitehall; but the Tower sounded ominous—irrelevantly, illogically ominous.

All the way up the river from Greenwich to Tower Wharf, he fretted about the possible purpose of the meeting. He was in the difficult position of being related to the Duke's chief enemy of the moment. There had never been much love lost between the Duke and the Earl. At the time of the Restoration, they had been the two officers most instrumental in securing the King's return. Albemarle, or Monck as he had been then, had the greater power, since he had the army. But there had been a mutual respect between the two. The King had rewarded them both—if not equally, at least satisfactorily. Sandwich had remained the brilliant naval strategist, but Albemarle had become the national hero, the bulwark of the Court in time of trouble. Now, however, the two men were at loggerheads. Sandwich had the disgrace of the prizes on his back while Albemarle had won broad acclaim for his courage in sticking with London during the plague. But more than that Sandwich now stood for the unpopular strategy of outwaiting the Dutch, while Albemarle represented the more exciting policy of getting out a fleet at any cost. The moment belonged to Albemarle, and perhaps the future did too. Samuel fretted over these matters and wondered where he stood. His heart, surely and forever, belonged to his patron; but what of the future, what of his career in the Navy? He had an uneasy feeling, vague and baseless, that this meeting with the Duke was crucial.

The Duke received him in the quarters of the Lieutenant of

the Tower. He looked no more perturbed or harried than he ever did. He waved Samuel to a seat and glared at him. Samuel looked bland and kept his own gaze fixed firmly upon him. He was used now to these ducal glares. The Duke snorted once, and then suddenly demanded, "What is the greatest hindrance in setting out a fleet when it is needed?"

"Victual," Samuel answered promptly.

"So I have heard," said the Duke, and he continued to look scornfully at the Clerk of the Acts.

"You have had some success, Mr. Pepys, in dealing with the victual for Tangier."

Samuel had had notable success. It was the one operation in the whole complex project of the Mediterranean base that had not suffered. Tangier had been well supplied with victual when it had lacked everything else, and Samuel felt no little pride in the efficiency of his service. He also felt considerable happiness with the £500 a year he was getting from his victual contractor for yielding a profit both to the contractor and to the King.

"Some success," he admitted.

"The Navy," the Duke shouted, "deserves as much care as Tangier." And then the old field general set in and delivered a blistering denunciation of almost everything that was wrong in the Navy, the strategy, the command, the financing, the victualing. Samuel noticed, as the angry tirade went on, that the Duke never mentioned the name of the Earl of Sandwich, and this he took for tact. Nor did he include supply and repairs in the list of evils. This he took for flattery. Both tributes he accepted gratefully.

At last the Duke stopped for a breath. Getting up from his chair, he stamped over to the narrow window of the little room. Without looking at Samuel, who had promptly risen from his chair, he said, "Mr. Pepys, if I have Sir William Coventry write you, offering you the place of Surveyor General of Victual for the Navy, will you accept?"

Samuel hesitated for a moment. "In place of or in addition to my post as Clerk of the Acts?"

The Duke whirled around and openly sneered at him. "In addition to," he bellowed.

Samuel dropped his eyes and looked down at his feet. This was what success sounded like; this was the flavor of triumph; closed up in a gloomy dungeon of a room in the Tower of London, a blustering old Commonwealth soldier shouting at him.

But what of the Earl of Sandwich? What of his patron? This man was the enemy of his gracious cousin. To accept this man's favor was, in a way, to reject the obligation a protégé owes to his benefactor. He knew that if he said yes to the Duke of Albemarle, he would thereafter no longer be the subject of the Earl of Sandwich. He would be free—his heart jumped at the word—and he would also be alone. And yet this man, this glaring nobleman at the tiny window, was also the voice of his country, his duty, and, perhaps, his future. Perhaps this was not the moment of crisis his imagination was making it. Stripped of the emotion, this was still a simple situation. He *could* improve the system of supplying victual to the fleet and he could also earn, justly, a healthy profit for himself in doing it. It was as simple as that; and yet he hesitated, until the Duke's throaty voice shook the room again.

"Will you accept it, Mr. Pepys?"

Samuel drew himself up. "I cannot, your Grace," he finally said, "refuse anything that His Majesty requires of me."

He was pleased with the answer, and so, apparently, was the Duke, for he waved him out of the room with a curt gesture and the parting advice, "Then go to work, Mr. Pepys. Your orders will be along directly."

Samuel walked out of the Tower through the Lion Gate and wandered out along the Wharf to collect his thoughts. This was a turning point, he felt, a milestone. Now he worked for the Navy, for the Crown, and not just for the Earl of Sandwich. It was bound to come to this sometime, he comforted himself. His lordship had known it and would understand it now. It would make no real difference in their lives. His lordship had never made demands of obligation. He would not even know that anything had happened, for it had only happened inwardly.

And yet when Samuel looked down and saw that he was standing over the scummy passage under the Wharf from the river to St. Thomas's Tower, called the Traitor's Gate, he pulled back his hand from the cold rail and hurried away from the place, disquieted and strangely unhappy.

XIII

How little we deserve of God Almighty

LATE IN NOVEMBER a hard freeze gripped the river and sent a chill wind into London. The little lake in St. James's Park turned to ice. The stone cobbles in the streets of the City became slick and dangerous, and the plague watchers huddled close over charcoal fires in protected doorways. The rats that had all summer enjoyed the freedom of the streets slunk back into the warmth of the dark cellars. London shivered in the first cold blast of winter—and rejoiced. Winter meant the end of the plague.

The plague had really been ended since that last fatal peak in September—statistically ended. The weekly Bills of Mortality had plunged downward consistently through October: from 5,000 dead in a week to 3,000, to 1,000. Following the great freeze, the curve of death by plague dropped even more precipitately: 600—300—and finally by the first of December to slightly over 100 dead in the week. London had never been entirely free of the plague. Death itself—scattered death—was no matter of alarm in the tough, dirty old seventeenth-century city. It was only quarantine they could not endure, enclosure, imprisonment.

As soon as the magistrates, under orders from the Duke of Albemarle, relaxed their firm watch on the quarantined houses, the tradesmen began to return to the City. Shutters were removed from the shop windows, vendors began to roam again, goods carts rumbled through the streets, apprentices brawled, merchants reassembled in the Exchange.

The King and the Court did not return to the capital until the end of January, and then only as close as Hampton Court. Samuel went at once with his brethren of the Office to greet the King and the Duke of York and to receive their instructions. Both the royal brothers pressed Samuel's hand warmly, and the King said aloud, so that all the Court could hear, "Mr. Pepys, I do give you my thanks for your good service all this year, and I assure you I am very sensible of it."

Samuel hoped that his colleagues had heard the royal compliment; but, when he looked to see, he saw that they were huddled in a far corner of the room conferring with Sir William Coventry. As soon as he could, Samuel began to edge across the room to see what business his colleagues were discussing with the Duke's secretary. When he was halfway there, just abreast of the great fireplace, he saw his cousin, the Earl of Sandwich, standing alone, his back turned to the roomful of courtiers, looking sadly into the flames of the log fire. Samuel stopped. The Earl's face was heavy with melancholy, his mustache untrimmed, dark circles under his eyes. It struck Samuel's heart to see him so. The man who had only a few months before been the hero of the Navy, the hope of the Crown, was now practically an outcast, out of favor with the Council, an easy target for his enemies, but forced, nevertheless, by his pride to stand here in the room with them and make a show of ignoring their triumph. And Samuel knew that he himself was on their side—York's and Albemarle's and Coventry's. When he took over the Victual at Albemarle's request, he had cast his lot. There was no way to ignore the fact, however much he might hope or pretend not to. To speak to Coventry was to slight the Earl; to speak to Lord Sandwich was to arouse the suspicions of the new rulers of the Navy. Samuel looked at his cousin gazing vacantly into the fire, and he looked at his colleagues over in the corner buzzing secretly to Sir William Coventry. He hesitated a moment —and then he stepped forward and touched his cousin on the sleeve.

The Earl turned slowly and gazed at him, as vacantly as he had been gazing at the fire.

Samuel said softly, "My lord?"

Without a gesture or a smile of recognition, the Earl muttered, "How do you, cousin?"

"Well, my lord," Samuel replied, his stomach tightening fearfully.

A suggestion of a smile touched the admiral's lips.

"You do not do well, Samuel, to speak to me so boldly in this cage of suspicious courtiers."

"Where may I see you, my lord?" Samuel asked quickly.

"Come to my lodgings, when you are free," the Earl almost whispered. More than he need have, Samuel felt. "Come to my cell and confess your sins." The suggestion of a smile was still on his lips.

That afternoon in the privacy of the Earl's cold chamber, Samuel poured out his heart: how he had agonized in making his decision to serve his lordship's enemies, how hard a game it was to play, serving two masters, his cousin and his king, when their ways became separate. In order to do his duty as an officer of the Navy, he had, he said, to serve whoever was in command. "That it is no longer your lordship is my grief," he concluded, almost in tears.

The Earl patted him kindly on the shoulder.

"I am sorry to see your distress, Cousin Samuel, and I am sorry also for all the inconveniences which are likely to fall upon you from your connection with me. You do have a hard game to play, but play it with courage, and credit, and honor. It is a prickly world we have the dubious pleasure of living in. A man has to be quick and tough and of good heart to avoid, or to bear, the slashes. Your good service to the Navy will aid the King when he needs aid, and it will not injure me."

Samuel grabbed his cousin's hand impulsively and kissed it. The Earl tactfully disengaged himself from this sudden show of emotion and went on to assure his grateful ex-protégé that his own condition was not irredeemable. The distribution of the prize goods was now cleared up, passed by order of the King under a privy seal. Albemarle, it was true, had done him much damage in criticizing his conduct of the summer's fighting, and had inclined the Duke of York against him; but the chief ministers of the state, Clarendon, Arlington, Manchester, had all expressed their confidence in him. And the King, of course, was still his unswerving friend. As a matter of fact, the King and Council had offered him an honorable place, to go as Ambassador Extraordinary to Madrid, where he would have the delicate and crucial task of combatting King Louis of France on the diplomatic battlefield of Spain.

Samuel was overjoyed at the news. An ambassadorship to Spain would remove the Earl, with honor, from the ugly factiousness of the Court, the vile slanders of the noble gossips, and the righteous anger of the Parliament. After Samuel had given his joyful congratulations to his cousin and left his lodgings to return to London, he also confessed to himself, with a twinge of shame, that it was also the best possible solution to the unhappy situation of Samuel Pepys. Now, with loyal love in his heart for his absent patron, he could pursue his necessary affairs with the Duke of Albemarle and the new leaders of the Navy without his old strictures of conscience. He was another step nearer freedom.

The Earl of Sandwich sailed for Spain on March 2 with a retinue of sixty-six persons, including his son Sydney, three shiploads of personal effects, and the best wishes of his family and friends, including King Charles II and his cousin, Samuel Pepys.

The next day Samuel called upon the Duke of Albemarle and reported on his study of the victual system in the Navy. The solution to the problem, Samuel pointed out, lay in making more specific and firm contract with proved victualers, like Mr. Dennis Gauden, and in instituting a better organization among the pursers of the fleet. Fleet pursers, Samuel had discovered, had had to cheat on their accounts in order not to find themselves in ruinous debt. Samuel had worked out a simple but unequivocal system of receipts and accounts whereby the pursers were held responsible only for victual actually delivered on board and not, as formerly, assigned to them in the Victual Office. A few well-trained clerks, Samuel insisted, could save the Crown thousands of pounds a year and insure that goods assigned were goods delivered.

The Duke commended the new Surveyor of the Victual and said that he was sure the fleet of 1666 would not suffer from the same failures as the fleet of 1665. Samuel said that he would know where to fix the blame if the failure was due to want of victual.

"And what of supply, Mr. Pepys? What of repairs and naval

stores? Are they ready? Have you had time for your regular duties as Clerk of the Acts?"

"They will be ready, your Grace," Samuel assured him.

"We can bring in someone to help you in the Victual if you need more time for Deptford and Chatham. Now that you have the Victual organized, we can find someone to help you with the contractors. Penn, I am sure, would be willing."

Samuel too was sure that Penn would be willing. Now that Samuel had done all the dull spade work, Penn would be happy to come in and enjoy the profitable business of making contracts. Samuel already had Mr. Gauden under instructions and he did not intend for anybody, much less Penn, to come in and get his hand into the profits. He put on a severely thoughtful expression and announced bravely, "I do not believe in divided responsibility, your Grace."

Samuel knew that was a dangerous tack. It sounded too much like the Earl of Sandwich. The Admiral was a staunch believer in single command at sea and rigid line-of-battle tactics in the fleet. Albemarle, he knew, was an open-command tactician, a melee-tactic man, believing in simply overpowering the enemy by force of numbers and rough-and-tumble, ship-to-ship brawling. The word *divided* was a touchy one and, at present, an unpopular one. He waited to see its effect on the Duke.

His Grace looked blandly at the stiff little man before him, standing chesty and bold, daring to throw his opinion into the teeth of the Admiralty.

"Do you not, Mr. Pepys?" the Duke paused a moment. "We have decided on a divided command for this summer. Prince Rupert and I go as joint commanders."

Samuel felt the sweat begin to form inside his clenched fists, but he did not move a muscle.

The Duke leaned back in his chair and looked hard at the arrogant little Clerk, waiting to see if he would break. But Samuel continued to look back straight and unwavering.

Slowly the Duke pulled himself forward in his chair until he was leaning well across the table.

"The Navy has a debt of over two million pounds, Mr. Pepys. We have a half-million provided to get out this fleet and to destroy the Dutch. This is the third attempt, Mr. Pepys. We have failed twice. If we fail again, heads will fall. The Parliament will see to that. If victual or supply should be at fault, they will know whose head to look for. Do you still want single responsibility, Mr. Pepys?"

Samuel knew all this. He had thought about it many times, alone in the office on Sunday, at night when he could not sleep, even in the midst of a tavern dinner when the bottles were circulating freely. He knew the dangers of his ambition, and the dangers frightened him. But he still wanted, or rather, somehow, he could not help but want, the right to see things done in order— and with profit.

"Yes, your Grace," he said steadily.

"Sweat, then, Mr. Pepys. Sweat the last drop of juice out of your well-furnished body. But get this fleet supplied. And quickly." The Duke swept his hand toward the door as if dismissing the problem of supply from his mind.

Samuel sweated. Throughout March and April, he rushed up and down the river driving the workers at the supply yards. He haunted the Victual Office to see that contracts were being made and met on schedule. He even took home a supply of specially varnished paper to have Elizabeth and Mercer line the pages, according to his invention, so that the pursers would have a uniform method of making their reports.

At the Board meetings he brooked no interference with his plans and contracts. He rode roughshod over the objections and hesitancies of his plodding colleagues. He had nothing to fear from them now. He was in charge and they would obey him or answer to the Duke of Albemarle.

It was only his own nature that he had to fear. Even in the sweat of his desperate ambition, he could not completely restrain his old love of pleasure. When Elizabeth prevailed upon him, without much difficulty, to spend an afternoon at home helping to entertain her dinner guests, Samuel punished himself by going back to the office after dark and working until midnight on his purser accounts. He made new pacts with himself, odd little vows to protect him from the demands of his lust. *"God forgive me!"* he wrote in his diary, *"I do still see that my nature is not to be quite conquered, but will esteem pleasure above all things. Music and women I cannot but give way to, whatever my business is."* He fined himself a shilling to be put in the poor box each time he left his work for his own pleasure.

Somehow he got the work done, fighting his way through the intoxication of April and the disturbingly lovely spring weather. The lower Thames was crowded with fire ships, victual barges, busy wherries scurrying back and forth between the supply yards. At Chatham and Portsmouth and Woolwich the great ships of the fleet were being assembled, a hundred sail of first-raters, like *The Royal Charles, The Royal James,* and *The Prince,* armed with ninety guns; second-, third-, and fourth-raters armed with fifty or sixty; ketches, armed merchantmen, fire ships, the dozens of auxiliary vessels that helped to keep a huge fleet mobile and flexible.

On April 23, the fifth anniversary of the King's coronation, the ships of the line moved into the Nore, their high sterns glittering with gilded scrollwork and long narrow pennons snaking out from the tips of the towering masts. The admirals in their cabins, surrounded by their commanders, broke the seals on their orders. Signal flags fluttered up to the yardarms. One by one the ships broke out their sails, weighed anchor, and maneuvered slowly and clumsily into position. A favoring breeze quickly filled the slack sails, cracking the taut silk smartly into powerful, pregnant motion. By sundown the fleet was well out into open water, the golden poops shining bravely in the dying sun.

As soon as the fleet had gone, Samuel experienced a sharp depression, a reaction of despair after the excitement of preparing the ships. If the fleet failed—and well it might fail under the blundering awkwardness of the joint command—Samuel would need to find a place of refuge. No one connected with the Navy would survive a failure of this fleet. All his hopes and ambitions rode with the ships that had gone out to destroy the Dutch navy. It was the best-equipped fleet that had ever gone out for England. He was sure of that. But there was too much of the training of the Earl of Sandwich in him to give him any confidence that it could do its work under the command of two landlubbers like Albemarle and Rupert. They were good enough men in the field

—tough, cut-and-thrust soldiers; but at sea they were bunglers or worse—arrogantly inept sailors.

Samuel busied himself fretfully with his accounts. It was almost impossible to disentangle his records, going through his bye-book to add up his expenditures, counting his scattered assets, his credits at the goldsmiths, his cash in his iron chest, the money due him from creditors, contractors, and the Navy. He worked for three days at the hateful task, straining his eyes to read Elizabeth's barely legible kitchen accounts, racking his memory to recall the source of a £50 gift of plate. Finally he arrived at a tentative figure. He was worth something in the neighborhood of £5,000. It would take a bit of doing to get his scattered fortune together; and he wanted it all together. He just might need to have it all at hand on a moment's notice. He went to the shop of Mr. Viner in Lombard Street and cashed in his credits with that reliable gold-smith. He received £2,200 from him in ready money, plus an interest payment of £35 for the quarter. It was tempting to let his money work for him at the goldsmiths' but he was afraid to let it get out of his hands now. He took the bags of gold home with him and locked them in his chest.

As May progressed the weather became hotter and hotter. The sky was dry and there was little rain. The dry boardings of the wooden houses of the City smelled like tinder and the wharves along the river reeked of warm tar and pitch. Everyone bought copies of the Bills of Mortality as soon as they appeared on the streets each Thursday to see if there was any sign of a return of the plague. But the Bills only showed their usual number of dead: 53 by dropsy, 166 stillborn, 3 of scurvy, 23 of rickets, 10 by vomiting, and 2 "suddenly." There were only 42 reported dead of the plague, a normal number. The Black Death was not returning.

June was always the month for great naval battles. Spring was occupied with fitting the ships. In May the fleet put to sea for shake-down and reconnoiter. By June 1, as if by custom and pattern, the opposing fleets maneuvered into position for battle. On June 2, Samuel at the Navy Office received word that the King had had a letter from the Duke of Albemarle stating that the Dutch had been sighted off the Gunfleet Sands and that he was preparing for battle. A ketch had been dispatched to notify Prince

Rupert of the engagement. Samuel hurried down to Greenwich to order a company of soldiers to the fleet. In the Park he found the King and the Duke of York listening for the sound of the fleet guns. From the top of the hill, removed from the noises of the river, Samuel could hear the distant rumble of guns very plainly. That is all they heard of the fleet that day. What they were all most anxious to hear was the news that Prince Rupert had joined the action.

There was a trickle of news the next morning. A disabled captain had put back in to Aldeburgh with the heartening news that he had seen one of the great Dutch ships blown up and three others on fire. As he left the scene of battle, he had sighted one of the King's ships approaching the line, and he assumed it was one of Prince Rupert's. Samuel was inclined to discount the optimism of the report. The first crumbs were always deceptive. He went to church—it was Whitsunday—and prayed that the afternoon would bring something more dependable, and equally cheerful.

The afternoon brought only a gabble of contradictory messages, one from Admiral Harman in the *Henry* that he had fought off three Dutch fire ships only after the loss of a hundred men and a badly damaged poop deck. There was no news of Prince Rupert, good or bad.

The next afternoon, four days after the beginning of the battle, Samuel was summoned to his office to see two seamen, just arrived from the *Royal Charles* with a contingent of wounded men. They sat huddled in Samuel's office, all muffled up, their faces as black as soot, covered with dirt, pitch, and powder. One of them—a young lieutenant named Daniel—had his right eye stopped with oakum. They had news, Daniel said, of the fleet, and it was not good news. Prince Rupert had not made contact. He had been at Dover, calmly taking on supplies when the Duke of Albemarle received the brunt of the Dutch attack. It was sixty ships against ninety and De Ruyter had not let the chance slip. He had scattered the English fleet all over the North Sea, firing some, running others aground, capturing at least two, and playing general havoc with the disorganized remnant. By the time the Prince arrived, the damage had been done and De Ruyter had cautiously retired to his own coast. It was a hit-and-run engagement, characteristic of the wily De Ruyter, who was always perfectly willing to leave his enemy in command of the field after he had done his damage.

Samuel hustled the two wounded men to Whitehall to let them tell their tale to the Duke of York. Young Daniel was a junior officer on the Duke of Albemarle's flagship and he had every opportunity to know the truth. The admirals in their reports would gloss the truth, claiming great damage done to the enemy, justifying somehow the injuries they had themselves received. As for himself, Samuel was ready to accept the unvarnished report of the young officer. In the end, he felt sure, the lieutenant's report would prove to be the true one. In the meantime, he was anxious to know what explanation Prince Rupert would offer for his failure to make contact with the beleaguered Albemarle.

He did not have long to wait. Two days later the Navy Board was ordered to meet at Whitehall with the Duke of York and the Privy Council. The summons was peremptory and terse: "You are ordered to appear." Samuel looked covertly at his colleagues—at their hard, uneasy faces. He forced himself to put on an air of bravado. "Come," he said loudly, "let us journey to Whitehall and hear the burden of the Admiral's music."

The Duke of York opened the meeting with a grim review of the damage the fleet had suffered. In addition to a score of ships which had received major injury, six ships of the line were missing, either captured by the Dutch or run aground on the treacherous shoals of the Dutch coast. Admiral Myngs was dead, Harman badly injured, and hundreds of seamen were in immediate need of medical care. To make matters worse, there was reliable information that the French were ready to join the Dutch in an all-out invasion.

The militia had already been ordered to guard the beaches and fortify the coastal defenses, but the most effective defense was to stop the enemy at sea. It was for this purpose that the Duke had summoned the Navy Board. The partially injured ships had to be made seaworthy within a month. The whole fleet had to be supplied and made ready for major action. Fresh seamen had to be found and equipped to replace the wounded. Each officer and commissioner would have to take responsibility for two or more jobs beyond his usual duties, and there would be no excuses accepted for failure. The Duke looked soberly at the gentlemen from the Navy Office. Samuel kept his head down over his notebook, writing furiously in his rapid shorthand.

As an afterthought, the Duke said that he had two letters from the generals at sea, which did not now need action but might be of interest to the Council. The Duke of Albemarle had written that a great part of the failure of the action would have to be borne by the new captains, the gentleman commanders, who had proved themselves either cowards or ignoramuses in the fighting. They would not or could not follow orders under pressure.

Samuel moved his foot under the table until he found the toe of Sir George Carteret's boot. He applied a gentle pressure. Sir George let no expression show on his face, but he lifted the index finger of his right hand from the table. It was signal enough between the two members of Lord Sandwich's family to express their covert satisfaction that Albemarle had had to pay for striking his lordship's old tarpaulins from the list of captains. The old captains, even if they had fought under Cromwell, knew how to obey an order. The Navy would miss the Earl of Sandwich before this crisis was past.

The second letter, the Duke went on, was from Prince Rupert; and he also had a complaint to make—but not against the seamen. The Prince's letter was full of abuse of the Navy Board. He placed the full blame for his failure to make contact with the Duke's fleet upon the Navy Board, or whoever was responsible for the tardiness in supplying his ships at Dover. He lost a full tide, he complained, by the slowness of the barges and tenders in getting his victual and ordnance aboard.

Samuel clenched his notebook hard in his hands and waited for something to happen. But neither the Duke of York nor any of the ministers made any comment. The Duke handed the letters to his secretary and went on to discuss the details of their work of preparation. Samuel made rapid notes, but half his mind stayed on the Prince's letter. The Prince was a blustering, loud-voiced old swaggerer, whose enmity could bring great damage, just by the volume of his complaint. If he had taken it into his head to blame the Board for his failure to relieve Albemarle, the Board, and therefore Samuel Pepys, might consider itself selected for the role of scapegoat. When great men made mistakes, lesser men had to pay for them—unless the lesser could find resources of greatness.

July was a hectic month. The weather was hot; tempers were feverish; the work was hurried. The merchants of the City finally, and reluctantly, agreed to lend the King a £100,000 (at 8 per cent) to meet the emergency expense of getting the fleet out. The press gangs roamed the cities and the towns, collaring almost any male they could find at large who looked young enough to walk without a cane or old enough to swing a hammer. Boys of fourteen and settled men of fifty were run down like vagrant dogs and shackled to a post until the press wagons could come and collect them for His Majesty's service. In a week the streets were practically bare of men. The few who did venture out wore their best clothes and a sword to show that they were gentlemen and not to be touched.

The last days of the month brought fresh troubles to the Navy Office, troubles that were not usually a part of their concern. Word came from the Lord Mayor, Sir Thomas Bludworth, that the pressed seamen, quartered in the Bridewell prison until needed, would not be released to the Navy until the City had been paid for its expense in lodging and feeding them. The ship commanders were sending violent messages to the Office demanding that the men be sent to the vessels at once, and the Lord Mayor answered all pleas of the Office by saying that not one would be delivered until the City had been paid the £15 bill for their lodgings. Samuel cursed the obstinacy of the dull-witted man and hurried to the Bridewell with £15 of his own money. He would get his money back, one way or another, but it would almost be worth the cost to get the men delivered and the fleet out of the river. He stayed at the prison until the last of the miserable men were delivered to the soldiers. He went down to the Tower to watch them being loaded onto the lighters that would take them down the river, and stayed until midnight, until the last vessel had pushed off from the dock. Then he made his way back through the crowd of wailing and cursing women who had come down to see their husbands and sons torn from them and sent away to fight a war they neither understood nor desired. It was a sorry spectacle, Samuel thought, a terrible tyranny. But there was nothing he could do for them, and he hurried away before it might occur to their frenzied minds that *he* was responsible for their grief.

The fleet at last was ready, not quite so large as the first fleet of the summer, but as well supplied and almost as well manned. Sixteen ships were inactivated and their personnel was sent to fill the rosters of the other depleted ships. Finally on the 23rd of the month, the Duke of Albemarle and Prince Rupert were piped aboard their flagships, the signal guns boomed out, and the fleet of eighty-nine ships moved out. Brittania was ready to contest again the rule of the sea with Holland.

Samuel needed something to keep his mind occupied and off the fleet. He needed something—a project—to keep him busy, one that would provide him nourishment now and in the future, when he might not have the means of seeking his enjoyment abroad. If he had to live in retirement, he would need something to occupy his thought, to fill his hours.

It was his books that held the greatest promise for ultimate pleasure. He had always loved to buy books, to own them, read them, handle them. There was not room in his study for all the books he had bought and wanted yet to buy. He would soon be running over with books. He needed cabinets to protect them and show them adequately. He called in Mr. Simpson, a reliable old craftsman who had done many jobs for him in improving the house. Although only a joiner, and not a cabinetmaker, Mr. Simpson was very skillful; and he would take orders—do a job the way it was described to him without argument. Samuel explained what he wanted: two cabinets high enough to have five shelves for folios and quartos and deep enough to hold octavos in front of the taller books. The two presses should be able to contain his 500 books. They should be fronted with glass doors so the books would show, and the wood should be sound oak capable of a good polish. Mr. Simpson suggested a carved base somewhat larger than the upper shelves and a cornice at the top to balance the heavy bottom. Mr. Simpson loved to show his skill in carving and Samuel shrewdly let him have his way. The presses would be soundly built if Mr. Simpson were allowed to indulge his pleasure. Every day or two Samuel went to his shop to see how the work progressed.

He sat in the musty old room among the shavings and dust, watching Mr. Simpson fit the beautifully made joints together, caressing the wood like fine leather. Samuel loved to watch expert workmen at their crafts in the back of the old London shops. He had very little else to do, until some word came from the fleet.

When word did come, Samuel was neither excited nor depressed. The fleet was now almost an abstraction to him; his imagination was not with it. The fleets, it seemed, had met and deployed around each other for two days. Two Dutch ships had been captured and burned, and one English ship, the *Resolution,* a third-rater, had run afoul of one of its own fire ships and burned to the water. On the evening of the second day the Dutch disengaged and retired to their own coast. Albemarle and Rupert sent in glowing claims of a victory, but Samuel knew that it was no victory to destroy two of the enemy's ships. In the meantime the English fleet would have to sail around in circles, waiting for the Dutch to reappear, using up its supplies.

Two weeks later, Albemarle, his patience and his supplies running low, sent a small force into the islands with orders to destroy whatever was at hand. In four hours the English invaders destroyed a dozen merchantmen, three men-of-war, and most of the houses that abutted on the harbor of Vlie. It was not a significant victory; but it was an action, something to fill a report and keep the seamen occupied. Having made his gesture, Albemarle ordered the fleet to retire and Prince Rupert sent a scorching letter to the Duke of York demanding to know what had become of their supply. York sent for Sir William Coventry, and Coventry sent for Mr. Pepys.

"The admirals are angry, Mr. Pepys. They have had to retire from the area of operations for want of supplies. They say they have not enough provision of victual or fire ships to stand a day against De Ruyter if he should come out. Why is this, Mr. Pepys?"

Samuel swore. "It cannot be true. No fleet since the King's return has gone to sea better provisioned, and auxiliary supplies are standing by at Southwold Bay ready for any ship that needs them. And," Samuel concluded angrily, "I have records to prove it."

"Bring your records," Sir William told him grimly, "and let us go to the Council."

At Whitehall Samuel showed the King's ministers his meticulous records. He read them the total amounts of beer, hard biscuit, dried and salted meat he had furnished the eighty-nine ships of the fleet. He listed the number and displacement of victual ships standing by at Southwold. He showed them the receipts signed by the pursers acknowledging the loading of goods to the capacity of the ships' storage rooms. He was about to open another box of fully documented accounts when the Lord Treasurer, the old Earl of Southampton, stopped him.

"There is no doubt," the Earl said in his high-pitched, quavering voice, "that Mr. Pepys's papers are in perfect order. It would be foolish, and perhaps foolhardy, to question them. But it is also going to be difficult to ask Prince Rupert to dine on his pursers' impeccable but tasteless receipts."

Samuel flushed. "The supplies have been delivered," he said tightly. The Duke of York quickly interposed. "Write the Prince and tell him so," he calmly advised his excited Clerk of the Acts. "The matter is between you and the Prince."

Sir William Coventry hustled Samuel out of the Council chamber. "The matter, Mr. Pepys, is between the Prince and ourselves. Come with me to my lodgings, and we will compose the letter together."

Samuel had a hollow feeling in the pit of his stomach. It was no easy thing to become embroiled in an admiralty fight. These great men fought ruthlessly, and they had too many weapons for a simple public servant. They could scuttle a man as high as the Earl of Sandwich without blinking an eye. What could they not do to a Clerk of the Acts if he became bold enough to give them the lie? If he had to become involved, however, and he could see no way to avoid it, he was fortunate to have as strong an ally as Sir William Coventry. Sir William was known at the Court as a man of the highest integrity. No one had anything on him; and he also enjoyed, which was his greatest strength, the full confidence of the Duke of York. Unless the political climate were to suffer a great change, the enemies of the Duke of York would think twice before they made too great an attack on the Heir Presumptive—or on any of his men.

Together the two servants of the Duke worked until two in the morning, framing their letter. The next day they met at the Victual Office and checked every invoice, every contract, every receipt. They called upon Mr. Hayes, Secretary to Prince Rupert, and made arrangements for the quick delivery of their letter to the Prince by special messenger. They met with the Navy Board, read them the letter and argued them into putting their approval on it. No one man, Sir William insisted to them, should have to bear the burden of defense alone. Mr. Pepys must have the total support of the other officers and commissioners of the Navy Board.

Under the icy stare of Sir William, the Board gave its approval; and Samuel and Sir William hurried to the Duke. The Duke read the letter carefully, made one or two minor suggestions, and then said that he thought the letter a fair presentation of the position of the Board. It was right and proper to send it to the fleet, but they would have to wait for a full settlement of the protest until after the admirals returned from sea. Sir William said that they would wait with confidence.

$\mathscr{A}$ great fire they faw in the City

SAMUEL WAS GLAD that Sir William was confident. He himself was not. He could muster no courage to tide him through the fortnight of suspense. He went home depressed and, for once in his life, listless.

At his house he found that Mr. Simpson had brought the new book presses. The beauty of them cheered him for a while. He sat on the floor fitting his plays and histories and sermons, his volumes of music, and his bound collections of prints into the uniform shelves. Elizabeth handed him the heavy folios, one by one, from the tables. He dusted them carefully, and put them in place.

When the last volume was cleared from the tables, the chairs, and the floor, he closed the doors of the cabinet and locked them with his new key. Now he had as fine a set of book cabinets as any man in town; as a matter of fact, they were one of the few sets he had ever seen, in the City or at Westminster. He would have to give a dinner on Sunday and show them to his guests. He always liked to have a new possession, a new piece of furniture or a new painting to show his guests. It let them know that they were dining with a rising man.

The wind was blowing hard when Samuel and Elizabeth went to bed that night. They could hear it soughing through the trees outside their closed windows, and the sound of it gave them a feeling of covered security inside their canopied bed. They were soon asleep.

But the wind outside increased in violence, ripping the dry leaves from the trees and tearing the shutters loose from their couplings. It was a banging shutter that awoke the maid Jane about three o'clock and sent her to the window to fasten it. Over beyond Mark Lane there was a light in the sky. She watched it for a moment, seeing the light rise and fall; and then alarmed by the strangeness of the light and the howling of the wind, she hurried into the master bedroom and awakened Mr. Pepys.

"There is a great fire in the City," she whispered to him excitedly.

Samuel crawled out of bed and went to the window. He watched the light in the sky for a few minutes.

"It is beyond Mark Lane," he said, "and the wind is blowing the other way. We are safe. Go back to bed." And Samuel slipped back into his own bed and quickly returned to his warm dreams of pleasure and security.

But over beyond Mark Lane, the citizens were not asleep—or secure. In Pudding Lane, a narrow little thoroughfare that wound its way between Thames Street and Little Eastcheap, just east of the Bridge, the courtyard of the Star Tavern was full of people watching Mr. Farynor's house and bakeshop go up in flames. Mr. Farynor and his family had barely managed to climb across the roof of the adjacent house to safety thirty minutes earlier. Mr. Farynor was swearing to all who would listen that he was sure the fire was dead in his ovens when he went to bed, but at two o'clock he had been awakened by smoke, his whole house on fire. No one listened to him. Everyone kept his eye on the flames that were leaping into the sky and being blown with fury by the wind from the east. Nothing could be done to save the house and the strong wind made the flames a menace to the whole neighborhood.

The roof of the house suddenly collapsed with a dull roar. A cloud of sparks shot into the air, carrying with it pieces of flaming board. The wind caught the boards like straws and sailed them across the narrow street toward the tavern yard. The people screamed in alarm and ran for their lives. The glowing boards fell among the piles of hay near the stables and burst into new flame. The wind snatched up the hay and blew it against the side of the half-timbered building. Before the watchers could gather their wits, the Star was on fire and roaring in the high wind. And then the two houses on either side of the bakeshop burst into flame. The people of the street ran northward into Eastcheap, knocking on the shutters to raise the householders and spread the alarm.

Someone had enough presence of mind to arouse the sexton of St. Clements Church and order him to ring the ancient alarm, a peal of the great bells backward. But through the howling of the wind the bells and the screams did not carry far. While the fire spread rapidly into Fish Street and then southward toward Thames Street and the warehouses along the river, most of London slept on, oblivious that the "great fire of London" had started.

When Samuel awoke in Seething Lane at seven, the maid came to him atremble with the news. The fire they had seen during the night was spreading. Three hundred houses had burned. The Bridge was on fire and the wind was carrying the flames uncontrolled into the City. Samuel dressed hurriedly and ran to the Tower. From the top of the Bell Tower he could see smoke pouring in dense clouds from the north end of the Bridge and all along the river as far as the Swan Tavern and up Fish Street Hill to Eastcheap. The smoke obscured the City beyond. He could not even see the square tower of the Cathedral. He hurried down the narrow stone steps and ran to the river.

At the wharf he hired a boat to take him through the Bridge to view the fire from the safety of the river. The warehouses along the waterside were packed with naval stores—pitch, tar, tallow, oil, hemp. The open wharves were stacked high with hay, timber, and coal: all the ingredients needed to give the leaping flames a base and a habitation.

There had been fires before in London, localized fires that had burned themselves out after destroying a timbered house or two, or had been quenched by the trained bands with water squirts, or pulled down with long fire hooks. A disastrous fire in 1632 had burned halfway across the Bridge before it was stopped. It was the unfortunate combination of the extremely dry summer, the strong northeast wind, and the fire hitting the incendiary riverside warehouses that brought about the tragedy of 1666.

In a stupor Samuel looked at the spectacle before him. It was too shocking to take in. St. Magnus Martyr, the ancient church at the foot of the Bridge, was ablaze. All the houses on the north end of the Bridge were burning, as far as the break a third of the way across which had never been rebuilt since the previous great fire. He could see a dozen structures that he had known since childhood smoldering or bright with flame, buildings that had seemed as permanent and indestructible as life itself—the Fishmongers Hall, the church of St. Lawrence Poultney, the Old Swan Tavern. Now they looked as unreal and stricken as an image in a dream. He turned his eyes from them and looked to the south bank to see if the whole world had turned suddenly into a hideous chimera, but the fields and buildings of Southwark beamed as pleasantly as ever in the morning sun.

Samuel's eyes lighted upon flocks of pigeons, the ancient owners of the eves and gables of London's buildings, flying madly in all directions about the burning buildings, hovering about the windows and balconies, sheering frenziedly away from a gust of flame, and then returning to their burning perches until the fire licked the feathers of their wings and sent them plunging downward into the holocaust, victims to the ritual of habit.

Along the edge of the fire, at the river stairs and on the unburnt wharves, Samuel saw the people acting as wildly as the birds. They hovered around their own houses until the very flames touched them; and then running into boats or clambering from one pair of stairs by the waterside to another, they flung their goods into the river or swam out to a lighter, a silly pot or a feathered hat clutched under one arm. Samuel ordered the waterman to take him up to Whitehall.

In the anteroom to the King's closet in the Royal Chapel, Samuel found a dozen courtiers waiting to attend Sunday service with His Majesty. He hastily told them the state of affairs in London. They were thunderstruck. They had seen the clouds of smoke and had gathered that there might be a fire in the City, but they were dismayed to learn the extent of it. One of the grooms of the bedchamber hastened to the King, and in a moment returned with word for Mr. Pepys to come into the King's closet. The Duke of York, the Earl of Arlington, and several of the chief ministers of state were closeted with the King, discussing household affairs before the service began. Samuel removed his hat, bobbed a quick bow in the general direction of authority, and poured out his tale.

London was in a panic; the fire was spreading westward and northward, uncontrolled. Samuel in his excitement even made bold to tell the King that unless His Majesty commanded houses to be pulled down, nothing could stop the fire.

It was not easy to startle King Charles. He was not an excitable man by nature, and he had long since learned to control his temper and his impulses. He was shrewd, detached, pleasure-loving, and slow to anger; but he had a conscience about people, unfortunate or dependent people, his illegitimate children, his untitled mistresses, or the hapless citizens of London when their houses were burning down about their ears. He leaned forward in his chair and listened to Mr. Pepys's breathless narration of the plight of the City. When Samuel had finished his account and boldly made his demand for royal aid, the King got up, paced about the room, shot a dozen quick questions at the nervous messenger, and then began to issue orders. He sent a groomsman scampering to get a coach ready for Mr. Pepys. He sent word to the Surveyor of the King's Works to gather all the fire hooks to be found in Westminster and to command enough laborers to man them. He ordered a system of couriers established to keep him in hourly touch with the progress of the fire. And finally he instructed Mr. Pepys to ride into the City as fast as the royal coach could take him and command the Lord Mayor to spare no houses, to pull down all necessary buildings before the fire in every direction.

The Duke of York broke in to tell Samuel that he should bid the Mayor to inform him if he needed any more soldiers. He could have as many companies of the Guard as he needed. Lord Arlington, not wishing to be outdone in the fever of royal concern, followed Samuel out to the waiting coach and voiced his assurance that the Guard would be sent into London if the Lord Mayor requested it.

Samuel's head was buzzing with the impetuous and, it must be said, the surprising burst of royal energy. This was a far cry from the almost callous disregard the Court had paid to the troubles of London last summer during the plague. Then, the Court had dallied its way from Hampton to Salisbury and to Oxford, always farther and farther away from the danger in the capital, until it finally, cautiously, reapproached, long after all threat of danger had disappeared. Samuel at least had waited until he was ordered to remove himself, and he had once a week made the hazardous journey from Deptford to Whitehall. Samuel's conscience did not hurt him about his behavior during the plague. Perhaps the King's did hurt. At any rate, the King was an eager bundle of concern now. His last word to Samuel was that he and the Duke of York would come down by barge into the fire area as soon as service was concluded. Samuel smiled grimly at the strange ways of crowned heads and held on for dear life as the bouncing coach jostled and tumbled him as it raced down the Strand, whip-bearing outriders clearing the way before them.

At St. Paul's, the coach came to an abrupt stop. The thick smoke from the riverside filled the air, making breathing difficult and seeing almost impossible. Samuel jumped down from the coach. The churchyard area was packed with frantic people, some of them running toward the fire to look for kinsmen living near the river or in the neighborhood of Fish Street, others running away from the fire, carrying bundles of clothing or pitiful loads of household goods, chairs, work benches, kitchen pots. The clatter of hand carts on the stone cobbles, the screams of terrified women, the din of the great bells of the Cathedral pealing out the disaster warning, and under it all the ominous roar of the flames a few streets away filled Samuel with a sick dread. He pushed his way into Watling Street through the press of people and carts and hastily made litters. He had to get to the Mayor, and that worthy gentleman would be—or should be—somewhere near the core of the fire around Fish Street Hill.

Samuel fought his way through the melee in the narrow, panicked street. He ran into an overturned cart. He was knocked against the wall. He barked his shins against the wheel of a stalled wagon. He was pushed down by a huge woman carrying a mattress on her head. He picked himself up from the filthy cobbles, his breeches torn at the knee and a trickle of blood running down his stocking, and hurried on toward Cannon Street. It was like a nightmare, but his mind was too numbed to dwell upon it. His whole attention was fixed upon one point, one fierce point that obliterated all the noise and motion and panic about him: *to find*

the Lord Mayor. He battled through the congestion at the intersection of Walbrook and slipped into Cannon Street. And there
in front of the Rhenish Wine House, his face streaming with
sweat, a large handkerchief around his neck, waving his arms
about like a man out of his senses, stood Sir Thomas Bludworth,
Lord Mayor of London.

Sir Thomas was the same silly man that Samuel had had
trouble with during the summer about releasing the pressed seamen from the Bridewell. He had been just as silly the night before when he had seen the fire starting in Pudding Lane and had
shocked the alarmed citizens by announcing scurrilously, "Pish.
This is no fire to wake a man for. A woman might piss it out."

Sir Thomas had spent the rest of the night paying for his foolish remark, raging through the hectic dawn ineffectually at the
frightened and disorderly citizens. And now when Samuel found
him late in the morning, waving his arms and sweating in front of
the wine house, he looked like a man bedeviled. Samuel interrupted his senseless gyrations and delivered himself of his royal
command. "This is the message of the King and of His Royal
Highness, the Duke of York," Samuel concluded a little grandly.
He thought that the distracted man needed something impressive
to penetrate his stupor. But Sir Thomas merely fell back against
the wall of the wine house, covered his face with his hands, and
almost sobbed out his words.

"Lord! What can I do? I am spent. People will not obey me.
I have been pulling down houses, but the fire overtakes us faster
than we can do it."

Samuel thought he sounded more like a fainting woman than
a man charged with rule of a city. But, his message delivered, he
left the Lord Mayor and walked on home. There was no more he
could do for the moment but eat his dinner and wait until the
afternoon when the King and the Duke came down the river to
give some command to the hapless, doomed town.

It was after three o'clock when Samuel saw the King's barge
putting into Queenhithe Wharf west of the Bridge. Samuel had
secured a wherry as soon as he had eaten his dinner. He now took a
stand in the middle of the surging traffic of the river and watched
the fire while he waited for the royal barge to appear. He could

feel the heat of the flames on his face even at that distance, but the smoke was so thick blowing back over the City that he could not tell how far northward the fire had advanced. The riverside, however, was blazing for a quarter of a mile west of the Bridge, as far as the warehouses in the Steelyard, pouring out great clouds of smoke and sending up spouts of burning flakes that whirled through the air and fell back upon the houses in a rain of fire drops.

On the river the boats and lighters and barges darted into the stairs, rushed back out again, or cruised up and down the stream, not one out of three loaded with household goods. Samuel noticed that one lighter had nothing aboard but a pair of virginals, bright, fragile, and ridiculous instruments, snatched by violence and foolish love from some music room in a merchant's house and sent to float upon the river in a boat that should have been busy in more essential salvage. The oddity of it, and the poignance, captured Samuel's eye, and he watched it moving slowly up the river until the King's barge came into view and put in toward Queenhithe Wharf. Samuel spoke to his waterman and set out to report to the King.

The King had not been idle in the time between service and his arrival at Queenhithe. He had summoned a meeting of all members of the Council who were at hand and charged them with the responsibility of organizing an orderly defense of the City. They had gone to work at once and were at the moment conferring with the magistrates and justices about setting up fire posts at adequate points around the periphery of the fire area, posts manned with soldiers, provisioned with food and drink, furnished with all available fire-fighting equipment, hooks, portable cisterns, manual squirts. Troops of the King's Guard had been sent in to help control the traffic and to assist in enforcing orders to pull down houses. The King himself had come into the City to confer with the more responsible aldermen and to put some backbone into the municipal officers. The Lord Mayor had long since disappeared into the limbo of obloquy, sweating and wringing his hands in despair.

As soon as the King saw Samuel, he commanded him to fetch Sir Richard Browne, Alderman and former Lord Mayor. Samuel located him in the pack of citizens crowding the wharf, and then stood by and listened to the King lecture the assembled City fathers like a schoolmaster impatient with the laziness of senior scholars. They must put an end, His Majesty told them, to the haggling about whose house was to be pulled down and whose house was to be spared. "*Any* house must come down, Sir Richard, if it stands in the way of the fire. Your house, the Lord Mayor's, or Mistress Quickly's. Any house that stands in the way of the fire—or there will be no houses at all in the City within two days."

Sir Richard pointed out that there was a law in the City that said that any man destroying another man's house should be at the charge of rebuilding it.

"I will take the responsibility of the charge. Let any protesters try to collect from me later. They may take a place in line with the rest of my ancient creditors." But Sir Richard did not know how to cope with courtly levity in so grave a crisis; he kissed the King's hand and went off to do as he was bidden.

Samuel, in turn, went off to fetch Elizabeth and take her to the south bank to see the fire from the safety of Southwark. From the windows of a little alehouse on the Bankside, they watched the inferno. As the sun went down and the skies darkened, the bright flames appeared out of the curtain of smoke, more and more, in corners and upon steeples, between churches and houses, as far as they could see up the hill of the City, a most horrid, malicious, bloody flame, not like the fine flame of an ordinary fire. The churches and houses and all that they knew of London, the ancient City, was ablaze, one entire arch of fire from the Bridge to the Steelyard, and in a bow up the hill forming an arch of more than a mile long. As they watched in wordless horror, they could hear, even at that distance, the noise the flames made, the cracking of houses at their ruin.

Neither of them spoke. Elizabeth held Samuel's arm fast, while he gazed, entranced, at the raging scene. From the light of the flames he could make out shops he knew, taverns, alehouses, or-dinaries. He could even see the street signs of some, waving and creaking in the wind—the Three Cranes, the Dolphin, the Saluta-tion, familiar emblems, gaudy, outlandish, unremarked in his daily passage, but now vivid and bright at the moment of their cremation. Samuel's mind snapped to attention. Why should he be able to see the sign of the Salutation, 200 yards *below* the Bridge? He looked again; and there it was—swaying in the wind, lighted clear by the illumination of the neighboring flames. The Salutation was but a step from Billingsgate! The fire was burning back along Lower Thames Street, *against the wind,* toward the Tower. Samuel snatched Elizabeth's hand and rushed to the river. Seething Lane was now in the path of the fire.

The alarm had been given at the Navy Office before Samuel and Elizabeth could make their way back across the river. A cart was backed up to the door of Sir William Batten's house, to take his goods to Bethnal Green, out of the City. Penn's servants were running back and forth between the house and the garden, storing his tables, his chairs, his bedsteads in a pile on the grass while Sir William searched out a cart to haul them to safety. The night was warm. A full moon shone down on the frantic scene, lighting the garden and the piles of furniture and the agitated people. Samuel dashed into his house shouting orders to the maids.

They worked all night packing dishes, rolling up rugs and draperies, hauling the mattresses and pictures and furniture out into the garden. While Elizabeth stood guard over their unhoused possessions, Mercer and the maids and the boy Tom carried the goods down the steps, out through the washroom, and into the garden. Samuel stayed abovestairs directing the servants and putting his books into wooden boxes. When the presses were empty, all the fine folios and quartos unshelved, he had a hard time repressing his tears. This was the reward of his care, his books again packed like hardware into wooden boxes, his beautiful glass-fronted cabinets ravished of their treasure, left to be burned in the house or subjected to a violent journey to safety. When Mr. Hayter showed up at midnight, with a few poor articles bound into a bundle, a sad face, and the distressing news that his lodgings on Fish Street Hill had burned to the ground, Samuel put him to work. They carried the presses out of the house. Tom Edwards held the carved top, Mr. Hayter bore the burden of the base, and Samuel walked alongside guarding the glass doors and keeping them from swinging. By two o'clock the house was stripped of the best furniture.

Samuel and his clerk went into the cellar to consider his iron chest. It was too heavy to move easily and it was probably safe from burning, but he could not persuade himself to trust his gold out of his reach. He loaded the sacks into Mr. Hayter's arms and sent them to the Navy Office. He told Hayter to store them in the small office just off the Board room and to stay with them until he was relieved. If he went to sleep, he was to sleep *on* the sacks. The gold might well be all he would have in future to protect him from the world.

It was four o'clock when Lady Batten suddenly appeared at Samuel's house to tell him that they had finished their move and that the Pepyses could have their cart to move their valuables to Bethnal Green. Samuel was astonished. He had never liked Lady Batten and he had learned to abide Sir William only by keeping a firm hand over him. That the Battens should now, in his extremity, do him a thoughtful kindness amazed him. He summoned his servants and put them to work loading the cart with his silver plate, his most valuable papers, his credits at the Exchequer, his books, his iron chest from the cellar. Dressed in his night robe, he mounted the cart with the Battens' driver and drove out Aldgate, eastward along Whitechapel Road to Bethnal Green, where Sir William Rider, a wealthy merchant, kept open house to his London friends in a fantastic structure called Kirby's Castle. The house had always intrigued Samuel as the supposed setting for the famous ballad of "The Beggar's Daughter of Bethnal Green," but now his only interest in the strange establishment was as a place of refuge for his valuables. Rider was a reputable man, a friend of the Navy, and he could be trusted to guard his friends' possessions. Samuel stored his boxes, his hampers, and his chest in the same room with Batten's and Penn's belongings, and hurried back to London to see if he could save his furnishings before the fire burned back to Seething Lane.

The Pepyses spent the day carting their furniture down to the Tower dock. Samuel hired a lighter to haul his goods to Deptford and store them at the Carterets'. From six in the morning until dark, the whole family packed their possessions across Tower Hill, down to the dock, and into the hands of the waterman, who lashed them securely in the wide, flat boat. All of them worked like laborers—the maids, Hayter, Elizabeth, Samuel, all except Mercer. Mercer had taken herself off, without a word, to see about her mother, whose house in the City stood in danger of the northward rushing fire.

When Elizabeth suddenly learned that Mercer had deserted, she threw down her burden of blankets and rushed out into the streets after her. She found the errant girl loaded down with kitchen ware, stripping her mother's house in Fenchurch Street of its portable goods. Elizabeth screamed at her to drop what she was doing and come back to Seething Lane where she belonged. Before Mercer could reply, her mother appeared at the door, sweating and breathless. She threw a desperate glance at Elizabeth, gave her daughter a sharp push in the direction of Cornhill, and then squared around to defend her household from the enraged Elizabeth.

"Mary has a duty here," she shouted. "She has a mother to help as well as a mistress. She will come back to you when she has done her duty here."

"Her duty is with me," Elizabeth screamed, trying to make her voice heard above the clamor of the brawling street. "She left us without permission. She has to come back."

"She will not come back until I tell her to. She is not a servant, not a 'prentice to ask leave to help her mother when she needs her."

The two women stood in the street, their feet spread, their fists tight against their hips, shouting at each other like fishwives, fighting for the services of a girl, while the fire roared through the town. Elizabeth was the first to break off the engagement.

"She need never come back," she screamed. "She need never come back." And Elizabeth turned and ran down Mincing Lane gasping and sobbing in the humility of her defeat.

While the Pepyses loaded the lighter with their chairs and tables and bedsteads and Samuel's presses, the fire swept westward past Queenhithe, northward up Gracechurch toward Lombard Street. By three in the afternoon, Lombard Street was consumed, Cornhill was a broad path of fire, and the Royal Exchange waited helplessly for its destruction. The great cloud of smoke, black and gray and yellow, poured back over the City in an unbroken pall, the steady, relentless wind carrying it over the hills and out into the country. Fifty miles away, as far as Oxford, the people saw it and wondered fearfully what omen of disaster it was.

At the heart of the fire, in Cornhill, the heat was so great that houses a hundred yards ahead suddenly burst into flames from the intensity of the blast carried by the hot wind. The air was filled with flakes of fire which sailed above the tallest houses and lighted new fires in Cheapside and Watling Street. As the fire swept on ahead faster than the mind could follow it, the panic of the people increased. The roads out of the City became clogged with carts and litters and scrambling, half-demented citizens. No longer did they try simply to move their goods from one house to another. Only the open fields north of the City were now safe. Moorsfields and Finsbury began to fill with exhausted refugees, their scanty possessions thrown onto the ground in little piles, entire families stretched out on the grass, huddled in misery and stupefaction.

East of the Bridge the fire crept slowly back against the wind, not wildly as it moved toward the Cathedral and the heart of the City, but gradually, relentlessly, like a sluggish tide. By six o'clock it had reached Billingsgate; by nine it was halfway down Fenchurch Street, nibbling its way, house by house, toward the Tower and the eastern wall.

At the Tower dock Samuel looked up at the sky and saw the reflected, pulsating light getting closer and closer. He looked down at the lighter. One more load would fill it and it could be on its way toward Deptford with half his household goods secure from burning, if not from water and careless handling. Elizabeth, now recovered from her wrath and her tears, had gone with Mr. Hayter to fetch the little table that had always stood in her bedroom, the well-made little table of walnut her father had fashioned for her as a girl and given to her as a dower gift, the only possession she had brought into her marriage except the clothes she wore.

Samuel waited for them by the boat, too tense to notice his weariness or his hunger. The wind blew his hair about his face, and the light from the sky deepened the creases that ran from the edge of his nose to the corners of his mouth, making his face seem like the placid mask of a puppet. He watched the light from the fire up the river play on the disturbed surface of the water. The heavily laden boat below him rocked and slapped the waves that fled under the pilings of the dock. Somewhere out at sea, heading for the Nore and the ports of the upper Thames, was Prince Rupert, nursing his anger and planning revenge against the Navy Office. Samuel smiled bleakly. The Prince would find a hollow vessel for his anger when he got home.

In a few minutes Hayter appeared with the little table, Elizabeth close beside him seeing that he did not trip or knock her treasure against a tree or a post. Samuel handed it down to the waterman, watched him lash it down to the top of the pile, and cover the whole load with a stiff and dirty tarpaulin. Then he stood back, aching with weariness. He gave the waterman his last instructions, made him repeat them, and then waved him away. The boat pulled away from the dock, moved slowly out into the mottled river, and finally disappeared into the darkness that lay beyond the Tower.

The three exhausted people, clerk, master, and mistress, walked slowly back to Seething Lane. The maids had put together the last remains of their Sunday dinner, scraps of beef, part of a hen, a few odds and ends of cheese and bread and anchovies. They sat on the grass in the garden and ate their supper, their first meal in a day and a half. Samuel opened a bottle of wine from one of the hampers in their now half-diminished pile of goods and passed it around, all of them drinking from the bottle. What with his weariness, his satisfied hunger, the sudden effect of the wine, and the image of them sitting there eating and drinking in the eerie moonlight, Samuel's head began to swim. With a feeling of horror, he felt a surge of laughter coming over him. It was ridiculous. The whole City was burning to ashes before their eyes, his possessions were scattered from Deptford to Bethnal Green, his whole career was hanging in the balance, and here they sat, like country folk at a fair, drinking from a bottle in the moonlight. He began to laugh. The sound of it came from the depths of him, shook him roughly as it rolled out. While Elizabeth and the servants stared at him open-mouthed, he held the bottle out at arm's length. He turned it upside down, emptied its few drops upon the ground like a libation, and then with all his might he threw the bottle crashing against the brick walls of the Navy building.

He felt foolishly but markedly better—relieved. He stopped laughing, took up a quilt from the pile of goods, and walked away toward the Office. When Elizabeth went in to him half an hour later, he was asleep on his thin pallet on the floor, snoring raucously.

While Samuel slept, the fire raged westward along the river. It hit the thick stones of Baynard's Castle and exploded them like gunpowder. It swept up the hill northward toward St. Paul's. If the Cathedral caught fire, the City was lost. There could be no stopping the flames if they once attained the command of that high eminence. Ludgate and Fleet Street, the Strand, the Temple, all Westminster lay beyond. And through the night, the flames moved relentlessly up the hill.

The authorities hoped that Cheapside could stop the sweep of the fire northward. Cheapside was the broadest street in the City and it was lined with the substantial shops of goldsmiths, good brick and mortar buildings, capable of withstanding the shock of disaster if any buildings could. But the goldsmiths had learned through ancient experience to trust only in God and their own ingenuity. They spent the night hauling their gold away to the security of the Tower; and since no man kept watch or gave his thought to the defense of the street, the fire entered it just before dawn and ransacked it with jubilation.

When Samuel awoke at dawn, aching in every joint, he went back to the river to locate his waterman. The near side of the Tower wharf was now too busy and cluttered for orderly business. It took Samuel half an hour to make sure that his lighter was not there. He checked every boat on the waterside, asked every waterman he could intercept, scoured the length of the docks, and finally found it tied up and waiting at the Iron Gate Stairs on the other side of the Tower. The portage to the river would now be more difficult than ever. They would have to come around the Tower over the hill and through the Postern passage, which was already jammed with carts and porters. Samuel went back to the Navy gardens and awakened the servants. The backburning of the fire was steady and threatening. They would have to work faster to clear their pile of goods into the lighter. Without breakfast or even a morning draught, they went to work, carrying the boxes and hampers and chairs through the crowded passage and down to the river.

During the morning the fire in the City moved beyond Cheapside into New King Street, the straight pathway to the Guildhall. The fire was not moving so fast now as it had among the timber buildings, but it moved relentlessly, like sluggish water, crumbling the brick houses, oozing through the windows and the doors, uprooting the very foundations of the street. Around ten o'clock, the flames washed broadly against the thick old sides of the ancient Guildhall, drew back for a moment, and then swept up to the top of the roof, catching the timbers, melting the lead sheeting, and finally plunging downward into the depths of the great hall.

At noon Mercer showed up in Seething Lane. Samuel saw her coming and turned his face away. But not Elizabeth. Elizabeth met her before she could get halfway across the yard.

"Go back," she screamed at her. "Go back to your mother."

"I have come to help," Mercer offered hesitantly.

"We don't need you now," Elizabeth shrilled. "Go back and never come near us again. We don't need you, now or ever."

Samuel watched the girl turn and go slowly out of the garden. He would have liked to say something, to soften the dismissal a little; but he could not without offense to Elizabeth. He kept his head down and went on with his work, handing a box to one of the maids, pointing out a chair that should go next to the lighter.

Farther up the garden Sir William Batten's servants were digging a large, deep hole in the turf. It was for his wine, Sir William explained to Samuel. "Jostling on a cart will do the wine no good. It is better to bury it here and take a chance on its being unmolested." Sir William prided himself on his taste in wine. He was receiving obvious satisfaction from this exhibit of his connoisseurship even in the hour of public danger. Samuel only looked at the capacious hole and thought of his Office records.

"Could we put the Office papers in with the wine?" Samuel asked. "They would be safer there."

Sir William considered for a moment. "Papers?" he muttered blankly. "Office papers? Oh, to be sure. They must be saved too.

Store them in. There will be ample room." And the Surveyor of His Majesty's Navy Office strolled away to supervise the men who were carrying his precious bottles and casks from his well-stocked cellar.

Samuel diverted Mr. Hayter from his furniture hauling to carting the heavy files and ledgers from the office to Sir William's wine hole.

It was shortly after three o'clock before Samuel had the last of his goods lashed to the lighter and on their way to Deptford. He came back into the Office garden just as Sir William Penn was emerging from his vacated house. Samuel told his colleague of the disposition he had made of the Office records, neatly stored with Batten's wine.

"And what have you done with your wine, Mr. Pepys?" Sir William asked.

"My wine?" asked Samuel wearily. "Nothing. It is still in the cellar."

"Why don't we dig a hole and bury our wine together?"

"I hadn't thought of the wine," Samuel confessed. He was about to offer an explanation, an apology for his dereliction, but he cut himself short.

"Let us do it," he said tersely. "We can save that too."

So while their servants dug the hole, Samuel and Sir William Penn sat on one of the garden benches and talked. Sir William had just returned from a walk around the City, making a survey of the fire. "It is burning all around St. Paul's," he reported. "The School is gone."

For the first time it occurred to Samuel how little he knew now of the actual progress of the fire. In the last thirty-six hours he had been so occupied with salvaging his own goods, so weary from the labor and the loss of sleep, that he had not thought of the fire as an active, advancing reality. It had been just a thing—a thing of horror over his shoulder, menacing and threatening, but still, unmoving. Now Sir William had brought it back to life, and with a word had destroyed old St. Paul's School—the ancient rooms, dark and musty, where Samuel had studied his Latin, felt the sting of the birch on his backside, and begun his climb from the tailorshop to Cambridge to Whitehall and finally to the Navy

Office. And now the School was obliterated. The casual, matter-of-fact words shook him. "The School is gone."

"And the fire rolls on down Ludgate Hill and into the Liberties," Sir William went on. "Christ Hospital is in danger. The masters have already moved the children to Islington."

Beyond Ludgate was Fleet Street and Salisbury Court, St. Bride's, and the old tailoring shop, Jane Turner's house, and Mr. Holden's shop. His whole past was being wiped out.

"Can nothing stop it?" Samuel asked in despair.

"Nothing but gunpowder," the Admiral replied mildly.

"Gunpowder?"

"Blow the houses," explained Sir William. "Pulling them down does no good in this wind. Not fast enough."

And the blunt old seadog got up from the bench and walked over to examine the hole.

Samuel's mind began to work, clearly and smoothly like the mind of a proper Clerk of the Acts. The Tower was well stocked with gunpowder—that was part of its present danger. And at Deptford there were at least a score of men whose business was to know how to use it, ordnance men, experts in blowing a dyke or firing a ten-pound shot. It needed only organization. He jumped from the bench and hurried over to Sir William, nearly slipping into the hole in his excitement.

"What's possessed you, Mr. Pepys?" Sir William demanded, as he held Samuel fast by the arm and pulled him back to safety.

"Gunpowder," Samuel blurted. "We have gunpowder and we have the men to use it. There are ordnance men at Deptford. All we need is permission to use them."

Sir William turned Samuel around and looked at him admiringly. "Mr. Pepys, you were not born to hang. Get permission. Write a letter. Entreat the Duke. Do what you need to make it official. I will get the men from Deptford and we will blow the fire to hell." And the Admiral, having found a task to suit his talents, dashed out of the garden and toward the river, fire in his eyes, and the promise of explosion in his ears.

Samuel hurried to the office and wrote a hurried letter to the Duke. He sent it off to Whitehall by Mr. Hayter with instructions to search the Court and the City until he found him, if it took all night. While he waited for the Duke's permission or Sir William's return with the ordnance men—whichever came soonest (for he knew that Sir William would not wait for the formality of official approval)—he put his wine in the now-finished hole. He also stored on top of the bottles and the two kegs of good claret, his loaf of Parmesan cheese and a crate of apples. Then he watched the men fill up the hole with the loose dirt.

He and Elizabeth ate their supper that night in the office—a shoulder of mutton he had ordered from the cookshop. They ate it like laborers, without napkins or dishes, cutting off hunks of the meat with the one knife they had, and eating it from their fingers. It tasted better than many a dish Samuel had eaten at Court or in gentlemen's houses. "Hunger is the best sauce," Samuel announced sententiously as he left to walk up Tower Street to see how close the fire had come.

Just beyond Mark Lane he felt the heat strike him. He went only close enough to see that Trinity House was in flames and the Dolphin was smoking and crackling. Alas! No more ale and good talk at the Dolphin. But his stomach now was full of good meat, his possessions as safely dispersed as possible, and he had done something specific about the fire. The thought about the Dolphin was just a thought—not like his agony about St. Paul's School in the afternoon. He went back to the office to wait for word from Mr. Hayter or Sir William. But in half an hour he was sound asleep on the office floor, and no word had come from either.

At eight o'clock the fire that had been burning around the base of St. Paul's for over two hours suddenly leaped to the roof of the great Cathedral. It caught the boards that were exposed in an opening of the lead roof and began to eat its way down through the timbered supports. The lead sheeting of the roof melted from the intense heat underneath and began to run down the face of the stone walls. After an hour of resistance to the volcanic heat, the old stones of the building began to calcine and explode off in great chunks into the churchyard below and to plummet straight down through the roof into the choir of the Cathedral, bursting through into the chapel of St. Faith's below, casting a shower of sparks among the books and pamphlets which the stationers and booksellers of the City had hurriedly stored in the safest place in the town. Within an hour, half the books in London were aflame.

Having conquered St. Paul's high prominence, the fire raged on unimpeded into the Liberties. It swept past Christ Hospital and into Newgate, through Ludgate into Fleet Street. By nine o'clock, the fire that had started two days before in Pudding Lane had made its way to Pie Corner, Smithfield. By ten o'clock the flames in Fleet Street were throwing their brightness against the ancient stone buildings of the Temple. The Church was gone and now the home of the Law was threatened. The Court lay straight ahead.

While stately carriages rushed through the streets of Westminster, carrying plate and jewels and frightened ladies to the westward safety of Windsor and Hampton Court, Samuel slept exhausted on the hard board floors of the Navy Office. Around midnight he stirred briefly when a loud explosion shook the windows of the building. He put his hand on Elizabeth to calm her. "Sir William is back with the gunpowder," he said softly, and turned over and went back to sleep.

Throughout the night explosions rocked the City. The ordnance crews put their charges under each house in a street bordering the line of the fire. Fuses were lighted and in a few minutes a whole block seemed to rise a few feet in the air and then collapse, sending a cloud of dust shooting up into the air. Little by little the line was made before the fire, a rubbled clearing which the flames could leap only with a giant step. But the steady, incessant wind had also grown into a raging gale.

At two o'clock Samuel awoke with a start. A great crying and shouting came up from the street. "Barking Church! Barking Church!" was all he could make out from the din. He was immediately at the office vault taking out his sack of gold, preparing to leave, when Will Hewer came in with the news. The fire was at the Church of Allhallows Barking, at the bottom of Seething Lane!

Without a word, Samuel threw on his boat cloak. Elizabeth tied a scarf around her head. With Hewer holding the sack of gold, the little party set out for Tower Wharf. The time had come to flee.

At the Wharf they found a boat and a waterman willing to take them down the river to Woolwich. Elizabeth and Will Hewer sat in the stern holding the gold sack between them. Samuel sat in the bow. None of them spoke. The only sound was the splash of the oars and the only sight was the murky darkness ahead. Behind them the sky over London glowed orange and yellow, angry and doomed.

At Woolwich Samuel installed Elizabeth in her old lodgings, the rooms she had occupied during the plague. He left Will Hewer with her to keep her company and to help her guard the gold. "Keep the door locked," he told her, "and never leave the room, both of you at once, until I return. The gold is all we have now; all we have for certain." And then he left them in mutual custody while he went back to London to see the end of the City.

Out on the river the boat bobbed and dipped distressingly. The waterman had a hard time of it keeping the little wherry out in the stream. He feathered his right oar and pulled hard with both hands on the left. The boat eased out gradually from the turning bank of Limehouse Reach.

"The wind's veered to the south," the waterman explained irritably.

Samuel stood up in the boat and the wind swept his hair back from his ears. It *had* veered. For the first time in three days the wind was blowing *toward* the river, from north to south and not from east to west. Perhaps the wind had changed in time to save what was left of the City. But Samuel had no great confidence in it. By this time, surely, the fire was in Seething Lane.

It was seven o'clock in the morning when they put in to Tower Wharf. Samuel almost hated to leave the boat, to walk up the hill and see his own house on fire, see flames shooting from his own office windows in the Navy Building. There would be an outrage, an obscenity in it that he had rather not witness. He walked slowly up the hill.

When he got to Tower Street, he glanced quickly down toward Barking Church. In the smoky morning light, he was not quite sure at first what he saw; but in a minute there could be no doubt. It was *there*—the porch scorched a little, the clock in the tower defaced—but the church stood, unburned. He rushed up Seething Lane. The fire was dying at the wineshop, smoking a little, but dying. And on the side of the street, black as a chimney sweep, grinning and happy among the equally dirty and sweating crewmen, sat Sir William Penn.

"The Office is saved, Mr. Pepys. We had a fine shooting."

Sir William was in his element, at rest after a victorious action, sitting with his crew on an imaginary gun deck, waving a bottle in cheerful exultation. Penn was good only for action, but in action he was impressive. At the moment Samuel felt a strong admiration for him, an affection even. But he refused the offer of a pull from the communal bottle and hurried down to Allhallows Barking. He wanted to see—he needed to see—the sight of the damaged City.

From the top of the old church's brick tower, he looked westward over the smoldering town. The fire was not out yet. There were still patches here and there, isolated torches of flame that marked the location of oil stores, wine and spirit cellars, stores of pitch and tar. But most of the view was composed of great stretches of flattened rubble, field after field of jumbled debris crisscrossed by a maze of paths that had been the streets of London. The strangest view of all, however, was row after row of chimneys, erect and useless, a forest of skeletal fingers. The sight fascinated Samuel, and horrified him.

St. Paul's still sent up a great cloud of rolling smoke, coiling down across the river, southward, blocking his view of the City beyond. He was almost grateful for the decency of the pall, but his curiosity was frustrated. He wanted to know the fate of the western part of the City. He crept back down the dark and narrow stairs of the church and located Sir William. They must walk through the town and survey the extent of the fire. Sir William brushed some of the dust from his clothes, threw a cheerful blasphemy at the lounging crewmen, and set off with Samuel to survey the devastation.

They walked along Fenchurch Street, up Gracechurch Street, and into Lombard Street. The view was all the same—rows of chimneys stark and rigid in the smoking rubble. Underfoot the cobbles were thickly overlaid with gray ash, still warm, ankle deep.

They went up Cheapside and saw the Cathedral still burning and occasionally flinging off an exploding stone. They skirted the churchyard and went up Newgate Street toward Smithfield. Anthony Joyce's house was gone. Samuel could not even tell exactly where it had stood. His bare chimney looked like all the others. It was this that bothered Samuel—the anonymous look of everything. Standing at Pie Corner and looking southward, he could see the river itself. There was nothing to block the view. For the first time in over two hundred years, a man could stand in Smithfield and see the Thames!

They did not venture any farther westward. Soldiers stood in the street and asked what business they had in the burning area. Houses were being blown near the Temple, and no one should go in that direction except from necessity. Samuel and Sir William had no necessity save curiosity; so they walked back eastward along the line of the northern wall of the City. The thick stones of the old London Wall had formed a bulwark against the fire, offering no purchase to the running flames. When the wind had shifted, the flames had turned back into the already consumed streets and died. The northward march of the fire had stopped dead at the northern wall.

By the time Samuel and Sir William reached Moorgate their feet were hot and painful. The heat from the thick carpet of ash over which they had walked had finally seeped through the soles of their boots. They went into the fields, among the hundreds of refugees who cluttered the ground with their little piles of salvaged belongings. Each family sat dejectedly by its little store of goods, stunned, waiting for they knew not what.

Samuel and Sir William sat on the grass and took off their shoes to cool their feet, feeling a little like intruders at a private grief. When a baker came by vending his penny loaves, Samuel bought a loaf of the tough stale bread and shared it with Sir William. When their shoes again felt cool to the touch, they put them on and walked to a brewer's tent. A tankard of ale revived them, and they set out to walk home through Moorgate and the hot dust of Coleman Street.

At the intersection of Old Jewry and Cheapside, Samuel came to a halt. Sir William wandered on down the street aimlessly, while Samuel stopped and looked at the ruins of the old building on the corner. This wreck, at least, he recognized. This was the

Mercers' Hall, the ancient hall and chapel of the worthy company of mercers, the trustees of St. Paul's School, the guild of Dick Whittington and Sir Thomas Gresham. This was the site of the birthplace of Thomas à Becket. From this spot the history of London moved out in all directions, touching, at one point or another, almost everything that had always been London, from St. Paul's to the Royal Exchange, from St. Thomas à Becket to Dick Whittington, from Sir Thomas Gresham to Samuel Pepys. If a center could be found, a symbol that made tangible the whole tragedy and loss of the burned City, it would be found here. Samuel felt a need to find something that he could hold in his hand, keep in his possession to memorialize the event that he knew in his heart was the end of a world. The historian that lay beneath the surface of the busy clerk, the poet that slept within the coarse-grained materialist, made him stop before the destroyed shell of the Mercers' Hall.

He walked up and down before the wreck, looking at the tumbled walls, the smashed windows. He looked on the ground at the broken shards of glass that littered the burned grass. He reached down and picked up a piece of glass, a fragment from the great window of the chapel. It was so melted and buckled from the heat of the fire that it looked more like parchment than like glass. It was still warm as he held it in his hand. He touched it to his cheek and ran his fingers over the strange texture of it. It *was* parchment—and glass too. A window *and* a record. A memorial and a symbol, created out of time, by fire and destruction. He slipped it carefully into his pocket and hurried on through the thick dust to catch up with Sir William.

XV

The glut of mirth I hoped for

THE GREAT FIRE OF LONDON burned for four days. The sun that rose over the City on Thursday morning shone brightly on an ugly scar of stone and rubble that stretched along the river from the Tower to the Temple and from the river northward to the wall, a path a mile and a half long and half a mile wide. Three hundred and seventy-three acres of the congested old medieval town lay as lifeless and desolate as a Yorkshire moor. Over 13,000 houses and shops had been reduced to ashes, their inhabitants sent wandering, almost empty-handed, into the open fields around the City. The miracle was that so few of London's hapless citizens were killed in the holocaust. Only six were reported by the Bills of Mortality, but many more than this, a hundred or more, died of exposure and hardship. Only the quick action of the King's Guard during the last day of the fire had prevented a greater mortality.

It was Sir William Penn's gunpowder that caused the trouble. As the fire swept down Fleet Street, closer and closer to Westminster, gunpowder was brought into the West End to blow up intervening houses to save the Inns of Court. The sudden violence of the explosions in the night immediately set off a series of wild rumors that the Dutch had come up the river and were bombarding the town, or that the Papists had started the fire in the first place and were now keeping it going by starting new fires. The rumors quickly brought on panic. By midnight crowds of enraged citizens were running through the streets of Westminster looking for foreigners and Papists. A French cook was seized in Charing Cross and hanged from a post. The Guard, alerted to the mob violence that had suddenly sprung up, hurried to the scene and cut the poor man down in time; but all foreigners were careful for a day or two to stay off the streets.

The panic died with the fire on Thursday, but other dangers remained. Flash fires occasionally sprang up all over town, catching the searchers unaware. The water conduits were destroyed or made useless. The markets had been burned and the brewers and bakers were practically out of business. London stood in imminent danger of starvation.

King Charles again showed a real concern for the welfare of his people. He issued royal proclamations commanding the magistrates of outlying counties to rush into London as great quantities of provisions as could possibly be furnished. He ordered temporary markets to be set up at Tower Hill and in Smithfield to distribute the food to the refugees as soon as it arrived. He ordered all churches, schools, and public buildings to be made available to houseless people for the storage of salvaged goods. And finally he made an urgent request that all towns and villages in England receive as many of the distressed refugees of London as they could accommodate. Under the new, magnetic leadership of the King, England responded, quickly and generously; and the people of London were saved from almost inevitable disaster.

But there still remained, of course, much to do to relieve the City, to make it again a habitable place, a living organism. This was a work of weeks, of months, of years. Only little by little could it be done, an acre of rubble cleared, a house rebuilt, a street remade, new goods and tools and merchandise obtained. It was like the work of patient ants rebuilding a torn hill, grain by grain.

Samuel Pepys borrowed a clean shirt from Mr. Creed, washed the grime and the dried sweat from his face, and set out to retrieve his scattered household. He rode out to Bethnal Green in a cart and fetched home his plate and his private papers, his books and paintings, from their storage at Sir William Rider's. He went down the Thames to Deptford and made arrangements for his furniture to be returned by lighter. He went on farther down to Woolwich and relieved Elizabeth and Will Hewer of their stewardship of his gold. Together they came back to Seething Lane and replaced the money in the iron chest in the cellar. They spent the night sleeping on the floor, the three of them together, under a blanket, with only a quilt between them and the hard floor.

While St. Paul's was still smoldering and the oil stored in the cellar of the Clothworkers' Hall continued to burn inexhaustibly, Prince Rupert's fleet sailed into the Downs. The Prince was, of course, ignorant of the catastrophe that occupied the City. He was full of pride and high spirits that he had brought the fleet home intact after a summer of busy if inconclusive fighting. When the couriers met him with tidings of the fire, he took it as a personal insult. The fleet's return was not news now. He might as well have been returning from a summer training cruise for all the country cared. He was hurt and angry. He set off at once for Whitehall, spoiling for trouble.

He got it almost at once. The Duke of York, despite his weariness from long hours of fighting the fire and directing in person the blowing up of houses, immediately called a meeting of the Council to consider the condition of the Navy. He summoned the Navy Board to appear and give an account of the over-all expenditure of the four million pounds that the Navy had received to conduct the war against Holland.

Samuel groaned when he heard of the summons. He was tired: not in body, for he had caught up with his sleep. He was tired inside, deep down. He had not thought of the Navy, in any specific way, for a long time. It was only a week really; but it seemed like months. He and Coventry had spent many days and nights before the fire going over Sir John Minnes's accounts, but the Comptroller kept such vague records that it was only with the utmost difficulty that they could make heads or tails of them. And they dared not let Minnes attempt an explanation. He would land them all in the Tower.

At the meeting next day at Whitehall, all the Board was present: Minnes, Penn, Batten, Brouncker, Coventry, Sir George Carteret, and Mr. Pepys. Only the chief ministers of state were present for the Council: the Chancellor, the Secretaries of State, the Lord Treasurer, the Duke of York, the Duke of Albemarle, and, of course, Prince Rupert. The King came in after a while.

Sir William Coventry, as secretary to the Lord High Admiral, reported on the general condition of the Navy. Over two million pounds, he said, had been paid out in verifiable contracts, accounts for £900,000 remained to be paid, and present charges for the care of the fleet were as yet indefinite.

"What, in general," the Lord Treasurer asked, "will the present charges come to?"

No one replied.

"Do the gentlemen of the Navy Office," he persisted, "have a means of knowing the extent of the present charges?"

Sir John Minnes was absorbed in the view outside the window. Coventry looked at Samuel.

"The Office has the means, my lord," Samuel said tentatively. The presence of these great men intimidatd him. He was used to the Duke of York. He had talked Navy business to him enough to be at ease. And he had learned to face up to the Duke of Albemarle during the plague. But he was not used to talking to the Chancellor or the Earl of Arlington or the Earl of Southampton. The King had come in during Coventry's speech, but somehow that did not bother Samuel as much as the glowering scowl of Prince Rupert on the other side of the table. He cleared his throat and began again.

"The story of our present charges, my lord, is not a cheerful one." He kept his eyes fixed on the Lord Treasurer. The Earl of Southampton had a gentle, kindly face, and Samuel knew that the old man was scrupulously fair and honest. He could think better by keeping his attention rigidly on Southampton. "Nor is it one to give me pleasure in the telling of it; but since your lordships would hear it now, I shall do what I can to acquaint you with our condition."

For thirty minutes Samuel acquainted them with the unvarnished ill state of the Navy—the huge debt, the vast amount of work to be done to fit a fleet for the next year, and their incapacity to do their work as it needed to be done because of a lack of money to do it with.

"The present fleet," he concluded, "the greatest fleet that His Majesty has ever sent to sea, is now in the Downs in as bad condition as the enemy and the weather combined could put it. It is impossible at the moment to estimate what it will cost to restore the ships to fighting strength. The full charge of the Navy and the present need for money cannot be fully known until the surveyors' report has been completed, but there is nothing that I know of to give me cause for optimism."

Samuel sat down quietly; but before he could take a second breath, Prince Rupert jumped to his feet, purple in the face, and shouting.

"Whatever the gentleman has said, I have brought home my fleet in as good condition and with as good a record as any fleet in our history, including the last fleet of the Earl of Sandwich."

Samuel turned white and his stomach became a stone.

"Twenty ships," the Prince thundered, "twenty ships will be as many as the fleet will have need to repair, and all the anchors and cables lost in the late storm can be taken up by any officers that know their business."

The furious Admiral, breathing hard, stared straight at Samuel, snorted contemptuously, and sat down.

Samuel put his hand to his stomach to press down the heaviness. He had to say something—now, in the thickness of the silence that hung in the room, into the teeth of an angry prince of the blood.

He rose to his feet and stood silently for a moment. He caressed the tip of his nose thoughtfully, looking neither at the Prince nor the Treasurer nor the Duke. He looked straight at the King.

"I am sorry," he said quietly, "that my words have given offense to His Highness. I have simply stated what has been reported to our office by those in the service whose duty it is to inform us. It is not within the function of the Clerk of the Acts to criticize the officers of the line nor to pass judgment upon the accuracy of reports made by officials entrusted with the duty. I have stated only reported facts without prejudice and without favor."

He sat back down again. The room was a vacuum. No one said a word. The Prince muttered something inarticulate and then relapsed into speechless fury. The Lord Chancellor squinted hard at the Clerk of the Acts and turned his head toward the King.

King Charles smiled wryly at the silent table. "If our loyal

Officers and Commissioners of the Navy have no further enlightenment for us," he said, "we will excuse them to continue their labors in our behalf."

The gentlemen from Seething Lane arose from their seats, bowed stiffly to the King, and left the room. They needed fresh air.

Samuel needed more than that. He needed some word of encouragement, some word that he had not disgraced himself. But his colleagues walked quietly away, troubled and unhappy. Samuel let them go. As far as he was concerned, they were an incompetent, skulking crew of deserters. He strode off to the Matted Gallery to wait for the meeting to break up and for Sir William Coventry to join him.

In the privacy of Coventry's lodgings later in the afternoon, Sir William gave him a token of comfort. He said nothing of Samuel's words with the Prince, but he did say that Sir George Carteret had explained to the Prince that the Clerk of the Acts had been concerned only with the expense of preparing a new fleet and had not intended any judgment upon the conduct of the war. The Lord Treasurer had said that that also was his understanding. When the Prince had tried to make a further protest, the Duke of Albemarle, his co-commander in the fleet, had cut him off with the rebuke that their present concern was the fitting of a new fleet and not the conduct of the old one. "Furthermore," he had said, "I know Mr. Pepys as an honest officer, not given to quarrels or insubordination."

"He is a creature of my Lord Sandwich," the Prince had sneered.

The Duke of York had interposed before the touchy subject of the Earl of Sandwich could get placed on the agenda. The meeting had rambled on to an inclusive but peaceful end.

"I think we should document our reply," Sir William said when he had finished his narration. "We do have documentation?"

"Yes, we have the surveyors' report, or we shall have in a day or two." Samuel was pleased that Sir William was saying "our" reply. "Batten can send it under his signature."

"Did not Penn join him in the survey?" Sir William asked.

"Yes," Samuel acknowledged. "The report may go under their joint signatures."

"It should go under all our signatures," Sir William said mildly.

Samuel squirmed. He had exposed himself enough, he felt. Let the others carry their share of the cross. He started to protest, but Sir William cut him off, quietly but firmly.

"We are an office, Mr. Pepys. If the Office falls, we all fall."

Samuel nodded unhappily. This, of course, was the truth. He could not deny it, but he did not see why he, with the obloquy of Lord Sandwich already on his back, should assume the personal hazard of having to defend the corruption of Batten, the incompetence of Minnes, the laziness of Penn, the carelessness of Lord Brouncker.

Sir William put his hand on Samuel's arm.

"We all know, Mr. Pepys. We all know whose care keeps us all afloat."

Samuel sat back in his chair. There was no contending with Sir William. From another man this would have been flattery—but not from Sir William. He was, if anything, too blunt, too honest in his dealings with courtiers and public servants. Sir William always spoke the truth. And this was the truth, Samuel admitted. It *was* his care that kept them afloat. It was only his weariness, perhaps, that held him back, that made him afraid to accept his duty.

"Very well," Samuel said at last. "We will all sign it."

He rode back home in a coach through the City. The sun was setting and a hazy dusk hung over the ruins, making them more bleak and forbidding than they had seemed in the immediate afterdays of the fire. The excitement had cooled down with the heat of the embers. Now there was only dust, endless dreariness, and a pervading suspicion of danger. So far very little work of reconstruction had taken place. The principal streets had been cleared of debris. Some of the chimneys had been knocked down and the brick stacked in neat rows but the general view was still one of dry, dispirited disorder. During the day the ruins were fairly busy with work crews clearing the streets, householders scratching among the ashes of their destroyed houses, looking for tools and utensils. The trained bands patrolled the streets to restrain the pilferers and the scavengers. But at night the streets were deserted. An occasional constable crept along in the dark, making himself as inconspicuous as possible. The graveyard silence and the smell of desolation in the huge area discouraged casual traffic; but there were little gangs of prowlers who worked a lugubrious trade, pilfering half-destroyed shops and preying upon citizens who dared to venture into the ruins after dark.

Samuel had forgotten how quickly the days began to shorten in late September, how quickly sunshine turned to dusk and dusk to darkness. By the time the coach was climbing Ludgate Hill, the light was gone and a thick gloom surrounded the skeletal chimney spires. When the coachman started to light his link, Samuel stopped him. There was no need, he snapped sharply, to attract the wolves with a light. He also drew his sword and laid it across his knees.

He felt as if he were adrift in an unknown sea. He could not recognize any landmark. He assumed they were moving down Lombard Street toward Fenchurch, but the hazy ruins here looked as anonymous as they did in Cheapside or Fleet Street. He could be anywhere—or nowhere. All was flatness, dullness, inexpressible dreariness.

Just before the coach turned southward into Mark Lane, a dark figure shot out into the road ahead of them. The shape called out and put out a hand as if to catch the harness of the horse, but the coachman brought his whip down hard across the flanks of the startled animal and then with a cross stroke caught the intruder flush on the face with the tip of the cracking thong. Samuel pressed his face against the glass of the coach and he could see a blood-red welt suddenly appear on the cheek of a frightened man before he clapped his hand to his face and screamed. The coach jerked sharply from the sudden plunge of the horse; and when the coachman took the turn into Mark Lane without slowing, Samuel was thrown hard against the far door. He shouted to the coachman to slow down, but neither the coachman nor the startled horse cared to linger in those threatening environs.

The coach raced pell-mell all the rest of the narrow way to Seething Lane. When Samuel got out he discovered that his sword had fallen to the floor. It had never once occurred to him to use it in the emergency. He slipped it back into its scabbard disgustedly. It was a silly, foolish weapon. Whips were better in his world. Whips and words.

But he resolved never to go again through the City after five in the afternoon.

It was easier for Samuel to think about going back to work than to do it. Somehow he could not make himself take hold again. He could do the routine things that came up in the office, keep Hayter busy, send Hewer out on trivial errands. But he could not attack a new problem or summon the energy to think creatively and closely about the old problems that he knew deserved his attention. His own fire was out. He was caught in the flatness and bleakness of the moment that either followed a disaster or foretold new catastrophe.

At night he had nightmares about the fire, dreaming that it was flaming against the windows of his bedroom and that he was for some reason powerless to move or cry out. He would awaken in the morning exhausted.

Elizabeth was restive during the day, easy to tears, and easy to anger. She was consumed with idleness. She had nothing to do, nowhere to go. At night in bed the unhappy couple quarreled and bickered, took mutual offense at the slightest provocation, went off to sleep in cold reserve, or stayed awake in the lonely darkness brooding. They could not find the comfort and release that their strong passion for each other usually brought them.

Now they slept apart, untouching and hag-ridden.

Samuel sent Will Hewer to the Mercers to see if Mary were willing to return to Seething Lane. But Mary was *not* willing. She would be glad to come from time to time, she sent word, as a guest and a friend; but she would not again put herself in the position of being taken for a servant. Samuel had to confess the justice of the reply. He did not love the girl the less for her spirit. As a matter of fact, he loved her more. He found himself brooding about her absence. He thought of the little pleasures that were associated with her in the good days before the fire—they seemed good now—her happy singing with him on the leads at night before supper, the cheerfulness of her laughter at dinner when they talked about the play they had seen the day before, the sweet modesty with which she allowed him little intimacies with her body when they were alone together in the music room after Elizabeth had gone to bed. Her absence became a narrowing focus of frustration. He thought more and more about the girls and young women who had allowed him liberties: Betty Lane, the girl at the linenshop in Westminster Hall; Mrs. Bagwell, the carpenter's wife at Deptford, who let him kiss her and no more; Mary Knepp, the actress at the Theatre Royal whom he had met at Woolwich during the plague and who in her own sophisticated way gave him the feeling of conquest without yielding the fact; Betty Michell, the daughter of his old friends the Howletts in Axe Yard, married now to an earnest young London tradesman, but who still enjoyed being called playfully Samuel's "other" wife and who allowed him a certain semiconjugal intimacy. He relived in his imagination his earthy, full-fleshed bouts with Betty Lane. He projected his half-successes with Knepp and Bagwell and Betty Michell into agonizing, consuming consummations. He became obsessed with sex, and launched out into a search for physical pleasure that would fill the vacuum of his desire.

His first instinct had been to lose himself in the attractions of the playhouses. At Drury Lane and Lincoln's Inn Fields he had always been able to find escape from the pressures of his work. Even when he did not care especially for the play or the acting, he could become absorbed in the music and the dancing and the high spirits of the audience. And now that he knew Mary Knepp intimately, he could go whenever he wished behind the scenes and see the players undressed, putting on their make-up, gossiping and quarreling. As Knepp's good friend, he was allowed the privilege of kissing the young girls of the company, Moll Davis and Nelly Gwyn. There was a liberty behind the scenes, an air of innocent debauchery, that should have satisfied his itch for dissipation. But he dared not go now to the theater. With his office and himself in their present condition, it would not do for the courtiers to see him wasting his time at the playhouses. He needed more private entertainment.

He went to see his old friend Betty Lane. She was not Betty Lane any more. She was now Betty Martin, the wife of a sorry, lumpish young fellow, a purser on one of the fifth-rate ships of the fleet. But she was still the same old Betty. Her husband, being a sailor, was usually away from home; and Betty kept open house in her modest lodgings in an obscure back street of Westminster. It was easy for Samuel to slip away from his morning's appearance at Whitehall and spend the afternoon with Betty. Now that she was married, he no longer had to suffer his old fear of consequences.

But Betty did not satisfy all that disturbed him. She was at best a sottish wench, with no style, and considerably stupid. Samuel needed some sense of conquest, and Betty was as invulnerable as a tavern jade. But Betty had a friend, a neighbor named Mrs. Burroughs, a fulsome young widow who found widowhood a tedious existence of empty days and joyless nights. She often came to Betty's house for conversation and company. Samuel had usually found her an inconvenience and a bore, but when he took her home to her own lodgings one rainy afternoon, he discovered that Mrs. Burroughs had charms that belied her stuffy manners and petulant voice. He took to alternating his visits between the lodgings of Mrs. Martin and those of Mrs. Burroughs.

But after a while the richness of the feast began to pall. Mrs. Burroughs was no more of a challenge than Betty Martin. A visit to one was very like a visit to the other, and he would sometimes forget which house it was he was supposed to visit next. Samuel did not like disorder, even in his debauchery; so he had just about decided to look for another arrangement when he found one day a new face at Betty Martin's, a younger face, suggestive of Betty's, but fresher and more innocent.

"This is Doll," Betty announced when Samuel had taken his seat. "She has just come to town to live with me and look for her fortune. She is my sister."

Samuel patted his knee. "Welcome to London, my dear," he said jovially. The girl came across the room and sat down dutifully on Samuel's knee.

"We must become acquainted," Samuel told her. "Fortune is not to be found like gold in the streets of London, anymore than it is to be found in the roads at home. It has to be earned by care and the proper use of whatever talents one has."

Betty interrupted her poking at the fire to tell Doll that Mr. Pepys always talked that way and that she must not be alarmed. He was a proper gentleman.

Samuel rested his hand lightly on Doll's thigh and went on with his conversation.

"You seem talented," he said, "and I dare say that Betty can teach you to be careful." He pulled the girl against him and reached into his pocket for a coin.

"Here is a crown." He put it into her hand. "Let this be a token of our friendship. And now if you will put on your cloak I will take you into King Street and buy you your first draught of London ale. It is said to make women as free as it makes men wise. Get your cloak."

This was not prudent of Samuel, not only because he ran the slight danger of being discovered by one of his servants or one of his neighbors, but more especially because, in his present need for excitement and conquest, he exposed himself to an attraction that he was unable to control.

Doll was not a beauty. As a matter of fact, she was plain. But she was young, sixteen at the most, and endowed with the fresh loveliness that comes with first ripeness. She reminded him a little of Elizabeth when he first married her. Elizabeth had been only fifteen, but *she* was French and precocious. Doll fascinated him now, completely, absorbingly.

He treated her with an almost courtly gravity, talking to her seriously, pointing out the Holbein Gateway and the Banqueting House where the first King Charles had been beheaded. He showed her the lodgings of Lady Castlemaine, the King's principal mistress. In the aleshop in King Street, he held her hand and whispered to her the names of the several courtiers he saw taking their afternoon draught: Mr. Baptist May, the Keeper of the Privy Purse; Henry Killigrew, Groom of the Bedchamber in the Duke of York's household; Henry Jermyn, Master of the Duke's Horse. Doll sat wide-eyed and speechless.

Samuel was to discover that speechlessness was Doll's natural state. She was not very bright or alert or gifted, but Samuel, in his infatuation, took her silence as wonder. She became a fixation to him. He took her to Vauxhall and showed her the entertainment booths, though they were closed for the winter and the weather too cold to enjoy a walk along the embowered paths. He took her up the river to show her the King's palace of Windsor. But principally he took her to taverns, where they could drink ale by the heat of the fire and let Doll look at the assorted citizens who she seemed to be convinced ruled the country and sat at the King's right hand.

Samuel let her think so. Her wonder pleased him and made her indifferent to the little liberties Samuel would take with his hands while she was gazing in open-eyed enchantment at a young lieutenant of the King's Guard downing a tankard of ale by the fire. Samuel was careful not to press the girl too fast. She was young and inexperienced. She must not be shocked too suddenly by what she would ultimately learn was the way of the world.

One day in November when he brought her home from a cold excursion to Hampton Court, he found that Betty was away for the evening. But she had left the door unlocked, the fire burning, and a note saying that there was ale in the kitchen and a dish of anchovies if they were hungry. This was a fortunate circumstance, Samuel thought, as he warmed himself by the fire and watched Doll take off her cloak and gloves. It was thoughtful of Betty to leave the note.

Doll brought the ale and they sat before the fire, thawing out from the chill that had pierced them on the river. Samuel chatted about the history of Hampton Court, how Cardinal Wolsey had built it for a palace for himself and in a moment of foolish generosity (or desperate necessity) had given it to King Henry VIII. He told her the secret of the maze in the gardens. You turned right at the first turn and left thereafter—or the other way round— he could not remember which. Doll listened sleepily and silently to his cheerful narrative, paying no apparent attention either to his words or to his hands which were moving more and more freely over her passive body.

The first thing Samuel knew he had undone her.

He was surprised and alarmed. But Doll was not. She was just speechless—and passive. She showed no more emotion than she had shown when he held her hand in the tavern. Either the girl had no morals or she was not as innocent as she seemed. In either case, Samuel was appalled. He had wasted his time and his money on nothing. He left the house in a dudgeon and resolved to have no more to do with the baggage.

One cold afternoon Samuel wandered into St. James's Park and walked along the winter-bleak paths to the new building that the King had built to house Queen Catherine's protégés, an order of Capuchin monks. Samuel had never visited the monastery before. His alert eye had seen the construction and his open ear had heard the gossip of the daring of the King in building a Catholic house so close to the Court; but his fundamental, inherent Puritanism had held him back from following the bent of his curiosity. Now, he felt, it did not matter much.

He made no ceremony of his approach. He just tapped the knocker on the great wooden door, as if he were making a visit to a stranger, and waited calmly for admission. When a sandaled and hooded monk opened the door, Samuel announced politely that he had come to visit the Capuchins. The monk, without hesitation, invited him to come inside and wait while he summoned the Lord Almoner, and then he shuffled off into the inner recesses of the spotless new building.

When the Lord Almoner appeared a few minutes later, he greeted Mr. Pepys courteously, saying that it was an honor for his house to receive a visit from an officer of His Majesty's household. Samuel did not know how the priest knew this (even if he had gotten it a little wrong) but he countered courtesy with courtesy and requested to see the monks at their daily tasks. The Almoner bowed and pointed toward a door on the right. They would tour the monastery, he said.

Walking slowly along the halls with the cowled and gracious figure, saying little, and that in a hushed voice, Samuel looked in at the chapel with its crucifix, an honored piece given by the Pope to Mary Queen of Scotland and containing, the priest whispered proudly, a splinter of the true Cross. His guide then led the way to the dormitory where the monks slept on hard beds, without sheets or mattresses, and to the refectory, a neat clean room, full of light and with a good view of the Park. The members of the order were eating a meal of boiled mutton on earthen plates and drinking wine from earthen cups. The monks ate in silence but, to Samuel, it seemed a peaceful, relaxed silence. His greatest pleasure of the visit, however, came when they entered the library, where he saw a gentle old man, his hooded head bent low over an opened folio. This, Samuel felt, was the image he had sought. The epitome of the monastic life—a quiet room, well-lighted, and filled with beautiful books, stout folios and slender quartos all bound in rich vellum, neatly placed on convenient shelves. This was the room for a recluse, a weary servant tired of the onslaughts of the flesh and the world. He wished devoutly that he could be a monk. And then he thought of the hard, cold beds, the silent meals.

He thanked his host for his hospitality, gave him two crowns for the charity of the order, and wished him good day.

The memory of that quiet afternoon in the peaceful cloister lingered in his mind. There idleness was a virtue and celibacy a necessity; in his own life in the winter of 1666, idleness was a disease, an incapacity from which he could not free himself, or make himself *want* to free himself. Of celibacy, he did not even allow himself to think.

Through December and the cold harsh weather, he threshed about in his unhappiness. He returned to his fleshpots, his private fleshpots, going to Deptford to visit with Mrs. Bagwell while her husband was away at Chatham working on the damaged ships of the fleet. He made assignations in Southwark with Betty Michell and got his hands slapped when he went too far. He even forgot his old regard for caution about going to the playhouses. He began to visit Mrs. Knepp at the Theatre Royal after the play, sitting in on rehearsals in the almost empty theater, taking her at night to a house in Holborn where artists gathered and sang bawdy songs and hacked away at each others' reputations. His reward for this nonsense was that in the coach going home, the ingenious Knepp allowed him all the liberties the limitations of a jouncing coach permitted.

It was a winter of discontent, a doldrum of lost ambition and helpless despair in which he tried to support himself by a release of the erotic turbulence that always lurked beneath the surface of caution that he held between himself and the world. He gave full rein to his lust, with no thought of consequence, as he sought mirth and desire.

Then Will Hewer came to see him.

Hewer, now a sober young man of twenty-five, had matured greatly from the awkward boy who had joined the Pepys household seven years ago on the day they had moved from Axe Yard to Seething Lane. Samuel had always known that there was good stuff in the boy. After all, he *was* a nephew of Mr. Robert Blackburne, who had been secretary to the Commonwealth Admiralty Committee. The boy had been brought up in the tradition of public service, and it took only a little sharp tutelage from the Clerk of the Acts to cure him of his boyish faults of occasional idleness, impertinence, and intemperance. Now he was a responsible, valuable servant. In his whole household, and therefore in all the world, there were only two persons in whom Samuel had total trust—Thomas Hayter and Will Hewer. Mr. Hayter was Samuel's identity at the office, his constant, loyal clerk. Will Hewer, on the other hand, was Samuel's peripatetic self, his errand boy, his agent at one place when Samuel could not be at two. If Hayter was his good right arm, Hewer was his legs, his eyes, his ears. Between them they composed a most formidable, a most complete alter ego of Samuel Pepys, Clerk of the Acts.

Will Hewer had come, his courage screwed tight, to offer to be his conscience as well. He stood stiff by the table in the study, his hat in his hands, waiting for Samuel to notice him.

Samuel sat dully in his chair wondering what in the world possessed the boy to stand there so stupidly. He was not really interested; he was just annoyed that Will was being so tense and dumb. He let him stand. Perhaps in time the boy would speak his mind or give up and go away. Samuel much preferred the latter.

But Will did not go away. He clutched his hat, shifted his feet, took a deep breath, and at last blurted out his mind.

"The people are talking, Mr. Pepys."

Samuel nodded and waited for him to go on, but Will had fired the only shot he had ready.

"What people?" Samuel prompted. It was well to get first things first.

"The clerks," Will stammered. "The clerks here and at White-hall, and some that are more than clerks."

Samuel smiled tolerantly at this promise of gossip.

"And what do they talk about, Will? The weather?"

"No, sir." Will had turned red in the face. "They talk about you."

Samuel stiffened. He looked angrily at his clerk, and then he thought better of it and relaxed.

"It does not surprise me that people talk," he explained gravely. "I have felt my share of their venom. Nor am I surprised that they talk about me. A man who dares to take a stand or to act with decision is bound to make enemies and stir up idle tongues. But how," he added as an afterthought, "have I injured clerks and servants?"

"You have not injured them, sir. The clerks I mean are not your enemies. They are your friends. They think you injure yourself."

Samuel turned his head and looked blankly at Will Hewer.

"How do I injure myself?"

Will dried his palms on the skirt of his coat and licked his lips.

"Come, Will, tell me," Samuel insisted. "How do I injure myself?"

The blood drained out of Hewer's cheeks, and his eyes opened very wide, like a man mesmerized. The words began to come in a torrent, rushed and overlapping. "They say you mind your pleasures to the injury of your work—and your reputation. They say you live at the playhouse, consort with the players and tavern wenches and other wasteful people while your work is left undone or is badly done by others. They say you have forgot your duty and your upbringing and have begun to act like a Whitehall rake. They say these things, sir, not to hurt you or blacken you but because they love you and fear what might happen if others should notice. And I tell you what they think, sir, because. . . ." But Will stopped cold, in midsentence, breathless and terrified.

In a thin, quiet voice Samuel asked, "And you, Will, do you tell me also because you love me?"

But Hewer could not answer. He broke down completely and wept, his face distorted and running with tears. Samuel turned away from him and walked slowly to the window. He kept his back to the unstrung, hysterical boy. He looked out the window at the leafless trees. Just so, he recalled, had he three years ago screwed up his courage to speak a personal rebuke to Lord Sandwich. It seemed longer ago than three years, much longer; then he had been the clerk agonizing about his master's dereliction and fighting for the courage to reprove him with gentleness and honor. And he had not quite had the courage. He had written a letter, unable to face him squarely with his censure. He had sent the letter by this same Will Hewer and he had waited a long and painful week for the Earl's reply, which did not come. He had waited a month for some word, some gesture that he was forgiven or understood. Now he understood why it had taken the Earl so long to give a sign. It was not easy to confess your sins to a servant—or to yourself, when the knowledge came from a servant.

"Quit crying, Will," he said at last. "It is all right."

He did not turn around. He spoke his words quietly out the window. "I do not blame you for the ugly report you bring me. I know you love me and tell me for my good—or what you think my good. You may tell your friends that Mr. Pepys has not taken leave of his senses. If he has taken a holiday from his work, they may be sure that he knows what he is doing."

Will Hewer rose slowly from the chair into which he had collapsed and walked to the door. With his hand on the knob, he said hoarsely, "I am sorry. Thank you, sir."

Samuel did not answer. He continued to look at the stiff trees outside the window. The wind assaulted them in sudden, impetuous gusts, cracking their branches against each other. With an angry jerk, Samuel snatched the draperies together, blotting out the ugly scene and enclosing himself in the obscurity of the suddenly darkened room.

The Dutch are come with a fleet

AT THE END OF THE YEAR a heavy snow fell on London and covered the broad scar of the burned City. As far as Samuel could see across the leveled acres, an unbroken whiteness lay over the charred ground. He walked up Tower Street as far as Mincing Lane, watching the tracks that he made in the frozen crust and playing a guessing game with himself about the location of former shops and taverns. London had many faces to show a knowledge-able man, all vivid and different and strange; but none that Samuel had ever seen in his thirty-three years of living in this great city was more strange than this sight of London leveled to the ground and paved with a pure white sheet of snow. He walked back to Seething Lane trying to step in his own original tracks.

But in two days the snow was gone, or as well as gone. Carts and coaches turned the streets into frozen mud, and the feet of laborers and tradesmen trampled the shop sites into a quagmire as they went on doggedly rebuilding the City. The loveliness disappeared and left only harsh cold weather to offend the dispirited citizens.

The government was almost bankrupt. There was no money to fit out the fleet, no money to pay the seamen who had fought in the campaigns of the past summer, no money to stock the supply yards. The contractors would not extend credit and the gold-smiths would not agree to an uncertain loan. The King appealed to the Parliament, and the Parliament bluntly asked to be in-formed how the King had spent the four million pounds that had already been furnished him to defeat the Dutch. It was a shocking question, not only because the Privy Council could not say exactly *how* the money had been spent, not in detail and on a moment's notice; but the question itself, by its very nature, put the Crown in the shameful position of having to account to its own subjects for the expenditure of Crown funds. The King did not like the position, just on principle, but neither did he like the excruciating embarrassment of letting his fleet lie idle, having his pay offices attacked by rioting seamen, or submitting himself to the wrath of his impoverished household. King Charles believed in the Divine Right of Kings and the sovereignty of the Crown, but he also believed in personal solvency. He was a Stuart and proud, but he was also half-French and shrewd. He ordered every department of the Navy to come to Whitehall and give an accounting to the Parliament of their expenditures during the wars.

Samuel gathered together his records and met with the accounting committee of the House of Commons. He answered a hundred sharp questions about the supply and the victual. He sent Hewer back and forth between Whitehall and the Navy Office fetching contracts and checking accounts. He stood about the anterooms awaiting the committee's pleasure. He sat in the committee room listening with awe and satisfaction to the chairman ordering the officers of the ordnance to ransack their records, working all night if necessary, until they could give a better account of the amount spent on powder during the first summer of the war. The committee was thorough and firm and knowing, and only when the Parliament was at least partly satisfied after a month of close questioning did it vote to grant the King more money. But it also voted to request that the King raise the money by a poll tax and that he practice a closer economy in the future.

The request did not make the King happy. The poll was an unpopular way of getting money. Chimney taxes and window taxes were unpopular too, but chimneys and windows were constant and stable, could be counted and checked; heads were variable. If more numerous than chimneys, heads were also more difficult to count—and to locate. Neither the King nor his subjects liked the tax on heads, but it was the only means the King had at the moment to replenish his treasury—there were no windows and chimneys left in London to speak of—so he applied the tax and hoped it would suffice.

Oddly enough the Parliament's recommendation for economy caught the King's fancy. Economy became the fashion. The idea which pleased him best was his design for an "economy suit," a long cassock of black cloth pinked with white silk, tailored to fit close to the body, and a simple coat of black velvet to be worn over it. The pantaloons were ruffled well below the knee with a large cluster of black ribbon. The new costume was not inexpensive but its funereal tone seemed appropriate to the somber restrictions of an enforced economy. The new fashion took on immediately, and Westminster tailors were busy for a month making copies of the King's new suit for courtiers and would-be courtiers. Whitehall looked for a while like a gathering of gayly mourning tradesmen, until word came from France that King Louis XIV had prepared a surprise for the English ambassador by outfitting all the lackeys at Versailles in King Charles's "pigeon-leg" black suit. And black immediately disappeared from Whitehall.

There were some, however, who did not have the King's genius for enduring a financial crisis. Sir William Coventry resigned his place on the Navy Board. He called Samuel aside at Whitehall and told him his decision.

"I cannot find it in my conscience to accept the King's salary for a duty I cannot perform. Without money we can do nothing, and I will not be paid to do nothing."

Samuel was nonplussed. It bothered him, too, that there was not enough to do now at the Office to earn his salary, but he had not thought of resigning. It was different with Sir William, of course; his place in the Navy was only one of several places he held. He was still secretary to the Duke of York and Commissioner for Tangier. Sir William would not suffer. But it was a pretty piece of conscience, nevertheless, and Samuel admired him for it. More shocking to Samuel was the thought of his now having to face the Board alone without the powerful support of the Duke's secretary. He was not sure how much his own power on the Board lay in Sir William's personal backing and how much in his own mastery of the details of the Office.

"I do not know how to receive your news," he told Coventry sadly. "I admire your honesty and envy you your conscience, but I cannot think of my life in the Navy without your aid or of the Navy itself without your energy and your wisdom. If you must leave us, may I ask that you not leave me. Could I, as a parting gift, extract from you the promise that I will not be forgotten in the continuance of your favor?"

Sir William smiled at the earnest, formal words.

"I promise," he said.

Nor was Coventry's the only resignation that came during the hard days of the winter. Sir George Carteret announced that he had had about all the criticism he cared to take for the Navy's inability to borrow money on the King's credit. The contractors were evasive and the goldsmiths were adamant. There was no money to be had until the returns of the poll tax began to accumulate, and that would take more time than the Navy had at its disposal. Sir George applied to the King for relief from his dilemma, and the King with his usual tact, and unusual promptness, arranged a swap whereby Sir George would take over the place of Deputy Treasurer for Ireland from the Earl of Anglesey and the Earl would assume the responsibilities of the Treasurer of the Navy.

That solved it, Samuel thought, for Sir George; but the addition of an earl to the Board, whatever it was worth in prestige, did not add a penny to the treasury. Sir George was wise to swap the Navy for Ireland. If Ireland was insolvable, it was not likely to sink and take its administrators down with it.

It was almost spring before the Privy Council evolved a fixed policy for the year. The poll tax had brought in something, more than the Crown had anticipated, but still not enough to conduct a full summer campaign against the Dutch. The Lord Treasurer allocated £10,000 to the Navy and told them that they would have to operate within that sum. The operations would have to be entirely defensive, or as nearly so as it was possible within the needs of the merchant fleet. An armed escort would have to be furnished to take the West India merchantmen out to sea before the Dutch could come out to molest them. In the meantime, the

Council began to make exploratory investigations of the possibility of a treaty of peace.

The Dutch, according to reliable reports, were as weary of the expensive war as the English, but an open gesture toward peace was a tricky business. Neither side desired to be thought to be taking the initiative; neither was willing to admit defeat and thereby have to come to the table as seekers and petitioners for terms. The King, after careful investigation, appointed a peace commission to go to The Hague to discuss with the Dutch the conditions under which a treaty for peace could be mutually established.

No one could tell, however, at this early date, how the negotiations were likely to go. King Louis of France kept his skillful fingers busy with the outlying strings of the business, keeping both sides off balance and suspicious. Intelligence spies reported that the Dutch were preparing some sort of fleet for summer work, how big or for what specific purpose no one could say. It was necessary, therefore, for the Navy to protect itself against attack. The Lord Admiral ordered all sound ships of the line to retire down the Medway and anchor in the protected waters of Chatham. The fortresses at Sheerness, which guarded the entrance to the Medway from the Nore, were heavily armed and manned. As a further precaution, an extra-heavy linked chain was dropped across the channel passage of the Medway above Chatham and attached to winches on the shore so that at an hour's notice it could be raised to hull level to block off approach to the anchored fleet.

Samuel had little to do in these plans for defense. Shoring up a fleet required little in the way of supplies and victual. Only a handful of men were needed to man the chain, and only a handful of men were available. All seamen stayed clear of the dock areas. They haunted the taverns along the riverside and made an occasional riotous appearance at the Pay Office.

Spring inertia began to take its toll on the morale of the Navy Office in Seething Lane. The thin bond of mutual trouble that had held them together in tentative harmony throughout the autumn began to slacken, and open, petty conflict broke out in the meeting room. Sir William Penn and Lord Brouncker fell out over the trifling matter of whose clerk should read off the Petty Warrants at the meeting. They squared off into a loud and fierce battle of angry words, until Samuel had to settle the fight by offering to read the Warrants himself. Penn demanded space in the office for a private room; and when Samuel pointed out that no space was available, Sir William gave the Clerk of the Acts a harsh raking, pointing out that the reason there was no space available was that Mr. Pepys had taken it all for himself. Samuel defended himself loudly and angrily, and the two men shouted back and forth at each other for half an hour like school-boys.

When a more serious matter, like corruption in the Ticket Office arose, the whole Board fell apart. Brouncker blamed Batten for condoning the corruption. Penn and Samuel charged Brouncker with protecting his friends in the Ticket Office. Minnes damned them all for bringing the trouble about by trimming his authority as Comptroller. The whole matter had to be taken to Whitehall and settled before the Duke. The Navy Office, under the strain of having nothing to do, was coming apart at the seams.

Samuel began to keep clear of the contentious premises. He went home to his quiet study where he could read in peace or think out a plan for his own security in the despairing times. If the peace commission at The Hague was not successful in its negotiations, or if the Dutch should send out a fleet and take it into their heads to make an assault upon the chain, then it might well be that Samuel's career in the Navy and his life in London would be at an end. There would remain nothing for him to do but retire to Brampton and live the life of a country gentleman. That prospect, at the moment, was not without its attraction. He would be free of Batten and Penn and Brouncker and Minnes and the whole bickering lot. He would have time for music and reading and collecting materials for a history of the Navy. Perhaps he could learn to garden, like Mr. Evelyn at Sayes Court, and write little pieces on farm economy.

But Brampton was farther away from London than Sayes Court was. It was a two-days' journey to Huntingdonshire. He would be trapped in a provincial prison months on end, surrounded by illiterate countrymen. In the country his household would consist only of his improvident brother, phlegmatic, unattractive sister, aged parents, and Elizabeth.

Samuel gave considerable attention and time to preparing Elizabeth for a life in the country. He had always, of course, concerned himself about Elizabeth's education. She could now dance a bit, after a fashion, and she could play a few card games and sketch and draw passably. Never, however, had he been able to bring her to any competency in music. She had no ear and her fingers had never been able to master the technique of playing a stringed instrument of any kind. She had a sweet, untrained voice, but she did not know how to use it as a musical instrument. She just sang when she felt like it, any old tune in any old key. If Samuel were going to have to live in Brampton, he needed a fellow musician. He would not be able to afford a Mary Mercer. He would have to train Elizabeth to bear her share of his musical necessity.

He went to Westminster and consulted with a flageolet maker. The flageolet was an easy instrument. It played itself almost, if the player could only learn to read notes, master a simple system of fingering the holes, and develop a proper lip. Even Elizabeth, he felt sure, could learn to play the flageolet. Samuel placed his order and took down the name of a teacher who might teach her to play. He found a music master near Covent Garden, a Mr. Thomas Greeting, a serious, middle-aged man, who had written considerable music for the flute and felt that he could teach anyone to play acceptably on the flageolet. For four pounds, he said, he would come twice a week for a month and teach Mrs. Pepys.

Samuel listened to their lessons every Tuesday and Thursday afternoon. It grated on his nerves when Elizabeth flatted a note, which she did frequently, and when she could not keep a tempo; but he felt that his money was well spent when after only five lessons Elizabeth was able to play, all the way through without flatting or missing the tempo once, a simple pastoral tune that Mr. Greeting had written especially for her. It was a haunting little melody and very easy to play. With that good beginning Samuel hoped that she might progress to better things.

As the weather became warmer, the officers of the Navy Board began to take themselves out of town to their country estates. Batten and Minnes and Brouncker went away to rusticate in Sussex and Kent. Penn spent more and more time at Chatham and Sheerness, helping Commissioner Pett in providing for the anchored fleet. In unmolested solitude Samuel attended to what little business there was to attend to. He had plenty of time to go over his personal accounts, reckoning himself to be worth, in cash and goods, somewhat more than £6,000. He spent much time on his diary, elaborating his brief notes from the bye-book, writing long accounts of his conversations with Sir George Carteret and Mr. Evelyn, making full analyses of the unhappy conditions of the Court, minute records of his uneventful days in the Office.

He took to taking long naps after dinner at home, sleeping hard and wretchedly from the time he got up from the table at two until Elizabeth woke him at five or six to go into the garden for a breath of air. He dreamed constantly during his hard afternoon naps, dreams of violence and anguish, that the fire was still burning, trapping him in the Office, suffocating him with thick acrid smoke.

One afternoon late in March he dreamed that his mother died. He thought that he was kneeling beside her bed crying, that her face was covered with hair, although it was not really the face of his mother as he knew it, but another face. He, in his dream, put his face against hers and wept. He awoke in great sadness, convinced that something was amiss at Brampton, either his father or his mother was sick or dead. For the next two days he could not free his mind of the presentiment that there had been a death at Brampton. But he was afraid to speak of it, and he drew back from writing a letter to Brampton to inquire; instead he sent his brother John to his father and watched the post to see if any message came from the north.

Two days later Elizabeth sent word to Samuel at the Office that a letter had come from Brampton. She had opened it but feared to send him its news. He must come at once. Samuel walked across the garden calmly. He knew what the letter would say. He had known for several days. The dream had been too vivid for fantasy. His mother was dead.

Elizabeth was waiting for him in their bedroom, John's letter in her hand and a stricken look on her face. Samuel took the letter from her and sat down on the edge of the bed. Elizabeth sat down beside him and put her hand on his arm. Their mother, John wrote, had died on Monday afternoon between five and six o'clock in the afternoon, having been in a coma for three days. She died peacefully and without pain. Her last words in this world had been on the Friday afternoon before, when she had said, "God bless my poor Sam!"

Samuel crushed the letter in his hands. His emotions caught him by surprise. He had known she was dead. He knew it was best that she was dead. She was old and helpless and unhappy and an embarrassment in the family. But now that she was dead and had spent her last breath to say "God bless my poor Sam," Samuel's control collapsed. He rolled over on the bed and wept. It had been a long time since he had been aware that there was anyone in this world who could even think "God bless poor Sam!"

Elizabeth, with her sure instinct about overwrought emotions, let him weep, only keeping her hand on his arm so that he might sense that she was there. This was Elizabeth's great strength; she was sure in her understanding of emotions and she had instinctive sympathy for distress.

After a while Samuel was himself again. He finished reading John's letter. Their father requested that Samuel not try to come for the funeral. They would bury their mother before Samuel could get to Brampton. But Samuel was asked to send mourning for the family and to provide mourning for his own household— Samuel and Elizabeth, Barker and Jane, Will Hewer and Tom Edwards, and hoods and scarves and gloves for the two under-maids. The old woman must be properly mourned. Even if she had had her origins in a Whitechapel butchershop, she must now be mourned as a daughter of the ancient house of Pepys.

Samuel and Elizabeth went up to Westminster to the best of tailors and spent fifty pounds on the best mourning clothes they could find. They sent the Brampton clothes by public coach the next day, and the house in Seething Lane, from undermaid to master, dressed in black for a month to mourn the death of Margaret Kight Pepys.

In a few weeks John brought his father back with him to London, leaving Pall at Brampton to try her hand at running a household on her own responsibility. Samuel received his father gladly. Now with the exception of sister Pall, he had his whole family under his roof and under his own administration. They were his care, and he intended to provide for them. John was suited to be a country clergyman, and must have a benefice; Pall must have a husband and a home in which his father could end his days.

John was sent out to call upon the bishops, the deans, the owners of estates who held country livings. Old Mr. Pepys was sent by coach to search out his old friends and neighbors who used to live in Salisbury Court, to visit with relatives and his dead wife's kin, to inquire of a likely prospect for a husband for Pall.

Late in April a small fleet of twenty-four Dutch ships were sighted off the coast of Scotland. It was assumed that they were lying in wait for the Newcastle colliers. If that were true, there was nothing much to be feared. This was only a nuisance raid, for the colliers knew how to hug the coast and avoid trouble. But early in May the little Dutch fleet sailed into the Firth of Forth and threw a bombardment of shot into the port town of Burntisland. The alert shore batteries immediately answered, and the Dutch quietly slipped back out of the harbor and disappeared over the horizon. No damage had been done, but the Crown had been put on warning: the Dutch were out looking for trouble.

Samuel kept close to the office, tense and vigilant. In sole command of the almost empty office, he felt a pleasure in his responsibility, but he also felt an acute apprehension that something might break, at a moment's notice, which he was not prepared to handle or to cope with. He sat about the office making work for himself, putting up a pretense of calm business for the benefit of Hayter and Hewer and the other office clerks. But he kept an eye on every messenger who came into the building.

At home he gathered his family about him, Elizabeth and John and his father, and told them the situation. The Navy was in no condition to defend the country, or perhaps even to defend itself. The Dutch were on the prowl, and if they decided to invade in force before a peace could be concluded, there was no telling what consequences might befall them personally. They might have to fight or they might have to flee. In any case, the career of the Clerk of the Acts was at a crucial point. If worse came to worst, they might all have to escape to Brampton and eke out their lives on what little he had been able to save from his career in the Navy, a matter of some £6,000 in all, with about half of that in cash.

He was not trying to frighten them or impress them. He thought they needed to know what was ahead for all of them. John said nothing. He looked at the floor, unable to think of anything he could say that would give comfort in the situation. Samuel's father just smiled weakly and gave the impression that he had known crises before and could weather another. Elizabeth was the only one who spoke.

"When we were first married, Sam, and lived in the one little room at my Lord Sandwich's lodgings, I used to make the coal fires every morning and wash your dirty clothes with my own hands every Monday. I did not mind it then and I would not mind it again, if God should reduce us to it."

Elizabeth said the words simply and quietly. She meant them, too; and Samuel knew that she meant them; and he admired and loved her for them. But he could not help thinking them a little amusing, coming as they did, not from a young, untried girl of fifteen, but from a grown woman of twenty-seven, a somewhat plump and richly dressed matron who had not done a lick of work about the house in years.

It was the morning of June 8 that the expected messenger finally arrived, with word that the Dutch had come to Harwich with a fleet of eighty sail and that Sir William Rider's people at Bethnal Green had heard the guns plainly during the night. Samuel receipted the messenger's letter and gave it to Mr. Hayter to copy into the official letter book. He also sent Will Hewer to Whitehall to see what he could learn at the Admiralty, and dictated a letter to Penn and Batten, suggesting that they return to the office at once.

That was all he could do for the moment, and he was pleased at how calmly he had done that. Will came back in the afternoon with word that it was true that the Dutch were out in force off

Harwich and that the King had dispatched the Earl of Oxford to raise the militia and prepare for an invasion.

The next morning Samuel went to Whitehall to gather his own news. He found Sir William Coventry in the Duke of York's chambers. He asked what service he could perform. Sir William said that the greatest need at the moment was maps. The officers of the militia were crying for maps and not enough could be found. Samuel said that he had a set of Hollar's six maps of the kingdom and Sir William could have those if he wanted them. Sir William said that he wanted them very much, and Samuel sent Will Hewer down the river to fetch them. That, apparently, was all that Sir William could think of for the Clerk of the Acts to do at the moment; so Samuel hired a boat and spent the rest of the day enjoying the fine weather up the river and pretending that nothing unusual was afoot.

But when he got back to Seething Lane at dusk, he found both Penn and Batten returned from the country and huddled together in the office with the clerks, poring over a late-afternoon order from Sir William Coventry demanding that fire ships be dispatched down the river at once. The Dutch were in the Nore.

Samuel threw off his coat and called for Mr. Hayter. With his two colleagues standing by to read off the list of fire ships located at Deptford and Woolwich, he rattled off orders to the shipmasters until midnight. If the dockmasters were on the job, every available fireship in the river should be under way by dawn.

When Samuel got to the office the next morning, however, he found not only another urgent order from Coventry to get the fire ships under way, but he also found Captain Sir Fretcheville Hollis, commander of fire ships for the Royal Navy, waiting impatiently.

"Why have the Duke's orders for fire ships not been executed?" he demanded sharply as soon as Samuel entered the room.

"They have been executed," Samuel answered. "They should be at Gravesend by now."

"They have not moved from their docks," Sir Fretcheville barked, "not one."

"Then there is trouble," Samuel replied. "Can you give us fast passage to Deptford?"

They met Penn and Batten in the garden. Samuel hurriedly explained the situation, and all four of them ran down to the Tower Wharf and jumped aboard Sir Fretcheville's twelve-oared barge. They were at Deptford before Samuel could make it entirely clear to Penn what had happened. He knew the orders had been sent. Hewer had taken them personally and Hewer could be trusted.

But what they saw when they pulled into the docks at Deptford appalled them. Not a fire ship had moved; every vessel lay tied at the dock, slack and still. The docks themselves were filled with yard laborers, sitting around on the capstans or stretched out on the bales of ship goods. A few shipmasters stood on the decks of their ships, glaring angrily at the lounging men, but the workers just sat there ignoring them, looking placidly at the idle ships. The yard workers had ignored orders and were defying authority. And Samuel knew why: they had not been paid in half a year, and would no longer work without pay.

Samuel jumped from the barge and hurried to the office of the yardmaster. "Did you receive our orders?" Samuel asked, just to get the conversation started.

"The orders were received and issued to the men," the master answered in an abused tone, "but the men will not work without pay. They have reported to the yard, but they will not load the supplies."

"The Dutch are in the Nore. By noon they may be shelling the batteries at Sheerness. It is a matter of the greatest urgency that the fire ships go down the river to meet them. They are all we have, and we must use them—*now*."

"The men won't work," the master answered feebly.

"There is such a thing as mutiny," Samuel suggested.

"On land?"

"Admiral Penn can make them think so. Let Sir William rattle them a bit and they will think so."

The yardmaster looked questioningly at the Clerk of the Acts and drew a mark in the dust with the toe of his boot.

"The Admiral can try, but these are obstinate, freedom-proud men, free citizens of London, not cowed seamen. But the Admiral can try."

Samuel rushed back to the docks and held a hurried conference with Penn and Captain Hollis. Penn jumped at the plan. He strode across the docks like an avenging angel. He mounted to the top of a huge crate and in his booming voice ordered all hands to stand by. The men continued to sit where they were, but they turned their heads toward the towering naval officer.

"The Dutch are in the Nore," Sir William shouted. "By tomorrow they may be at Chatham or at Deptford. Are you willing to sit around on your fat butts whining about pay when the enemies of the King are loose in the river? If you are cowards with not enough decency to defend your own homes, then you should be patriots enough to furnish the supplies so that men who love the King and are not afraid may face the enemy and at least fight for the right to be free Englishmen."

For ten minutes Sir William blasted them in quarterdeck eloquence, and when he was finished, he thrust his fat old head out at them like an angry turtle and glowered.

The men glared back at him, sullen and scowling; and then one man got up, seized a crate in both hands and with fierce violence threw it on the deck of the nearest fire ship. Another man got up slowly from the coil of hemp he was sitting on and rolled it angrily toward the loading net. Gradually, one by one, the men got up and went to work. In a minute or two the dock was busy with the efficient if not enthusiastic labor of getting the supplies aboard.

The four officers of the King scattered to a variety of urgent tasks. Sir Fretcheville sped off in his barge to inform the Duke of Albemarle at Gravesend that the fire ships were coming. Batten and Penn stayed on at Deptford to supervise the loading, and Samuel hurried away to Woolwich to order the *Golden Hind,* one of the Dutch prize ships captured last summer, to proceed to Gravesend.

Albemarle was placing a blockade across the Thames at Gravesend, towing frigates out into the river and sinking them in line, confiscating all ships that lay at hand, loaded or unloaded, and knocking holes in their bottoms. It was desperate, high-handed work, and it hurt Samuel deeply to see the fine, trim frigates sinking slowly into the river, only their top housing and spars showing above the water.

He could learn no news of the Dutch. There was a report that they were already firing on Sheerness, but Samuel could hear no sound of the guns. He felt sorry for poor Pett over at Chatham, responsible for the fate of the *Charles,* the *James,* the *London*—all the great ships of the line—idle and useless now, a burden and a care rather than the great floating fortresses that they had been built to be.

When at dark Samuel started to go back to London, he lay down on the wet boards of the boat and slept until the waterman awakened him and said that they were back at Tower Wharf. He dragged home wearily and fell into bed exhausted.

Before he could get to the office the next morning, a messenger from Coventry was at Samuel's door with urgent orders for more fire ships to be sent to the Nore. And as soon as Coventry's messenger was gone, a breathless courier hurried in with a message of anguish from Pett at Chatham. "For the sake of God and the King and the Kingdom, send help. Sheerness is lost. Chatham is next. Send help."

Lord Brouncker and Minnes took horse at once and set out at a gallop to aid and comfort the panicked Pett. Samuel and Batten went back down the river to Deptford to spur on the dispatching of fire ships. They found Admiral Penn striding the docks, shouting encouragement to the exhausted workers. Everything was under control at Deptford. Penn was getting the ships out.

At dinner time Will Hewer came in with the news that the Pay Office had funds on hand for the payment of the last quarter's salaries. Samuel left his dinner and ran to the Pay Office to collect what was due him, £400 in bulky silver. Samuel needed every penny now that he could get his hands on. Flight might be necessary in a matter of hours. He lugged the heavy sacks home and locked them in his iron chest in the cellar.

Back at the office waiting for him was a terse order from the Council. The officers of His Majesty's Navy were ordered to seize any ships that lay in the river. Under an invasion, the King could by law, the Council ruled, take any man's goods that were needed in the defense of the realm. Samuel thought of his iron chest and groaned in agony, but he called Mr. Hayter and began to send off orders to execute the law of royal seizure.

All day he stayed in the office waiting for news of Chatham. Word came up the river that the Thames was blocked at Gravesend and that the Dutch had made no gesture toward London. They were concentrating on reducing Sheerness and getting at the English fleet. But no news came from Pett.

That night the drums of the trained bands beat a steady summons in the streets. All members of the bands were ordered upon penalty of death to appear in arms at dawn with bullets and powder and enough money to supply themselves with victuals for a fortnight. The soldiers of the King had been ordered to Chatham. The defense of London was now entrusted to the amateur soldiers of the City. Samuel and Elizabeth sat in the office garden until eleven listening to the drums and talking in whispers of what they would do about their servants if they should have to flee.

Nor was there any news the next morning at the office. Samuel took a boat and went to Whitehall, but Whitehall was strangely quiet and deserted. No courtiers were to be seen in the streets, no clerks appeared in the taverns, no women rode in the Park in their private coaches.

Samuel searched an hour for Sir William Coventry, at the Palace, at his lodgings, in the Hall, but he could not find him. At last he met Coventry's boy in King Street and asked him what news he had of his master. The boy said that in a letter from the Duke of Albemarle last night, Sir William had learned that the Dutch had made no further move after reducing Sheerness. The Duke was optimistic that the chain would hold and save Chatham, but Sir William had ridden off to learn the fate of the fleet for himself.

Samuel wandered around Westminster the rest of the morning trying to learn the truth, but he could find no one who knew the truth or else had the courage to tell him. He went back to Seething Lane to see if any word had arrived at the office.

Mr. Hayter met him with a sealed dispatch from Coventry just brought by courier from Chatham. Samuel broke the seal and read the bitter news. The chain was down and the Dutch were among the anchored ships.

Samuel put his head down on his desk and wept.

In a little while he pulled himself together and went across the garden to his house. He summoned his father and Elizabeth to come to the study. John had gone to Brampton to prepare Pall for their coming; only his father and his wife remained to help with the flight. He locked the door and told them the end had come. The Dutch had invaded the fleet and all was lost. The time had come to flee. Some violence might very well come to the Office. The country would not accept the loss of the fleet without anger. Their only hope was to send what money they could into the country before disaster struck. They would scatter their portable goods as best they could so that discovery in one place would not ruin them completely. The important thing was to get their money out of the City and safely hidden at Brampton.

At four o'clock the next morning, the royal barge slipped past the Tower on the way down the river to Barking Creek. The King and the Duke of York were taking personal charge of the defense of the Thames.

As soon as the night watchman passed the word to Samuel, he called Elizabeth and his father from their beds. They must get up and make ready to catch the morning coach for Huntingdon. He brought up his gold from the cellar and packed £1,300 of it into a night bag, as much as the two of them could carry without suspicion. With Will Hewer to serve as an escort, he took them to the Post House in Holborn and got them seats on the inside of the Huntingdon coach. He told them that they were not to leave the coach at any stop along the way or to allow the bag out of their hands for a moment of the journey. When they got to Brampton they were to dig a hole in the garden and bury the gold, deep enough to leave no mark and secretly so that their neighbors would not know.

As soon as he was back in Seething Lane, Samuel sent Will Hewer into Lombard Street with his £400 of new silver. Silver was too bulky to carry. Hewer was to try to change it into gold at whatever price the goldsmiths were asking. While Hewer was away, Samuel packed £300 of the remaining gold into a money belt and strapped it around his waist next to his skin. It was awkward and uncomfortable, but it kept him reminded that his life's work was now concentrated into portable coin and that his future depended on the ingenuity with which he could carry it with him into seclusion.

Next he filled a small chest with his most valuable papers, the legal documents that attested his clear title to the farm at Brampton, his dead brother Tom's old tailoring accounts, and his diary. He sent these by Tom Edwards to his cousin Sarah Giles in Bishopsgate to keep for him until he required them again. He did not know what to do with his silver plate. It was not easy to hide two and a half dozen heavy silver plates and he did not know to whom to trust them. He decided to gamble on the safety of the plate at home, but he sent the maid Jane to the Joyces with his pair of silver flagons. Even the Joyces could not lose or mislay anything as large as the flagons.

When Will got back from Lombard Street, he reported that he could not buy gold at any price. The goldsmiths had sold their last gold coins the night before, and now were turning away their creditors by the hundreds, saying that all credits were now payable in twenty days. Lombard Street was in a panic—and so was Samuel. How could he dispose of £400 of silver? He thought of flinging it into the privy, but he gave up that notion and resigned himself to hiding it under the beds where he could reach it if he needed to get it quickly.

The securing of his personal goods was interrupted by a commotion in the garden. The Navy Office was being besieged by the Deptford laborers. They had worked, they shouted up to the windows, and they wanted their money. They had gotten the fire ships loaded and Sir William had promised them their pay.

Samuel hurried to the office to quiet the disturbance. He had no fear of them. He knew them and they knew him. They were entitled to their money and he was willing to do what he could to get it for them; but they must not be allowed to create a riot and bring open shame to the Office.

He selected three men whom he knew as reliable workers and took them up to his office. He would send his own clerk, he explained to them, to the Pay Office and get what money he could for them, but the men must be peaceful and not stay in a crowd. He would keep in touch with them and as soon as the money came he would notify them. One of the men could stay upstairs in the office with him and another could stay in the garden to relay the word when the money came. The three men accepted the arrangement as reasonable, assured Mr. Pepys that they trusted his word, and went out to scatter the workers off the premises.

The rest of the morning at the office was pandemonium. Couriers ran in and out bringing orders and carrying messages. The clerks worked in frantic haste, getting in each other's way, snapping at one another. Masters of some fire ships came in to report that the Ordnance had delivered them unmixed ingredients and not ready powder as they were supposed to do. Samuel met each crisis as it came up. He sent off a sharp note to the Ordnance demanding that they deliver ready powder or be held accountable for dangerous delay. When Will Hewer got back from the Pay Office with enough money to give each worker a part at least of what was due him, Samuel set up a line downstairs to pay the men as they filed through the building.

He buttonholed the messengers when they came in and quizzed them about the temper of the City and the progress of the barricades down the river. But he could learn very little. The trained bands were growing restless, standing about in the streets without orders. There was no news from the lower Thames and no news from Chatham. They were in a vacuum, isolated and barren, while the fate of the fleet and perhaps of the country was being decided elsewhere.

At noon he sent a courier on horseback out the Great North Road to overtake the Huntingdon coach and to learn what he could about the safety of his family. He wanted clear news of that operation, at least.

Throughout the afternoon came rumors and little fragments of news, unofficial and unconfirmed. Three of the great ships had been burned to the water, another had been captured and towed unceremoniously up the Medway. Samuel cursed the inadequacy of fragmentary reports while he feared the truth that official news might bring. He rubbed his back where the money belt chafed the skin. He was in sole command of the office, but there was no pleasure in it. It was command without knowledge, without direction, without power. He sat in the office and fretted.

At last darkness came. The last messenger departed. The clerks went home. The doorkeeper locked the doors of the building and stationed a guard to receive any messages that might come during the night. Samuel summoned Hewer and Hayter and took them to his house and gave them supper. They all ate in silence, too depressed to talk. After supper Samuel took his two clerks upstairs to his study. He sat down at his table and wrote out a new will, simple and brief. He left all he had in this world jointly to his wife and his father, with affectionate request that they provide comfortably for John and Pall. He had Mr. Hayter make three copies of the short document and then Hayter and Will witnessed Samuel's signature. He gave a copy to each of his clerks and bade them good night. After they were gone, he folded the other copy and put it into his money belt with the heavy gold. Making a will always gave Samuel some comfort. It gave him a feeling that he had made the ultimate gesture for order.

At nine o'clock the next morning, Samuel's courier from the North Road rode into Seething Lane. The Huntingdon coach, he reported, had got as far as Royston, two-thirds of the way to Brampton, by ten last night. Mr. Pepys's father and wife were well and safe. They should be at Brampton by noon today. Samuel gave the man a pound in silver and told him to get some sleep.

When Mr. Hayter came into the office a little later, he had disturbing news of the City. A mob had swarmed last night into the grounds of the Lord Chancellor's fine new house in Piccadilly, cut down the trees, broken his windows, and set up a gibbet before the gate. The trained bands had removed the gibbet, but the damaged trees and windows remained as ugly tokens of the people's revolt against authority. In Charing Cross great crowds had assembled and chanted the old Civil War cry of "A Parliament. A Parliament." The trained bands had done nothing to disperse the seditious gathering.

At noon Sir William Batten came back from his vigil down the river. The Thames was now blocked, he reported to Samuel, but in the greatest confusion possible. Good ships, full of supplies and valuable cargo, had been commandeered on the Council's order and sunk while empty hulls had been ignored. But there was no news, Sir William said, of the Dutch. At least they were not in sight at Gravesend.

No news of any consequence came during the afternoon. There was a report from Deptford that some of the fire ships which Samuel had sweated so hard to supply and send off had been commandeered and sunk into the barricade. Word came that it was the *Royal Charles* the Dutch had captured and towed off. None of the news was good or reassuring, but even these bad reports helped to break the strain of their isolation.

It was almost dark before the official courier from Chatham arrived, and Samuel was so weary now with waiting and so sure of the tale of disaster that the report was almost an anticlimax. The fleet was lost, the report said. The Dutch had broken the chain without the slightest trouble. The shore batteries had fired upon the invaders for a while, raking them with nine-pound shot; but at the crucial moment, when the Dutch were in their most vulnerable position, the powder gave out and the defense guns fell silent. The English command had disintegrated. Albemarle had damned Lord Brounker for not having the idle ships manned, and Pett had been arrested for negligence in spending more time on saving his models than on carrying the ships higher up the Medway. Chatham was at the mercy of the Dutch.

Samuel and Sir William Batten walked home together across the garden. They sat down on a bench behind the Surveyor's house and watched the darkness take the trees. Neither of them spoke. Samuel looked at the squat little man beside him. All fire was out of him now. The testy old officer lay back, his head resting on the hard edge of the bench, his face tired, seamed, and dirty. Samuel felt a sudden urge to touch him, to give him some word of comfort. But he could not. Batten would have to find his own way. No one could help another now. It was every man for himself.

Samuel got up without a word and went into his own house. He went up to his bedroom and lay down upon the bed and closed his eyes; but he opened them again quickly. The thoughts came too fast and they were too unbearable. He lighted the candles and wandered around the room, touching the furniture and the thick, rich draperies. On a table by the window lay Elizabeth's flageolet, untouched in a month, he mused, and probably unmissed. He picked it up and fingered the stops. He put it to his mouth and blew a thin, weird note, shrill and sad. He thought for a moment, and then slowly and carefully he played Mr. Greeting's little pastoral exercise from beginning to end. The sad little tune floated through the room, poignant and melancholy. Samuel was very pleased. He had not known he could play it.

XVII

A greater omen of ruin

THE DUTCH FLEET, having had the satisfaction of ravaging the English Navy in its own anchorage, sailed back up the Medway and into the Nore. The hundred ships of Admiral De Ruyter moved leisurely up the coast, threw a final contemptuous volley into Sole Bay, and then, with mainsails billowing and prows jutting triumphantly, disappeared into the North Sea.

The invasion was over. The Dutch had accomplished what they wanted. They had made a practical demonstration for the benefit of all Europe that they held mastery of the ocean seas, and they had made their demonstration while the politicians were still struggling over the terms for peace at Breda. Now the English peace commissioners could think further about what they were demanding, and the merchants of Holland could go about their business of piling up fortunes without the expensive necessity, for a while at least, of having to fit out a fighting fleet to protect themselves. Mighty England had been put in her place, and the merchants of London could digest the bitter knowledge at their leisure.

But England did not have the leisure—or the desire—to swallow the pill. Rumors came quick from Whitehall and Westminster that heads would fall for this disgrace, and the Crown was determined that the heads that fell should not be royal. The King prorogued the Parliament for the summer. Word went to Breda to conclude the peace on whatever terms were available and as soon as possible. The Council summoned the Principal Officers of the Navy Board and let them listen while they charged Commissioner Pett with willful negligence and ordered him to the Tower. The gentlemen from Seething Lane crept back to their office white-faced with terror.

As soon as word came from Breda that the peace had been signed, the King sent Secretary Morrice in his robes of office to the Lord Chancellor to demand the Great Seal. The Earl of Clarendon, after seven years of rule in the government and a lifetime in the service of the House of Stuart, was stripped of his power and thrown to the wolves. Clarendon was selected for the leading role of scapegoat. The errors of the past were to be the errors of Lord Clarendon.

As son-in-law to the disgraced Chancellor, the Duke of York came under the general suspicion. Also as head of the navy that had failed, the Duke bore the brunt of the public attack upon the service. To be a servant of James Stuart now was to be guilty, by association, of treachery and dishonor.

Into the place of power left vacant by the dismissal of Clarendon stepped the Duke of Buckingham, the vociferous champion of trade and Protestantism. Buckingham was the avowed enemy of the Duke of York, the Earl of Clarendon, and Roman Catholicism. He was also the hero of the House of Commons and of the London merchants. The Crown stood in dire need of a minister popular with the Commons; so the King permitted his lifelong mentor to be dismissed, his royal brother, the Heir Presumptive, to be pushed aside, and his troublesome cousin, the Duke of Buckingham, to be raised to power in the Council.

Resignations came thick and fast. Sir William Coventry resigned his place as secretary to the Duke of York—not because he was fearful of the enemies of the Duke, but because he had made the mistake of censuring the Earl of Clarendon in the Duke's hearing. This was no treachery in Sir William, for the Duke had in his time been equally severe in his criticism of the Chancellor. If now the Duke had reason to alter his judgment, his secretary had not; so Sir William resigned his office with brave words, "If a servant of a prince does not know how to retire from office and lead a private life, he is not fit to serve a prince."

The Duke accepted his secretary's resignation and replaced him with a politically colorless but veteran administrator, Mr. Matthew Wren. Samuel went at once to Sir William's lodgings and offered him his steadfast friendship. Sir William thanked him and gave him a warning. "These are dangerous times. Look to your own security and be prepared to suffer disgrace even when you know you are innocent. It will require more than innocence to survive the rigors of the days ahead. Be ingenious, Mr. Pepys, and think what you are doing."

Samuel went home and thought. He had really come off better than he had expected. Elizabeth had returned from Brampton with assurance that their gold was safely cached in the garden of the farm. He had recovered his silver flagons from the Joyces and his papers and his diary from Sarah Giles. He had restored the gold from his money belt and the silver from under the bed to the iron chest in the cellar. Although he had been frightened out of his wits by the Council's treatment of Pett, and had dreamed horrible dreams for a fortnight about being committed to the Tower, nothing really had happened to him yet.

But he felt that he could afford to take nothing for granted. He had to anticipate trouble. When the Parliament reassembled in October, there was bound to be a clamor for investigation. He had the summer in which to prepare himself.

He began by resigning his place as Surveyor of the Victual. It was a profitable plum and he hated to surrender the £800 a year it had been bringing him, but he needed to simplify his situation and to concentrate his area of defense. He collected his last commission from the contractor and sent in his resignation to the Duke.

Then he set to work on his records. He brought Will Hewer into the office and joined him with Mr. Hayter in making abstracts of every scrap of possible evidence he could find. Through the long, apprehensive summer, Samuel and his clerks labored at their records, piling up his evidence of good stewardship. He kept in touch with Whitehall, going often to visit with Mr. Wren, the Duke's new secretary, to make his acquaintance and to gain his confidence. It did not take him long to settle his mind about Mr. Wren. The new secretary was following a policy of making no mistakes; and Wren, in a very short time, knew who it was at the Navy Office who made no mistakes. Mr. Wren and Mr. Pepys were very soon of one mind about the conduct of Navy administration in the face of public censure: compile the evidence and say nothing until the time for judgment came. Samuel felt that he was fortunate to have so sensible a man in Coventry's old place. He could work with Mr. Wren.

But he could not work with his colleagues of the Navy Board. Either they were not aware of the gravity of the situation or they did not know how to meet it. Penn was no good for quiet work. He was excellent in action, but he was a fish out of water in the tedium of office strategy. Lord Brouncker was able and a good student, but he was impolitic and butt-headed. He would not surrender a position once he had taken it, no matter what new evidence came to light. Minnes was a charming and gracious man, personally attractive, but he was ill fitted for his duties as Comptroller. His work had been divided and taken away from him because he was not able to perform it, and now he was angry and obstructive. Batten seemed like a man in a swoon. He could not recover his wits from the shock he had received at the realization of the Dutch invasion. He sat around the office in a daze, unable to fix his attention on anything. Then suddenly he took to his bed, burned two days with a raging fever, and died. Samuel was shocked at the suddenness of it. It had not occurred to him that a man could disappear so completely so quickly. He was sorry to hear that he had died and left only £800 in this world for the care of his family. A man should be more provident than that.

But Samuel's brief pity did not let him lose a minute in getting Penn to join with him in writing a letter to the Duke urging that Colonel Thomas Middleton, the Commissioner of the Navy Yard at Portsmouth, be appointed to Batten's place. Middleton was an old hand in Navy administration. It would not be necessary to waste time breaking him in. The Duke quickly acceded to the Board's wish and Middleton came in as Surveyor.

Samuel went on doggedly with his slow work of preparing a defense. He explained his procedure to Colonel Middleton and asked him to keep quiet and keep his ears open. He had more difficulty with Penn and Brouncker and Minnes. Penn was too busy and too impatient to pay attention to Samuel's lectures. He squirmed and fretted. He agreed to anything and understood nothing, but Samuel made him read the records and sign his initials to the abstracts. Minnes and Brouncker were more responsive, but also more obdurate. They wanted to argue everything, put off, deliberate. Samuel had little patience with them. The work could never get done in this bickering atmosphere. So he went on without them, briefing them only when it was necessary, giving them completed reports to read and sign at their quarrelsome leisure.

When September came, Samuel felt that he was entitled to a rest before the ordeal of October came. He proposed to Elizabeth that they go to Brampton and fetch their gold from its grave in the kitchen garden. He notified Will Hewer that he was to accompany them, to help them salvage the gold and to serve as escort in bringing it back to London. Elizabeth put in that she wanted to take her new girl with her, young Deb Willet, a young girl of a good family who had just come to Seething Lane to serve as companion and maid. Samuel was willing. The girl was very pretty, and the gravest little thing that Samuel had ever seen for one so young. It would be refreshing to have the child with them in the coach to help relieve the weariness of the journey.

They spent two days at Brampton. Samuel walked through the fields with his father, projecting improvements, making plans for additions to the house when, and if, he should have to retire from London. He discussed with Pall the merits of the young farmer from nearby Ellington, one John Jackson, whom their father had selected as a possible husband. Samuel told Pall that she must consider the judgment of her father in this matter. Her dowry was set aside and waiting for the moment that the negotiations were completed. She must not be impatient or headstrong. It was important for her to have a husband and a household where their father could live out his last days.

Six years in the country, away from the temptations of idleness and pride, had chastened Pall. She was willing to be submissive, for she wanted a husband and a household of her own. She would do what was necessary to get one: accept her father's choice and obey her older brother. Mr. Jackson would suit her very well, she said, if he suited Samuel.

But getting the gold was Samuel's principal business in Brampton. As soon as it was dark at the end of his first day there, he lighted a dark lantern and went into the garden with Elizabeth and his father. When they had pointed out the spot where they were sure they had buried the sacks, he took an iron spit and poked around in the loose dirt. But the spit did not strike cloth bags or anything else. Samuel looked at them inquiringly.

They had put the bags in a wooden box, they explained, so that the bags would not rot and lose their coins.

Samuel probed again—and again. But his iron found nothing whatever under the dirt. In growing excitement, Samuel jabbed the spit all over the area, not only in the hidden place behind the hedge, but also out in the open, in the center of the garden, where any passer-by on the road could have seen if it had been light. Elizabeth and her father-in-law stood by helplessly, protesting that they were sure they had not buried it out so far from the hedge, while Samuel jabbed and sweated and swore. Just when he was really about to lose his temper, the iron spit made a dull sound as it hit something solid. Samuel jabbed two or three more times to make sure, and then he snatched the spade from his father's hand and began to dig. In two scoops of the shovel, the blade hit wood. Samuel fell to his knees and pulled away the dirt like a dog digging a hole for a bone. In a few seconds he uncovered a box, mouldy and half-rotted, buried only six inches under the ground.

He threw down a handful of dirt and cursed aloud. This was a fine way to secure his money, he shouted—only six inches under ground and in plain view for the whole world to see. They would be lucky if a single coin remained. He snatched up the spade again and plunged it under the exposed box. With a breaking sound the box split open and gold coins scattered wildly into the air. Samuel dropped down to the ground on his knees and lifted out the broken container. He pulled aside the boards and felt for the sacks. They were soggy and rotted, spilling their coins into the box and onto the ground. Samuel beat the ground with his fists.

While Elizabeth held the light and the old man went back to the house to fetch a barrow, Samuel searched the ground for the scattered coins. He had found only a dozen when his father returned with the barrow. Samuel hoisted the broken container into it and told them to take it into the house, to the inmost room, and lock the door, and then to send Will Hewer to him with a lantern, a sieve, and two pails of water. They would sieve for the scattered coins until they had found every one, even if it took all night.

By two in the morning, they had found forty-five pieces by panning the earth through the sieve. They stopped then for the night, to get some sleep, so they could continue the next morning.

They got up at five o'clock and went back to work, shoveling the dirt into pails and hauling the pails to the summerhouse where they could pan it in privacy. By nine o'clock they had found thirty-four more pieces, within twenty or thirty, Samuel reckoned, of the number that had been lost. They all spent the rest of the day washing the money, counting it, resacking it in fresh cloth, and packing it carefully into a basket. Samuel charged his father to continue to look every day for the remaining coins, until he had found ten or twelve of them at least.

When they loaded into their coach the next morning to return to London, Samuel put a cloth over the basket as if it were a lunch basket; but every quarter hour, he looked under the seat to see if it were still there. When the roughness of the road jounced the basket so that it seemed about to break, Samuel took out the sacks and put them in Elizabeth's lap. If the heavy burden made the last miles of the trip uncomfortable for Elizabeth, it was no more than she deserved.

On October 10 the Parliament reassembled in Westminster. The King greeted that body cheerfully, reported that since they last met he had disbanded the militia, put out of employment all Catholics and all persons who had been proved to have done their business ill. For the rest, he would leave it up to the Parliament to call to account whom it pleased. The House thanked the King for his words and for what he had done in the members' absence, including the dismissal of Lord Clarendon.

The ceremonies over, the House got down to its principal business, investigating the disastrous conduct of the war with Holland. A Committee of Miscarriages was appointed and instructed to hear evidence and search out any case of negligence, error, or corruption in the late war.

One of the first acts of the Committee was to ask the Navy Office to supply them immediately with a list of all ships and commanders engaged in last summer's action. Samuel sent them the information the next day and accompanied it with the earnest desire of the Office to cooperate with the Committee of Miscarriages in every way possible.

The Committee wasted no time and put no limits on the area of its investigation. It heard everything that anyone had to say about Commissioner Pett's failure to carry the fleet above Chatham away from the guns of the Dutch ships. It took note of every complaint against the Ordnance for failure to supply ready powder when it was requested in the emergency. It inquired into the practice of the Pay Office in paying the sailors by ticket instead of money. And it went farther back in time than the invasion. The Committee wanted to know who was responsible for dividing the fleet during the summer and thus missing the opportunity of a decisive victory. Even the old matter of the prize goods bobbed up from time to time in the committee room.

None of these matters touched Samuel closely, except the old scandal of the prize goods, and he felt that he was safe there. But he had to spend hour upon hour waiting about in the anterooms to be called as a witness. He did not mind testifying very much. The Committee treated him with the greatest respect, thanking him many times for the clarity and promptness of his evidence.

But one day the chairman warned Samuel that he seemed to be hedging in his answers, when he had been pushed hard about Lord Brouncker's paying off a whole ship with tickets before he had received orders to do so. Samuel was alarmed that the Committee should think him anything but clear and open, but he was also distressed that it was trying to get simple *yes* and *no* answers about a matter that was too complicated and ambiguous for that. Samuel assured the chairman that he was trying to protect no one, but Lord Brouncker could not be held wholly responsible for a condition over which he had no control. Paying by ticket was an evil necessity. If there was no money when a ship discharged its crew, a ticket or a negotiable promise-to-pay was better than nothing at all. The center of the trouble lay in the fact that the Office just had not had the money to meet its obligations.

The chairman looked soberly for a moment at the Clerk of the Acts. The delicate matter of inadequate funds, he said, was not the concern of this committee. Doubtless the House would in time appoint a commission to investigate the accounts of His Majesty's household, but that was neither the business of Mr. Pepys nor of the Committee. In the meantime, he said, the witness should take heed of this warning not to try to protect anyone. Samuel thanked the chairman for his kindness and said that nothing was further from his mind.

Samuel brooded for several days about the chairman's rebuke. What position *should* he take when one of his colleagues was attacked? Brouncker had handled the pay-by-ticket badly, to be sure, but Brouncker's faults had not brought about the bad morale of the seamen. The system of paying by ticket was not Brouncker's invention. He had used it only when there was no money to pay with at all. Was it the business of the Clerk of the Acts to reveal the individual faults of the members of the Board, to wash the Office linen in public? He had no love for his colleagues on the Board, but he did feel that the integrity of the Office depended on his ability to justify the acts of that agency. The chairman had presented him with a dilemma too difficult for his handling.

The only two men whose advice he had ever sought were no longer available to him. Lord Sandwich was in honorable exile in Spain and Sir William Coventry was in virtual exile in Westminster. There remained only the Duke of York, and the Duke had so far given no hint of being willing to concern himself with the troubles of the Navy. He was himself too high for the Parliament to touch, but the King had warned his brother to keep silent and inactive in this period of jockeying between Parliament and the Crown. The Crown wanted money and the Parliament wanted an accounting. To gain the one the King was willing to submit to the other.

Samuel debated with himself for a day, and then he decided to chance it. The Duke could only refuse to see him.

But the Duke did not refuse. He received Samuel cordially and almost wittily. "How goes your attendance upon our masters of Parliament, Mr. Pepys?" the Duke asked, smiling broadly.

"I still have my head, Your Grace, and hope to keep it."

"You will, Mr. Pepys, you will," the Duke assured him. "There is no head in London so firmly fixed as yours, I warrant. But tell me your troubles."

Samuel told him. He told him in detail of his exchange with the chairman of the Committee on Miscarriages, related the whole history of the perplexing matter of the tickets, analyzed Lord Brouncker's doubtful handling of them, and then asked for advice.

"What is my duty, Your Grace? Do I defend only myself or do I defend the whole Office as well?"

The Duke looked thoughtful for a moment and then touched Mr. Pepys on the shoulder. "Defend yourself, Mr. Pepys, to be sure. And I am sure you can. One sound ship has saved many a battered one. I do not think you have to make a choice. You and the Office are one. But defend yourself, Mr. Pepys, and know that you have my blessing if not, for the moment, my support."

Samuel kissed the Duke's hand gratefully. He gave Mr. Wren a cheery smile when he passed through the outer chamber, and rode back to Seething Lane with a grim resolution in his mind. It was his duty then to support the Office. Therefore it was his responsibility to rule it.

The Parliament continued to sit until Christmas, bringing a bill of indictment for treason against Lord Clarendon and submitting an act for the King's signature to investigate by commission the accounts of all officers of the King concerned with the expenditure of Crown funds during the Dutch War. The King signed both bills. Lord Clarendon hurriedly and secretly slipped away from England and returned to his second exile in France, this time without the care or the comfort of Charles Stuart. Samuel Pepys went to Westminster to locate a copy of the specifications of the act that empowered the Commons to investigate the accounts. He found also a list of the men who would compose the commission.

They were powerful men; or rather, the Act gave them power. They were empowered to call before them all persons employed in the management of the late war and to demand an accounting for every penny spent for whatever purpose. Samuel knew only one member of the commission, Alderman Sir William Turner, a merchant tailor and a former sheriff of London. Turner was an able and honest man, but he also knew the value of a shilling.

There would be no nonsense if the whole commission was of the caliber of Sir William Turner.

The Parliament adjourned on December 19 and the King named February 6 as the date for reassembling. Samuel was grateful for the respite. He would need every minute of the time to get himself in condition for the ordeal. He called a meeting of the Board and laid down the law. He would assume the responsibility, he told his colleagues, of organizing the defense of the Office accounts if they would grant him the power of decision and if they would give him their fullest cooperation. They had surely read, he told them, the specifications and would know the necessity of unity in presenting the case for the Office. They promised him what he wanted without demur, and Samuel went to work.

He requisitioned the full-time service of old Mr. Gibson, the veteran chief clerk of the Office. Gibson knew the history and the duties of every department of the Office. He was a collector of Navy memoranda and he had, in his files or in his well-stocked head, a precedent for every action the Board had taken.

He joined Mr. Gibson to his own team of Hewer and Hayter. They held regular meetings every morning at ten and plotted the tasks that each should tackle for the day ahead: Gibson on the Surveyor's records, Hewer on the Comptroller's accounts, and Hayter on the contracts. At night they would all assemble in Samuel's study at home and discuss strategy. Samuel gave them free reign to dissent and to suggest. Will Hewer very quickly rose above his fellow clerks in these discussions. He had a better head for strategy and more experience than Hayter or Gibson in observing the tactics of politicians in committee meetings. After they had been laboring for weeks in preparing a defense of denial, Hewer argued stoutly one night for a strategy of admission and justification. A flat denial of facts, he urged, would arouse the suspicions and the anger of the Parliament. Its members were convinced that money had been misspent. Their only convincing argument, Hewer went on, was to admit that short cuts had been taken, irregularities observed, but only for the reason that the work had to be done without adequate money. The tide did not wait on the humors of goldsmiths.

Samuel thought about Hewer's suggestion overnight. It was a

clever and honest position to take, one that would appeal to the Parliament because of its humility. The only trouble was that the admission of irregularity depended on his ability to use the justification of no money. The justification could be taken as an attack upon the Crown, whose responsibility it was to furnish the money that the Parliament had voted. He would have to have high approval to make the charge. He could not visualize himself appearing before the Council with a petition to accuse it of irresponsibility.

But after a sleepless night he had the sudden inspiration of going directly to the King. He *could* visualize himself before the King, laying his problems at his feet, and asking his aid. Whatever faults the King had, and he had many, he was humane. He would be sympathetic to the problems of a simple, care-worn servant.

Samuel went to Whitehall. He asked for a word with the King and was immediately summoned into His Majesty's private chambers. Not only was King Charles inherently sympathetic, he was also available—too available, some of his critics maintained. In a matter of five minutes, Mr. Pepys of the Navy Office was in the King's presence and explaining in detail the nature of his problem. Could he, he humbly asked his Sovereign, tell the commission of the Parliament that most of his Office's difficulties came from want of money?

The King smiled cheerfully at the Clerk of Acts' worried countenance. "Why, of course, Mr. Pepys. It is the truth. God-fearing men need not be troubled to tell the truth."

Samuel started at the words. Somehow he had not expected such old-fashioned piety from the witty King. Charles Stuart was too complicated a man for his understanding. He kissed His Majesty's hand and hurried back to Seething Lane. Now he was free to work out his strategy.

When the Parliament reassembled in February and the Commission of Accounts organized to begin its hearings, Samuel was almost numb with weariness. His eyes were troubling him sorely. An hour's reading by candlelight after dark would make him feel that his eyes were about to pop out of his head. A new pair of spectacles from the glassmaker in Westminster did not help him at all. He began to have Mr. Hayter read the figures of an account to him while he did his best to understand them without seeing them.

When the Commission sent word to him to deliver all records of accounts, Samuel took them to Westminster and delivered them with relief. He had squeezed every drop of useful knowledge out of the thick books by now. He was weary of them. He and his clerks had pored over them until they almost knew them by heart. At least they had in abstract and in memoranda all that they would need. There only remained to organize the defense into a coherent document.

He spent the mornings dictating to Mr. Hayter, with Gibson and Will Hewer sitting by to check dates, amounts, bills of receipt from their memoranda. Mr. Hayter wrote it all down quickly in shorthand, and then in the afternoon he would copy it out in full script. At night the four would gather again in the study, and Hewer would read the day's work aloud while all of them made notes and corrections. It was slow work, but it was accurate and exact.

When the long document was at last complete, in first draft, Samuel took it to Sir William Coventry. Coventry would be the best critic of its value. He knew the background and he knew the temper of the Commons. Samuel asked Sir William to read it and give him a judgment.

Sir William took two days on it and made a long list of questions and suggestions. He went over the document with Samuel, point by point, explaining his objections to some minor points and offering his advice about a phrase or two. "But," he said, "the narrative is good. It is honest and clear. There are, of course, a thousand handles here for captious men to snatch at if they are of a mind. The important thing is to make a good impression and the details will be overlooked. Much depends on that first impression. Be calm, speak clearly and with quiet confidence. The House loves a confident, quiet speaker and hates a bumbling, sullen one."

"Speak!" Samuel exploded.

"Why, yes, Mr. Pepys. You will be a witness before the House.

The Commission will read your document, but the House of Commons will hear you speak it."

Samuel sank down into his chair. Somehow he had not thought of the document of defense as being a speech. He had heard speakers perform in the crowded little House of Commons, and he had heard them hissed off the floor like actors at the playhouse. He had never in his life made a speech. He had spoken at meetings, hundreds of them, with confidence. But he had been sitting down and talking to a few men about something he knew. He could not make a speech, standing exposed and alone before a hostile audience. He felt suddenly sick and defeated.

He thanked Sir William limply and walked back toward London. He wandered down the Strand and into Fleet Street. The rebuilding of the burned areas was now beginning to show some progress. Wide, straight streets were being staked off where only narrow, crooked lanes had once threaded through the congested shops and houses. He stood on St. Paul's hill and watched the workmen tear down the fire-ruined tower of the old Cathedral. The great stones plummeted down so fast before his eyes that he felt seasick. He walked on quickly down Cheapside to Cornhill where a new cornerstone had been recently laid by the King for the reconstruction of the Royal Exchange. A new London was gradually rebuilding, stronger, more modern. But he was not at all sure that he would be here to live in it when it was done. He might well be up in Huntingdonshire, surrounded by bumpkins, tending his little farm, and remembering the great days. He walked home, wrapped in despondency.

In the last few days before their appearance before the Parliament, the Commissioners and Principal Officers of the Navy Board met daily. Samuel read them his document of defense, explaining the reason for every argument. When they became too captious about details, too sensitive about an admission of a fault, Samuel cut them off. He was too tired to argue, too dispirited to pay attention to their carping. But he won at last their general approval of the document.

Samuel took his clerks home with him and closeted himself with them in his study. He had to digest the whole body of the report. He could not memorize it; he did not trust his memory. He had to digest it, get every argument, every fact, in the right order into his brain, and then trust that the whole defense would come to his mind when he needed it—in the crowded room of the House of Commons.

He worked with the clerks until midnight. Fortunately they knew what they were doing. There were no extra words, no digressions, no interruptions. They took turns, each man presenting the facts that came from his own principal area of knowledge. Samuel lay back with his eyes closed. He held up a finger when he wanted a repetition. He extended his whole hand when he wanted to pause and think about what had been read to him.

The next day he did the same thing, and the next, and the next. On the last day he went over and over the document, reciting it tonelessly in a dull, flat voice, just getting the facts in order, while the clerks made notes or prompted him when he went astray. They kept at it, over and over, until Samuel felt that he was going mad. At midnight the weary clerks went home, saying that they would be at the office as early as Mr. Pepys wanted them. He told them to come at six.

In his own bed Samuel could not sleep. His threshing about in the bed awoke Elizabeth and she put her arms around him. The warmth of her body relaxed him a little and the tightness came out of his brain. This ordeal, he told her, was more than he could face. He had endured the plague, and the fire, and the invasion without too much fear—or so it seemed now—but he did not see how he could bring himself tomorrow to stand before the Commons and defend himself like a criminal in court. This was more than he had counted on when he took the job in the Navy, and now he was sick of it. He was ready to go into the country and live quietly if Elizabeth would go with him.

Elizabeth pulled up his nightshirt and began to rub his back. She was willing to go, she said. She had rather live in Brampton, away from the shops and from good company, than to stay here and see her husband kill himself with worry or blind himself with work. She had rather have a live husband in the country than a dead one in London. They talked in whispers, in broken sentences, in long-accustomed intuitions of communication. By two o'clock Samuel's mind was emptied of its burden and he fell asleep.

At five-thirty Tom Edwards came into the room and laid out his clothes. He awakened Samuel and helped him put on his new suit, the camlet coat with the blue silk breeches. He put on fresh linen, a neckband with lace and new full cuffs. Deb had dressed his wig and Tom had polished his sword the night before. Samuel put them on and looked at himself in the glass. He looked like a ghost, he thought, a well-dressed, respectable ghost.

Hewer and Hayter and Gibson were waiting for him at the office. Samuel made an outline in his own hand, filling in the headings with the key facts as the clerks read them off to him. As soon as Samuel finished a page, Mr. Hayter made a clean and legible copy of it on good stiff paper which he had cut down to pocket size so Mr. Pepys could hold his notes in his hand easily.

By nine o'clock the notes were all ready. Hewer bound them together into a neat sheaf and put them into his own pocket. They would be ready when Samuel needed them. Samuel told Mr. Gibson good-by, and with a tremor in his voice the old man said that he would be praying for success. And then with Will and Mr. Hayter on either side of him, Samuel walked down to Tower Wharf to get a boat for Westminster.

The trip up the river made his stomach queasy. The irregular motion of the boat churned his empty stomach and a cold sweat popped out on his forehead. He swallowed hard and took deep breaths of air.

When he arrived at the Privy Garden stairs, he sent Will and Mr. Hayter on ahead to the Hall to notify his colleagues that he was on the way. He needed a stop at a tavern. He went to the Dog in King Street and ordered a pint of mulled sack. He sipped it slowly so that the drink would not take him too quickly, and the warmth of the dry wine spread through his body and gradually settled his stomach. Feeling a little better, he walked on slowly up King Street toward Westminster Hall.

A crowd filled New Palace Yard. There was unusual excitement in the air. Clerks and members of the House hurried by in whispered conference. Messengers ran back and forth. Coaches hurried up to the door of the Hall and discharged their passengers. This was the characteristic stir that marked special days in the Parliament: a trial in the House of Lords, a bitter debate in the

Commons. For a moment Samuel felt the old thrill, the excitement of getting a place to watch the proceedings. And then it struck him—*he* was the cause of the stir; *his* speech was the proceeding. His breath stopped and the sweat popped out again on his brow. He hurried on into the Hall and ran to the first spirit stall he could find, ordered a dram of brandy, and tossed it down at a gulp. He leaned back against the wall and watched the milling crowd hurrying toward the chamber of the Commons. His breath began to come more easily and his heart settled down to a normal beat. A surge of peace and indifference took charge of him. He walked up the stairs to the Chapel of St. Stephen, where the Commons met, and joined his colleagues.

Will Hewer was there to give him his notes, which Samuel slipped into his pocket without a glance. All the Board were present, looking stiff and tense, except Penn, who as a Member was already in the House sitting with the Commons on the green baize benches. Everyone gave a formal greeting to Samuel and then the conversation died. They stood about singly and in pairs, abstracted, remote.

They waited for half an hour, in strained silence, until the door of the House opened and the Serjeant-at-Arms, in his robes of office and bearing the Speaker's mace before him, came out and announced in a strange formal voice that the House was now ready for the Commissioners and the Principal Officers of His Majesty's Navy to present themselves. Leading the way, he guided six gentlemen into the crowded, stifling room. They lined up before the long tables of the Clerks of the House and faced the Speaker, Sir Robert Brooks, sitting above them in his canopied chair. The Serjeant-at-Arms announced the identity of the strangers he had admitted, placed the mace in the two hooks at the end of the table and took his seat in a chair at the farther end of the chamber. The gentlemen of the Navy Office bowed to the Speaker and waited. Samuel could feel the stares of the Members at his back boring into him, but he kept his eyes fixed firmly on the Speaker. Sir Robert took his time, letting the House settle itself for a moment and then he began to speak, quietly and precisely, explaining to the Commissioners and Principal Officers that the House had felt a growing dissatisfaction with the conduct of the

Board as it was reported to them by the Commissioners of Accounts, and the House had thought it only fair to themselves and to the gentlemen of the Navy Board to invite the gentlemen to present themselves to the House and give them opportunity to say whatever they cared to say in their own defense. Samuel and his colleagues bowed again to the Speaker and stood perfectly still in their places while one of the three Clerks of the House read the Commission's charges.

Samuel knew the charges before the clerk read them. He could have written them himself—the tardiness of supply ships in making rendezvous with the fleet, the bad morale of the seamen by reason of their being paid by ticket, the poor coordination between the fleet and the services of supply, and so on. Samuel's mind ticked them off as the clerk read them in his stilted voice.

When the clerk had finished, Sir Robert paused a minute and then said that the Board might have as much time as it desired in answering the charges. He looked straight at Samuel.

Samuel bowed to the Speaker, took his notes from his pocket, and turned to face the Members. He made himself take his time. He looked at his notes for a minute and then raised his head and looked around the room. It was not easy, this sweep of his eyes around the tightly packed room, the bank of faces rising up to the right and to the left in the narrow, long chamber. He saw no face that he knew. They were all anonymous and hostile. He did not let his mind think about them. He was fixed on getting the phrasing of his first sentence just right. He licked his lips and began.

The nature and details of the charges of the Commission, he told them, were not unfamiliar to him. They were the charges that he and his fellow members of the Board had anticipated, and they were grateful to the House for giving them the privilege of discussing the charges with the honorable Members. The Navy Board, he went on, shared the grief of the House at the failure of the fleet to perform at the peak of its potential in the engagements of the previous summer. His Majesty's servants at the Navy Office had searched their hearts and their office records to discover wherein they had failed or to what degree they had failed. It was now his responsibility as Clerk of the Acts, and as spokesman for the Board, to explain, if he could, the nature of their duties and to describe, if he could, the conditions under which they had performed their duties.

Samuel spoke his words slowly and thoughtfully, as they came to his mind. He did not have to raise his voice. The room, because it was small, and because the Members sat close, had an atmosphere of intimacy that discouraged oratory. The Members sat quiet, listening intently. Samuel felt a growing satisfaction that so many were listening so attentively to what he had to say. He moved easily into the body of his argument, glancing only occasionally at the notes in his hand. The facts he and his clerks had so laboriously assembled came into his mind as he needed them: dates, names of ships, names of officers, amounts of contracts. He talked on patiently, explaining his points as he would have at a conference or a Board meeting.

Gradually the faces of the Members disappeared. Before him was only a clear picture of three years' work, orderly and conclusive. Subconsciously he became aware that he was enjoying himself. This was power. This was the realization of one's self, one's identity. He talked on, oblivious of everything but the completely fascinating details of the work of his office.

When he had finally finished, he thanked the House for its kind attention and turned around and bowed to the Speaker.

Sir Robert Brooks thanked Mr. Pepys for his clear and interesting narrative, nodded to the Serjeant-at-Arms, and dismissed the witnesses. As they filed out of the room and the chamber filled with a sudden noise, Samuel looked at his watch. It was half-past one o'clock. He had spoken *for three hours*. He could not believe it; it had not seemed that long. It had seemed more like half an hour, or an hour at the most. And then he became aware of something else. The sudden noise that had filled the House as they had filed out was applause. The House was applauding. Great God Almighty! They were *applauding!*

As soon as the little file of men were back in the lobby and the Serjeant-at-Arms had closed the door, his colleagues fell upon him. Lord Brouncker pounded him upon the back and swore that he did not know Mr. Pepys was capable of so great a speech. Penn came running from his place in the House and pumped Samuel's hand until his arm ached. Minnes just looked at him and let the tears of joy flow down his face, and Middleton rushed down to the spirit stall to get a bottle to drink the health of the Clerk of Acts. They rushed him away from the Hall to Lord Brouncker's house in Covent Garden where they could drink and shout to their hearts' content, without fear of disturbing the peace of Westminster.

No one thought of sending to the House to hear their decision. They knew they had won. Penn said that he had sat in the House too long not to know how to interpret its reactions. When it applauded a man, he had won. "Mr. Pepys has saved the Office," Penn shouted, and they boosted Samuel to the top of one of Lord Brouncker's finest tables and thrust a bottle into his hand. "Drink, Mr. Pepys, drink it to the bottom. You have earned a debauch."

Samuel turned the bottle up to his lips and let the wine flow. The good claret poured into his mouth faster than he could swallow. It poured down his chin and onto his fine camlet coat, soaking it. Samuel came up once for air, and then turned the bottle up again and did not take it down until it was empty and the contents of the bottle drained down his gullet and onto his coat and lace neckband.

An hour later the ecstatic brothers of the Navy Office roared out of the house and across the square into the Theatre Royal. They arrived in time to give a resounding hiss to the surprised actors who were just taking their bows at the end of the first interval. They commanded two coaches in Drury Lane and rushed their hero through the City and deposited him in triumph at the door of his house in Seething Lane.

Elizabeth and Will Hewer were waiting for him at the entry. They helped him up the stairs and guided him to the parlor. Mr. Hayter and Mr. Gibson, Tom Edwards and Deb Willet, Jane and all the maids were there waiting for him. Samuel held on firmly to the back of a chair and thanked them for the help that all of them had been in his time of trouble. He thought he had saved them, he said thickly, and he hoped that they would all be able thereafter to live in peace and content with each other and with the world. He patted Mr. Hayter and Mr. Gibson fondly on the cheek. He kissed Deb and Jane and each of the maids soundly on the mouth. And when they had all gone, except Elizabeth and Will Hewer, the strength went out of him and he collapsed on the sofa. Will picked him up and carried him into the bedroom and put him on the bed. Elizabeth undressed him and covered him with a blanket. While they sat on either side of him, holding him close, he released his pent-up feeling and sobbed uncontrollably.

He slept hard all the rest of the afternoon and all the night, the deepest sleep he had known in months. Elizabeth woke him at seven and helped him dress in clean clothes. It was fit, she told him, that he should go back to Westminster and hear the good things being said of his speech. She and Deb would go to Charing Cross and see what was being said in the shops. Samuel agreed readily. He did want to hear what was being said. Yesterday seemed like a dream now. He wanted to know that it was real.

When he arrived at Westminster, he went first to see Sir William Coventry. He could count on Coventry for the truth. Sir William greeted him with a deep bow. "Good-morrow, Mr. Pepys, that must be Speaker of the Parliament house," he said elaborately and in high good humor. "This is the same Mr. Pepys that was afraid to make a speech?"

"One does what he has to," Samuel passed it off lightly. "But what of the vote?"

"There was no vote. The vote was postponed, but that is only prelude to victory. The Navy Office is safe, at least from the Parliament."

Sir William went on to discuss the speech. He had heard one Member say, after the speech, that Mr. Pepys could earn not less than £1,000 a year if he would put on a gown and plead at the Chancery bar, and the Solicitor General himself, Sir Heneage Finch, had protested in public that Mr. Pepys spoke the best of any man in England.

"So come now, Mr. Speaker, let us go to the Duke and claim your triumph," Sir William concluded and opened the door for them to go to the Palace.

They found the Duke just leaving his lodgings to go into the Park to enjoy the fine morning air. The Duke, when he saw Samuel, stopped his whole entourage and held out his hand. "See what comes of diligence and loyalty," he announced loudly to the courtiers around him. "Mr. Pepys has single-handed converted the whole Parliament. The Bishops should offer him a mitre—if the Navy could spare him. But go and see the King, Mr. Pepys. He has good words for you."

The Duke put his hand on Samuel's uncovered head and tapped him twice. It was almost like being knighted, Samuel felt.

The King was sitting in the Park, beside Rosamond's Pond, tossing crumbs to the swans and placing wagers with the ladies-in-waiting on which of the lovely birds was the greediest and most agile in snatching the royal favors. When Sir William and Samuel came up and made their obeisance, the King turned his back on the water and looked up gaily.

"Mr. Pepys," he said, "I am very glad of your success yesterday and I can think of others who share my joy. One Gentleman of the Bedchamber swore to me this morning that you might teach the Solicitor General. Well, teach him, Mr. Pepys, if you care to, but save most of your energies for the Navy. The Navy needs you more than the Solicitor does."

XVIII

My wife was struck mute

THE GLOW OF HIS TRIUMPH in the House of Commons lasted Samuel throughout the rest of the spring. Whenever he went in the weeks that followed, he heard his name mentioned with praise, in the taverns in King Street, in the Royal Exchange, in the theaters in Covent Garden and Lincoln's Inn Fields. Mr. Pepys's name seemed to have become synonymous with the Navy and the Navy's name gradually became less and less a synonym for failure. The Commissioners of Account desisted from bringing in a vote of censure, and the Parliament voted the King £300,000 to put the realm in a proper state of defense.

The savor of the triumph in the House was not to last indefinitely, however. The Duke of Buckingham was too clever to be put aside by a temporary victory of the Duke of York's servants. If the Navy Office was blameless on one count, it was not blameless in all. There had been error and mismanagement and defeat. Samuel very soon heard reliable rumors that Buckingham was preparing to launch a bill of reform upon the Navy that would in reality be a condemnation of the organization of the Navy as it now existed. Samuel was alarmed. Reform was needed, to be sure, but not the kind of reform the Duke of Buckingham had in mind. He asked for a conference with the Duke of York.

His Grace received Samuel in his bedchamber and dismissed all his attendants except Mr. Wren. Samuel came right to the point. Did His Grace share the Duke of Buckingham's desire to write new rules for the Navy Office?

"Not at all," the Lord Admiral answered sharply. "The present rules are adequate. They were written by Navy men who knew the needs of the service. If there is fault, it is only in the proper administration of prevailing regulations."

"That is what I have come about," Samuel said. And he proceeded to reveal his mind to the Duke. He took an hour, going into detail about the looseness of the administration of the Pay Office, the lack of liaison between the Comptroller and the Surveyor, the inadequacy of the reports of the yardmasters. The Duke listened intently while Mr. Wren made notes. When he was through with his analysis of the faults of the Office, Samuel made a suggestion. He suggested that the Lord Admiral write a general letter to the Navy Office asking every officer and commissioner to give an explicit accounting of his duties and his procedure in executing those duties.

The Duke nodded his head. "Write the letter you think necessary, Mr. Pepys, and give it to Mr. Wren. I will send it under my own hand."

"My name will not be mentioned," Samuel suggested.

"Your name will not be mentioned," the Duke assured him.

Samuel spent two days on the letter, writing it out in his own hand, the drafts and the clean copy. He sealed it and sent it by Will Hewer to Mr. Wren. Then he settled down to wait. There would be explosions. His honeymoon with his colleagues would be over. They would suspect him, although they could not be sure. He was willing. It was better to beat Buckingham to the draw and save the Office from the hands of the politicians than to luxuriate in the doubtful pleasure of office popularity.

While he waited, he turned his attention to the comfort of his own house. He bought new draperies, new furniture, and a new dinner service. He gave Elizabeth money to buy a new pearl necklace and reckoned that she now owned about £150 in jewels.

Word came from Brampton that the marriage negotiations between the Pepyses and Mr. John Jackson as husband for Pall were completed, and Samuel arranged for Elizabeth and Deb to go to the country and help with the wedding. He went down to the cellar and fetched up a hundred pounds in silver for Elizabeth to take with her as an extra and surprise addition to Pall's dowry. She would now go into her marriage with a highly respectable value of £600. Mr. Jackson had a good farm and a good house at Buckden, only two miles from Brampton, convenient for Pall to look in upon her father. Samuel had had an interview with Mr.

Jackson and had approved of him. He was a stolid fellow, not much given to conversation, but a worthy, honest man. He was just the phlegmatic sort for Pall, and Pall was lucky to get him. He sent Elizabeth and Deb off with instructions to see that the wedding was handsome and a credit to the family.

While his wife was away, Samuel worked hard every morning with his clerks, getting his own department in shape for an accounting to the Duke. But in the afternoon and the evening he sought the pleasures of the town. The theater became again his baiting place. He went to the Theatre Royal with Lord Brouncker and with Penn or with anyone else who was worth an afternoon's pleasure at the playhouse. But principally he went alone, slipping off from the office at dinner time, getting a bite to eat at a tavern in Covent Garden, and then going into the playhouse in ample time to get a good seat in the pit. He went backstage frequently to see Mrs. Knepp and to look at Nell Gwyn and the other girls in their undress. After the play he would take Knepp to supper, or to the Tower to show her the Crown jewels, or out to Islington or Kensington to enjoy the night air.

In the coach when it was dark, Knepp would sit on his lap and sing naughty little songs into his ear so that the coachman could not hear. Samuel took a few liberties with her while she sat on his lap, and she did not mind, apparently. She neither encouraged him nor discouraged him. He was afraid, however, to press his luck too far.

One night, when he was at the Pierces, Knepp came in from the theater with a bad headache. Mrs. Pierce made her a pallet on the floor so that she could lie down and ease her head while she enjoyed the gaiety of the company. Samuel sat down beside her on the floor and sang her a naughty song he had learned at Whitehall that afternoon. Knepp asked him to rub her temples to take the tightness out of her head. When the rest of the company went into the dining room to eat supper, Samuel stayed with Knepp and extended his rubbing to the base of her neck and down her back. In a little while Samuel was lying down beside her and taking liberties that he had not intended or, before this, dared.

When he heard the company returning, he jumped to his feet; and at the first opportunity he said good night and made a confused departure. He had frightened himself. Knepp existed in another world, a world that charmed and fascinated him, but a world that he did not trust. He knew that Elizabeth was already vaguely jealous of both Mrs. Pierce and Mrs. Knepp. It would not do to give either of those doubtful women an opportunity to make witty allusions in Elizabeth's presence. He decided to stay clear of Mrs. Knepp for the rest of the summer, or until Elizabeth returned.

He went back to work with his clerks, getting supplies out to the summer fleet, making contracts, and reading a great deal in the records of the Navy Office during the Commonwealth. Much could be learned from the regulations and procedures of those incorruptible old Roundheads. He read all afternoon in his office and at night alone in his study by candlelight until his eyes rebelled at the punishment. He needed a visit to Dr. Turberville.

Dr. Daubigny Turberville had recently set up shop in Westminster after having acquired a considerable reputation as an oculist in Salisbury. He was an Oxford man, a cautious physician who considered the eye as an interrelated organ of the body and not an extra appendage to be supported by ingenious devices. Turberville, like most of his contemporaries, believed in physic as the beginning of all remedy. But he also believed in thorough knowledge of his patient.

When Samuel called upon him, Dr. Turberville first of all took down a careful history of Samuel's whole physical life. He quizzed him closely about his old operation for the stone, the performance of his bladder, the habits of his bowels. He turned back the lids of Samuel's eyes and examined the balls. The best cure, he told Samuel when he was finished, was rest. When Samuel protested that he could not rest his eyes, not now, the doctor said that in that case he would proceed with other indicated remedies. He gave Samuel a strong purge, four pills to be taken at a time. He gave him drops to be put in his eyes every night before he went to bed. Finally he bled him—14 ounces. "Now," he said, "we have done what man can do. Nature must help, and you must help. Use your eyes no more than you have to, especially avoid reading by candlelight. Nature did not intend man to read after dark.

The moon would be brighter if God intended man to read at night."

Samuel left the doctor's shop in deep depression. What the doctor had been telling him was perfectly clear. He might lose his sight entirely. And then what use would the Navy have for a blind Clerk of the Acts? He would have to give up his job and go to live in Brampton in retirement, in blindness. Samuel shuddered at the thought and went home in bitter gloom.

He decided that night to take a holiday. He could not stay at the office and not read. He would need to get away from books and papers and dispatches for a while, until his eyes grew stronger. The next day he stayed at home to take his purge and make his plans. Elizabeth had stayed on at Brampton after Pall's wedding to enjoy the country air for a while. He and Will would ride to Brampton and bring her home a roundabout way. They would hire a coach and return by way of Oxford, Salisbury, Bath, and the western counties. He had never seen that country, and Elizabeth had not seen it since her childhood.

Samuel stayed in Brampton only long enough to pay his respects to the newly married couple. Mr. Jackson was taciturn as usual but Pall, Samuel thought, already showed signs of contented pertness. He hoped that she would soon show signs of being with child and bear him a nephew. He would enjoy the role of uncle.

Will Hewer stopped off in Cambridge to arrange for a coach and driver. On Monday, June 8, Will and the coach arrived at Brampton and the party set off at once on their journey—Samuel, Elizabeth, Deb, and Will. They drove south and west and arrived in Oxford in time for dinner next day. Samuel paid a shilling to see Friar Bacon's study and ate strawberries for dinner. He jotted down in his notes that Oxford was "a mighty fine place; and well seated, and cheap entertainment."

On Wednesday they drove across the Salisbury plains at nightfall, the great steeple of the Cathedral looming large and beautiful in the twilight. They spent all the next day viewing the Cathedral and driving out to look at the mysterious stones of Stonehenge. Samuel conceded that the Cathedral was lovelier than Westminster Abbey, but of the strange stones on the plain he could make nothing at all. "God knows what their use was!"

On Friday morning they drove westward to Bath, through Somersetshire, where Elizabeth and Deb became excited because they had both been reared in the west. Samuel stopped at Breking-ton and paid a little boy a shilling to say the Lord's Prayer in *Zummerzet* dialect. Deb was so touched that she cried and gave the child a kiss.

They spent the weekend in Bath, taking the baths and drinking the unpalatable waters. Samuel hoped they might help his eyes, although he did not really think they would. He was much impressed with Bath, its good stone houses and general cleanliness; but he felt that it could not be very sanitary for so many people to bathe in the same water. He took a dim view of bathing anyway. He was convinced that it was dangerous to submit the body to the shock of full exposure to the air, but in Bath he did as the Romans had done and took a bath. He sat in the hot water for an hour and then was carried home in a Bath chair, well-wrapped in a sheet. He stayed in bed for two hours and sweated profusely. He had to admit, after it was over, that he did feel remarkably fresh and relaxed, but he could not see that it had done his eyes any good.

They drove over to Bristol on Sunday and visited with Deb's uncle, a hearty, respectable man, who showed them all the sights of the old town, including Marsh Street where Deb had been born. Samuel noted that Deb's uncle was "like one of our sober, wealthy London merchants." That was enough to endear him to Samuel and to raise Deb's standing in the family even higher.

On Monday they set out for London through Wiltshire, Berkshire, and Buckinghamshire. They broke their journey at Reading, and it was here that the reaction began to set in. Either they were all enervated from so much bathing or they had grown weary of each other's company in the narrow coach or the satiated gloom that usually comes with the end of a holiday had taken them. Deb had her mind on her childhood in Bristol. Elizabeth brooded darkly upon a casual reference that Samuel had made to Mrs. Pierce, his eating dinner with her while she was away. Samuel fretted about the careless way in which Elizabeth did everything, forgetting her fan and making him go back to fetch it, breaking into a conversation to say something foolish and irrelevant. Will

Hewer talked and joked, trying to keep their spirits up, until Samuel told him to be quiet and give their ears a rest.

The day after they got home, Elizabeth put on a good town dress and paid a call on Mrs. Pierce. That night she was very quiet at supper, saying almost nothing throughout the meal, and when she went to bed it was into Deb's room she went and there she slept all night.

The next afternoon she and Deb went together to the Theatre Royal. When Samuel got home from Whitehall, they had not returned from the playhouse, and he was puzzled about their going without saying a word to him. He asked Elizabeth about it when she came in at six o'clock. She had as much right to go to the playhouse without him, she snapped, as he had to go without her. Samuel retorted that she was a fool to prate about her "rights." They did not speak to each other the rest of the evening; but when they had finished their supper, Elizabeth went straight to bed—Samuel's bed this time.

Samuel walked up and down on the leads for a while, wondering whether Elizabeth had been to Drury Lane to spy on him. Something was afoot, Samuel knew; but he decided that it was best to hold his peace and see what Elizabeth's strange mind was hatching.

Whatever it was, she seemed to be sleeping on it when Samuel went to bed. He undressed quietly and slipped into bed without disturbing her. He did not care to have his night's sleep lost by a scene with Elizabeth.

He had just gotten into his first sound sleep when Elizabeth awakened him by shaking his shoulder. She was sitting up rigid in bed, looking fixedly into the dark. She had a request to make, she announced. She wanted permission to go into France, with her father, and live there out of trouble, away from a husband who did not love her.

"What did you say?" Samuel asked, confused and unbelieving.

"I want to go to France."

"Why?"

"To live. To leave you in peace to come and go as you like, without having to bother with a wife. I am only an anchor to you. You had rather have your freedom to go to plays and dine with hussies. You love pleasure more than you love a wife. As soon as I am out of town, you take yourself off dining and play-going with bitches like Mrs. Pierce and Mrs. Knepp. I will get out of your way and you can go ahead and live like the whoring dog you are."

Samuel lay back upon the pillows and looked at her. So that was it. She had heard he had dined at the Pierces and gone to the theater while Knepp was acting. What else had she heard? He could not be sure. Mrs. Pierce could not have been such a fool as to tell what she knew. This was only general jealousy, he hoped. It was best to let it pass.

"If you have a desire for France," he said quietly, "we will go to France, together, next summer."

Elizabeth looked at him sharply. "You did not listen," she said.

"I listened. I heard you speak in anger. I heard you berate me for taking pleasure without you. You know I must have some pleasure to make my work bearable, but you must trust me that my pleasure does you no injury. There would be no pleasure for me at all without you. You must not speak or think of that again. We will go to France next summer."

Elizabeth got up and walked about the room, saying nothing. When she came near the bed again, Samuel took her hand and drew her down onto the bed. He kissed her arm and smiled at her. Elizabeth scowled at him, but yielded to his pressure and got back under the covers.

Samuel was careful thereafter to give her more of his time in the afternoons. They went together to the playhouse, Samuel making it a point to find an excuse to attend the theater in Lincoln's Inn Fields rather than the Theatre Royal in Drury Lane. He wanted no chance meeting with Knepp. They visited Vauxhall and drove out to Islington. Elizabeth seemed to enjoy the attention; she said nothing further about going to France, but Samuel felt that they were living under a guarded peace.

The Duke's letter finally came to the Office late in August. It was basically the same letter that Samuel had drafted for His Grace, requiring that every commissioner and principal officer of the Navy Board make an explicit accounting of his stewardship. The members read the letter in amazement. What did the Duke have in mind, calling them all so suddenly to account? Samuel suggested that whatever the cause, they had all better make an answer, promptly and honestly. It was better to have a critical letter from the Duke of York than a summons from the Duke of Buckingham. The officers breathed hard and called their clerks. This was a funny business, they muttered, and looked quizzically at Samuel.

Samuel kept in close touch with Mr. Wren and read the answers of his colleagues as they came in, Penn's, Brouncker's, Minnes's, Lord Anglesey's. Some of them slipped in hints of dissatisfaction about Mr. Pepys, and Lord Anglesey suggested that the records of the Clerk of the Acts should be examined; but Samuel and Mr. Wren only smiled and made abstracts of the replies. Only when all the members had submitted their statements did Samuel, with painstaking care, write out his own reply. Mr. Wren protested that it was not necessary for Mr. Pepys to file an answer, but Samuel insisted that the record should be complete. He filed his answer with the others.

He and Mr. Wren worked for a fortnight, collating the answers. He took down an abstract of all of them and visited Sir William Coventry. He wanted the former Secretary to see if anything had been overlooked or unfairly stated. Sir William could find no fault. "This should do it," he said. "This is the proper road to reform. There is danger in it, however, Mr. Pepys. There is much admission of error here."

Samuel shrugged. "There is no alternative," he said. "And I am getting used to danger now. The worst that can happen is dismissal, and no man should serve a prince who cannot face dismissal." Samuel was pleased to recall Sir William's own words about retirement and to be able to paraphrase them to him.

By the end of September the Duke acted. He summoned Samuel to the office of the Admiralty and asked him to prepare a detailed recommendation for the improvement of the operation of the Navy Board. Samuel bowed gravely to the Duke and said that he would be happy to accept the charge.

Word of Samuel's new responsibility—and new power—beat him back to Seething Lane. Lord Brouncker offered his aid in writing the new regulations. Samuel thanked him and said that he would call upon him. Sir William Penn became very neighborly and jolly. He sent Samuel a quarter of venison to make his Sunday dinner. Samuel thanked him and invited him to come after church and help them eat it.

This was delicate business and Samuel had no desire to upset his colleagues. He and his clerks reestablished the old teamwork that had held them together so well during the preparation for his defense. They read to him to save his eyes, and he dictated to Hayter while Hewer and Gibson made abstracts and took notes. He saved his eyes as much as he could, but the work strained them and made them weep with fatigue. He tried an experiment of reading through paper tubes. Elizabeth and Deb made them for him, but the tubes were awkward and not very helpful.

On the last Sunday in the month, he went with Elizabeth and Deb to church to include his thanks in the regular prayers of service. Samuel and Elizabeth enjoyed sitting in the Navy's private gallery in St. Olave's and looking down upon the familiar heads of the parish. It was usual for the wardens of the church to look up at the Navy gallery and bow before they took their seats in the front pews. Samuel noticed now that word had gone abroad that he was the leading spirit of the Office, most of the parishioners of St. Olave's found occasion to bow to the Pepyses before they seated themselves. It was a quiet honor, not easily won, and Samuel was very proud of it. It was for this respectful homage, rather than Mr. Milles's tedious sermon, that Samuel went so often to St. Olave's on Sunday morning.

After the sermon and a good dinner of a hot shoulder of mutton and a lamprey pie, Samuel retired to his study and spent the afternoon listening to Elizabeth and Tom Edwards read to him his first draft of the bill of reform. It was good. There was much work yet to be done on it, but it was good.

Samuel did not go directly up to bed after supper. He stayed on in the kitchen and had Deb comb his head. Samuel did not keep his head shaved. He kept it cropped close so that his wig would fit snug, but he had found it healthier to keep a natural cap of his own hair growing on his scalp. But it was troublesome. The hair tangled badly after a week of enclosure under the wig, his scalp itched, and sometimes nits infested his head. He always had one of the maids comb him on Sunday night, but he preferred to have Deb serve as his barber. She was careful and conscientious. She was also the best company in the house.

While Deb ran the comb through his hair, Samuel chatted with her about their trip through the western country. He asked her questions about her Bristol uncle, his business, his affairs. He quizzed her about her life in Marsh Street when she was a child. Deb answered gravely, as she always did, telling him of little incidents in her childhood, her grief at the cruel death of a puppy she loved. The more she recalled of her life on Marsh Street, the more readily she talked, without Samuel having to prompt her with questions. When she had finished dressing Samuel's head, she came around and sat down on the floor beside him and let the flow of her homesick recollections pour out. She laughed, and Samuel laughed with her, at the mistakes she had made in trying to talk with the grown people of the neighborhood, using long, incorrect words so they would think she understood the adult conversation. She told of the lessons her mother had given her in cooking, and how she had burned her fingers (she still had the scars) when she had tried to lift a boiling pot from the fire without using a cloth. Samuel looked at the faint scars on the three middle fingers of her right hand and kissed them. Tears came into Deb's eyes and she said that he reminded her of her father, the way he had treated her when he once caught her in a lie. He had beat her across the palms of her hands with a switch, and then he had cried and kissed her hands until his tears wet her palms.

Deb cried too at the memory of it, and Samuel took her upon his lap to comfort her in this burst of homesickness. He put his arms around her and smiled down at her lovely, tear-wet face. He brushed the hair from her face and touched her lips with his fingers. In an outburst of gratitude, Deb threw her arms around his neck and kissed him passionately upon the lips.

And at this moment Elizabeth walked into the room.

She stood there perfectly still, struck mute. Samuel released the girl and stood up. Deb looked at Elizabeth and then at Samuel, as if not quite able to understand what was happening. Elizabeth did not say anything. A strange guttural sound came from her throat and she clapped her hand to her mouth as if to stifle the

330

ugly sound. Then she turned around and walked out of the room, stiffly, unnaturally, like a sleepwalker.

Samuel stood paralyzed by the chair, unable to move or speak. Deb sank upon the floor and buried her head in her lap. Then Samuel, as if rousing from a dream, sprang toward the door and rushed up the stairs. Deb remained on the floor, weeping like a deserted child.

Up in their bedroom Elizabeth lay on the bed, on top of the bedclothes, staring at the ceiling, expressionless. Samuel was afraid to approach her or to speak to her. He sat down in a chair by the chimney and kept his eyes on her fearfully. The little light from the embers of the fire gave the only light in the room. It flickered and threw darting serpents of shadow across the floor. The only sound was the occasional fall of a coal in the fireplace. Samuel could not even hear Elizabeth breathing. She lay perfectly motionless like one petrified. And Samuel sat in the chair, unmoving, while the fire burned out, slowly, and Samuel's head gradually relaxed against the hard back of the chair.

He must have slept, for he was suddenly startled by a fierce whisper in his ear. "I have received the Holy Sacrament," the strange voice whispered. "I have received the Holy Sacrament."

Samuel jumped to his feet and stared. It was Elizabeth, on her knees beside his chair in her nightdress, her hair unbound and falling across her face. She looked like a ghost.

Samuel quickly lighted a candle, his hands shaking so that he could hardly light the wick. He held the candle close to Elizabeth's face, to see if she were mad.

"I am a Catholic," she whispered, still on her knees. "I am not what you think me." She made the sign of the cross and then rose to her feet and went back to the bed. She got under the covers and returned to her former attitude of looking fixedly at the ceiling.

Samuel went to the side of the bed and kneeled down beside her. He wanted her to look at him, to give some sign that she knew he was there. But she did not look, and Samuel sat there pleading in the silence for one word to grasp and use as a cord of communication.

But Elizabeth said nothing; the candle burned out, and Samuel slipped from his knees to sit on the floor and keep dreadful vigil until the first light of dawn came into the room. Then he got up and went out of the house.

At the office during the morning he moved through his chores like an automaton. He spoke to no one and heard nothing that anyone said to him. His clerks looked at him and at each other, but they said nothing. Mr. Pepys was a man of moods. The Clerk of the Acts was concerned with his bill of reform. They kept their counsel and protected their master from visitors.

At dinner Elizabeth sat at the table encased in granite. The fierce light had gone out of her eyes and had been replaced by lead. This was not sullenness or petulance. This was paralysis. Samuel could not face it. He made a few efforts to swallow a mouthful of whatever it was on his plate, and then he left the table and the house. He wandered through the City, the ruins of the fire, aimlessly, willingly lost.

It was dark when he returned to Seething Lane. He went straight to his bedroom and fell into bed. There was no sign of Elizabeth—or of Deb. He wondered for a moment, before sleep overtook him, what had become of Deb. She was probably exiled in her room, imprisoned in her own grief.

He awoke in terror some hours later to hear violent screaming right beside him. It was Elizabeth, standing over him, her face contorted, and a sluice of words, foul and horrid, streaming from her mouth.

The dam had burst at last. The girl was a whore, Elizabeth screamed, a damned bitch who had come into the house to seduce her master and violate the bed of her mistress. And he, Samuel, was a false rogue who had not had the decency to keep his sluts away from the house, but had brought them home to shame his wife by flaunting them before her eyes.

Samuel let the words fall, cringing under the lash but welcoming the sting, almost, as penance, not so much for what he had done with Deb, for that had been innocent, but for all his unfaithfulness and for what he truly in his heart lusted to do with Deb. He let the words fall and was grateful that there was no word of the Sacrament or of his wife being a Catholic. That had been only perversity, a means to wound him mortally, to frighten him, to kill him, in a veiled way, without in fact being a murderer. He could only hold his breath and hope that the holocaust would in time burn out, like the great fire that had almost but not quite destroyed the City. He closed his eyes and received the scourge of her words, until the tears came and he could stand no more.

Elizabeth shouted and screamed her curses for an hour, like one possessed of endless strength of will to blast her enemy from his reason. She could not, she *could* not, Samuel gasped to himself, continue so for long. But she did. At last her strength gave out and she fell upon the bed exhausted, sobbing so violently that the bed shook. Samuel, released from his torment, slumped down in the bed and joined her in her sobbing.

They lay so for half an hour, neither speaking nor trying to speak. The sobs gradually subsided. They lay at last quiet and exhausted. Samuel reached out his hand and touched her foot. Elizabeth did not move. Samuel listened and heard her regular breathing. He turned his head and looked. She had fallen asleep. Samuel relaxed and, keeping his hand on her foot, he too finally slept.

Samuel did not go to work the next day. He sent word to the office that he was staying in to take a purge; but what he really did was to stay with Elizabeth in their bedroom all the day, seeking a peace upon any terms that Elizabeth wanted. Jane brought their dinner to them on a tray so they could eat in privacy while they worked out terms of their future accord.

The terms were surrender, complete and total surrender. Samuel would not in the future go abroad without Elizabeth or without an agent of Elizabeth in attendance. He would never go again to the playhouse without her, never dine, never so much as go to church without his wife. He would never again visit Mrs. Pierce or look at Mrs. Knepp. He would devote any time that remained from his work to the entertainment of Elizabeth at home, abroad in the City, on any journey that took him out of London. They would go to France next summer and visit her family's country. They would buy a coach and a pair of good horses so they could ride together in the Park or through the streets like a decent, respectable London family with good connections.

Samuel agreed to all of this, surrendering his sovereignty in his own household, accepting the stigma of being accompanied wherever he went by a bodyguard to protect him from his own weakness. There was nothing else for him to do. He wanted Elizabeth, even as she was, more than he wanted pleasure or independence or freedom.

At only one term did he boggle.

"The girl must go," Elizabeth said. She could not bring herself to use Deb's name. "The girl must go."

"Yes," Samuel said, holding his breath now that this specific cause of the agony had been stated.

"And you must send her," Elizabeth went on relentlessly.

"I will," Samuel agreed quickly, hoping now to hear some word of the injured girl.

"And you will call her a *whore* to her face and tell her that she has lost the right to live with decent people."

"I cannot call her *whore*," Samuel protested, "when she is none."

"The girl is a whore," Elizabeth suddenly screamed, "a whore, a whore."

Samuel grabbed Elizabeth to stop her screaming.

"I will send her away. I will send her away as you wish," Samuel hurried to agree. "Where is she? I will send her away at once."

Elizabeth's screaming stopped at once. "She is locked in her room, safe from you; and you will send her when I tell you." Elizabeth sailed to the door, blooming with her triumph. "And the girl is a whore," she shot back into the room as she went out to take command of her house.

Samuel did not see Deb for four days. He slipped a note under her door, telling her of his situation, praying her forgiveness, and demanding that she burn the note as soon as she had read it. But Elizabeth kept a close eye on every move he made. He dared not try too much to ease his conscience about the unfortunate Deb. Somehow he would find a way, he resolved, to comfort the girl and to avoid having to call her a whore to her face. He could not send Deb away in that horrid manner. He could not, because it was cowardly to do so, and also because he could not forget the experience of holding her in his arms and feeling her lips upon his mouth. He would find a way.

But Elizabeth gave him no choice. When he came home to dinner on the fourth day, Deb was sitting at the table with Elizabeth. Deb was very pale, Samuel noticed in the one brief glance he was able to make before he saw the expression on Elizabeth's face. This was a test, a twist of the knife, Elizabeth was putting upon them, an exhibit of her power to Samuel and a taste of her hatred of Deb.

They sat through the meal in silence, eating without looking at each other and without speaking. Elizabeth kept her eye on Samuel and Samuel kept his eye on his plate. Only Elizabeth, Samuel thought, could think of this punishment, to make them eat together and dare them to look once at each other.

As soon as dinner was over, Elizabeth told Deb to come into the parlor. "Mr. Pepys has a word for you," she said darkly. They all went into the parlor and Samuel and Deb sat on opposite sides of the room, with Elizabeth in between to supervise the dismissal.

Samuel hurried into the words of his dismissal before Elizabeth could prompt him and make the ordeal more excruciating.

"You must go from this house, Deb, and you must never see me again, here or anywhere else. I hope you have repented of your sins as I have mine, and I hope you will try to be a decent, chaste woman hereafter."

Before Samuel could finish his speech, modulated as gently as he could, Deb broke into a sob and ran out of the room before Elizabeth could stop her.

Samuel did not see the girl again for two days, and he could find no means of putting a note under her door. One of the maids stayed on guard outside her door all day, and Elizabeth stayed with Samuel every minute that he was at home.

On the last day of Deb's residence in Seething Lane, Elizabeth rose at dawn and went immediately to Deb's room to see that she was ready to leave. Samuel quickly tore a page from his notebook and wrapped 40 shillings into a tight package. He would try to find some way to slip this token of his sorrow to her. But Elizabeth came back into the room as soon as he had put the package into his pocket.

The girl was ready to go, Elizabeth reported, and Samuel was to stay in the bedroom until the coach had come for her. Samuel started to make an objection, but Elizabeth turned her back on him and took her stand at the window. Samuel sat down in the chair by the chimney and listened to the sounds in the house, to see if he could hear Deb's voice and tell how the girl was taking her disgrace; but he could only hear the feet of the servants moving about in the room below and the voice of Tom Edwards singing in the kitchen.

Finally there was the sound of a coach on the cobbles outside the house, the slam of a door, a chatter of several voices below, the sound of luggage being loaded onto the coach, another door slam, and then the wheels of the coach rattling harshly on the cobbles. Elizabeth kept her place by the window until the sound of the wheels died away; and then she dropped the curtains and walked triumphantly out of the room.

Samuel rushed to the window and looked out into the street. There was no sign of life anywhere. The sun shone brightly on the bare October trees and the bells of St. Olave's rang loud and clear. Samuel stepped back from the window and looked at the mullions that divided the panes. They looked like bars.

He took up his hat and went out of the house to go to the office. If he had lost sovereignty at home, he was still in command at the Navy Office. As he stepped into the garden, Will Hewer showed up from nowhere and walked with him, step for step, in solicitous, embarrassed silence.

XIX

The old freedom and kindneß
of England

SAMUEL PEPYS did not easily accept a prison. There were many hazards in his world which he carefully avoided, being willing to confess himself a coward rather than to take too great a risk. But when his liberty was challenged, his freedom of movement or of thought threatened, he stopped short.

He sent Will Hewer off on an errand to Whitehall and then set about the difficult task of finding Deb. If Elizabeth had decided to be his jailer, he would demonstrate his revolt by locating Deb. Deb had become for him a symbol of his liberty. Also he owed the girl something, some assurance that he was not the hypocrite she must think him, some token of his interest in her welfare and her happiness, which he had, by his stupidity, endangered.

He had only one clue as to where Deb had gone. Elizabeth had been careful to keep him in ignorance of what plans she had for Deb's removal, but she had let slip one piece of information. A Doctor Allbon of Lincoln's Inn Fields had been mentioned.

He spent the day tracing the whereabouts of Dr. Allbon. Samuel did not know anything about the mysterious doctor, what he practiced, or Deb's connection with him. It was a poor clue, but it was all he had. He inquired at every shop and tavern in the neighborhood of Whetstone Park, but for his morning's work he came up with only the uncertain tip that the doctor was a man of broken health and fortune and had moved from his former lodgings to a house in Eagle Court, a dark cul-de-sac off the Strand just opposite Somerset House.

Samuel made his dinner off two pennyworth of oysters in the Strand and tackled Eagle Court. In an hour he learned from a porter that Dr. Allbon had fled these premises also, but the porter refused to give the name of his new lodgings. The doctor was a good man and the porter was not going to give any information to his creditors who were hounding him. Samuel gave the man a half-crown and explained that it was not the doctor he wanted to see but a young girl who had recently come to live with him, a relative of the doctor's apparently.

The porter relaxed a little and said that he would take a note to the girl—if there was a girl—but he would not give the gentleman the address; and the gentleman would have to agree to remain in the company of another porter, a friend of his, so he could be sure he was not followed. Samuel agreed to the arrangement, promised another half-crown when the porter had fulfilled his promise, and scratched off a quick note to Deb. He told her that he must see her and would be outside her lodgings in a dark coach if she would return permission by the messenger. And then he submitted himself to his guard and watched the cautiously obliging porter walk off toward Lincoln's Inn Fields.

It was dark when he returned and gave Samuel Deb's answer. She would be on the lookout for him and would come out to his coach if he waved his hat.

Samuel gave the man his other half-crown, found a coach, and set off for his assignation. He felt very adventurous. He drew his cloak close about his face, not so much because the coachman might recognize him but because he felt that it was the proper thing to do if you rode to an assignation in a dark coach.

Deb was waiting for him, standing on the stoop of the sorry tenement in which she now lived with the unhappy Doctor Allbon and his family. She came out at once, as soon as he had waved his hat twice, and got into the coach with him. Samuel enveloped her in his cloak and comforted her while she cried. She would never recover, she sobbed, from the humiliation that she had undergone at Seething Lane. She did not blame Samuel; she knew how it was with him. There was nothing else that he could have done under the circumstances. But she did wish that she had never gone to

338

Seething Lane, or had not been so unfortunate as she had been in being surprised by Mrs. Pepys.

Samuel kissed her gratefully. He had no reason to expect her to be so generous. He gave her 20 shillings and told her that she could reach him any time she needed help by leaving a note for him at Mr. Herringman's bookshop in the New Exchange. She had only to call him and he would help her all he could. Before he kissed her good-by, he advised her to be careful of her honor. She must find a good husband who would love her as she deserved to be loved. In the meantime she should be careful of the men she trusted. Not every man would value her honor as he did.

But on the ride back to Seething Lane, he could not suppress the vision he had of getting the girl to bed.

When he got home Will Hewer was waiting for him in the entry full of distress. He was too upset to say anything. He only pointed up the stairs and held his head in anguish. Samuel walked up to see what reception Elizabeth had prepared for him. He was determined not to quail. He would lie like a dog, deny anything she knew, answer incrimination with incrimination; but he would not submit this time.

Elizabeth was waiting for him in the dining room, her eyes blazing and her mouth trembling. Samuel calmly asked what ailed her, and she let go. He was a false, rotten-hearted rogue. He had lied to her. He had spent the day with his strumpet Willet while he pretended that he was working at Whitehall.

Samuel shouted back at her that it was a damned lie. He had not seen the girl or wanted to. But Elizabeth let out a shriek and charged straight at him. She struck him in the face with her fist and pulled his wig from his head and threw it on the floor. She attacked his head and scratched him until the blood came. Samuel could only defend himself by throwing his arms around her and pinioning her arms to her sides.

In this awkward position he somehow got her out of the dining room and up the stairs to their bedroom, with Elizabeth screaming every step of the way. He kicked the door to with his foot and tumbled Elizabeth onto the bed. She immediately stopped screaming, but she returned at once to the attack, with words now, however, and not her fists. While Samuel wiped the blood from his

339

face, Elizabeth sat on the bed and spat her venom at him. If she could find the wench, she shouted, she would slit her nose for her. The girl was a whore and the gibbet would not be too good for her. Samuel could just give her £400 and she would go away forever; and if he did not, she would shout his baseness up and down the street until every man in London knew it.

Samuel ran to the door and shouted for Will Hewer. Elizabeth was too wild for him now. There was no telling what injury she might do, to him or to herself. He needed help, and only Will Hewer could be trusted to know of this disgrace.

Will came running up the stairs and into the room, tears running down his face. As soon as he came in, Elizabeth stopped her shouting and glared at Samuel.

"Do you intend to kill me and have your servant hold me while you cut my throat?" she demanded.

"No. No," Will Hewer cried. "You are both killing yourselves by anger, and for nothing."

Samuel took Will by the arm and drew him to the other side of the room. He told him of Elizabeth's threats to publish his name in the streets unless he gave her £400 and let her go. He had lost control of her, he said, and he needed help to bring her back to her senses. She charged him with seeing Deb when he had given his word that he would not.

Elizabeth took up the charge and elaborated it. He had indeed gone to see Deb, or he had tried to, or he had wanted to. She knew him well enough to know that he would try to see the girl if he had a chance, and he had made the chance by sending Will Hewer off on other business while he searched the town for his strumpet.

The words came tumbling out, but the violence and the volume decreased as she left the specific charge and entered into speculation. Will Hewer noticed the change and leapt to take advantage of it. He went across the room to her bedside and sat down in a chair.

"Mr. Pepys had good reason to send me abroad," he explained to her. "He gave me important business to do, that only I could do —but that is neither here nor there. This girl is not worth your anger. Forget her and Mr. Pepys will forget her. Let us make a pact, a written contract. You make the specifications and I will write them down. We will debate the points as we go along, compromising where we must, and then we will all sign the agreement. If you do not now trust your husband's word, I can tell you that you can trust his respect for a contract and so can all the Navy Board. Will you agree to negotiate a contract?"

This was a master stroke. Samuel *would* respect a contract. Elizabeth knew he would, and she also felt that she was in the saddle since she could dictate the terms.

Will looked at Samuel and Samuel nodded. He looked at Elizabeth. She bit her lip, glared again at Samuel, looked hard at Will, and finally nodded her head. Will took out his notebook and sat down at the table. While Elizabeth talked, Will wrote her terms in his book in shorthand.

Samuel was to agree never again to see or speak to Deb Willet while he lived. He was to write her a letter, which Elizabeth reserved the right to read and approve, calling her a whore and telling her that she had injured his wife by the greatest act of disloyalty he had ever known. He was to promise further that he would not hereafter go out of the house upon any cause without having the company of Elizabeth or, if it was not convenient for her to go, that of Will Hewer, Tom Edwards, or any other loyal servant approved or appointed by Mrs. Pepys. And finally he was to promise to say his prayers every night aloud and in the presence of Elizabeth, asking God to forgive him for his violation of His commandment and his acknowledged infidelity to his wife.

Samuel paced the floor while Elizabeth dictated. Once when he started to protest, Will Hewer cut him short.

"Let her dictate," Will insisted. "She is the injured party and has the right to state the terms."

Samuel bit his tongue and continued to walk up and down the room, fuming and seething; but Elizabeth kept on dictating and Will kept on writing. When she finally came to the end and could think of no other condition she wanted to impose on her erring husband, Samuel exploded.

"Only a craven puppy would put his name to so humiliating an agreement."

He stalked out of the room and slammed the door. As he went

down the hall he could hear Elizabeth shouting, "Does the dog fear to say his prayers?"

But Will was right after him. He took his master by the arm and said quietly, "We are not through yet, Mr. Pepys." There was something like a knowing smile on Will's honest face; and Samuel, trusting in the meaning of the smile, yielded to Will's pressure and came back into the bedroom.

It was only fair, Will explained when they were all seated again, that Mr. Pepys should promise not to see Mrs. Willet again.

Samuel nodded.

And it was also only fair, Will continued, that Mr. Pepys should write her a letter and tell her that he would not.

Samuel nodded again.

As for going abroad with a guardian, Mrs. Pepys had herself specified that he, Will Hewer, would be agreeable to her to serve this post. Now, since the world was used to seeing Mr. Pepys accompanied by his clerk, there could be no shame or injury to the Clerk of the Acts in having the constant company of Will Hewer. Unless, of course, Mr. Pepys preferred another clerk. . . .

Samuel put out his hand and touched Will's knee. He would prefer his usual clerk.

Will smiled gratefully and went on to the last of the conditions. A gentleman of Mr. Pepys's known adherence to the offices of the Church surely would not object to saying his prayers aloud at night.

"Certainly not," Samuel said stoutly.

"In my presence," Elizabeth interposed for the first time.

"In yours and God's," Samuel snapped.

"Then write the letter, Mr. Pepys," Will hurried to inject before this expression of religious zeal led them into another outburst. "Write the letter now and I will deliver it to the young woman with my own hand." Will stressed the "with my own hand" ever so slightly.

Samuel went to the table and wrote the letter, two full sheets of formal, elaborate language to say to Deb that he would not see her again. When he had finished the missive, Will handed the sheets to Elizabeth and she read them slowly.

"You do not call her *whore*," she protested loudly.

Samuel jumped to his feet and was about to answer, but Will grabbed his arm quickly and pressed him back into the chair.

"Write it by the agreement, Mr. Pepys, on this third sheet of paper and we can put it with the others." Will pushed a clean sheet in front of him and looked him straight in the face. While Samuel stared at him, and Elizabeth watched him from behind, Will slowly dropped the lid of his left eye.

Samuel turned and scrawled the hated words, "Deb, you are a whore." He signed his name and gave the sheet to Will. Will handed it to Elizabeth, who nodded her head and gave it back to Will to fold with the other sheets.

As soon as Will had gone, with the solemn promise to deliver the letter to Mistress Willet the first thing the next morning, Elizabeth left her seat, came across the room to Samuel and kissed him briskly on the brow. She would clean the scratches on his face for him, she said cheerfully.

Samuel permitted himself to be coaxed back into a semblance of good humor. He gave her the joy of the marriage bed that night, to her obvious satisfaction, and went across to the office next morning with Tom Edwards in conspicuous tow. He had to go to Whitehall during the morning, he told Elizabeth before he left the house, but he would not go until Will Hewer returned from his errand. Will, as a matter of fact, could even sit with him in the conference with the Duke. He was now permitted to have his clerk in private attendance to take notes for him.

When Will Hewer came back from Lincoln's Inn Fields about midmorning, he silently handed Samuel the undelivered third sheet of his letter. Deb had not seen the horrid page, he assured Samuel, and the girl had understood the necessity of the letter.

Samuel touched the sheet to a candle flame and watched it burn to ashes. "Now we will go to the Duke," he told Will.

The Duke of York was in an angry humor when Samuel and Will arrived at the Palace. Buckingham had succeeded in forcing the resignation of the Earl of Anglesey from the Board and had replaced him with two of his own servants, Sir Thomas Osborne and Sir Thomas Littleton.

"Buckingham," the Lord Admiral snorted, "is trying to gain control of the Board by replacing all my appointments with his own men. He is intent on putting Penn with the fleet, and he would remove you if he could. It is well that you have influential friends in the Parliament. The Council will not dare to touch you while Coventry has a voice in the House and while Sir Robert Brookes is Speaker."

Samuel was relieved to hear that his security was insured by the power of Coventry and Brookes in the House. These men he had won by his own merit. He had not inherited their love from his patron. With the Commons to support him from below and the Lord Admiral to guide him from above, he had no need to fear, too much, the influence of the Duke of Buckingham upon the Council.

But he could not think too harshly of Buckingham's changes in the Board, whatever the motive. Samuel had not been much impressed with the abilities of the Earl of Anglesey in the Treasury. His lordship did not have Sir George Carteret's ability to get money or his diligence in guarding it. As for Penn—well, Penn was a good sailor but a sorry office man. The Navy would be better off with Penn in the fleet.

Samuel did not mention these reservations about Buckingham to the Duke of York, of course. He spoke only of his work on the regulations. If he could bring his proposals for improvement of the regulations to an early conclusion and the Duke could present them to the Council and gain its approval, perhaps Buckingham could be forestalled.

The Duke said that he thought a good proposal would work wonders, and he urged Mr. Pepys to make all haste with his project. The Council would be impressed with a promising document of reform.

Samuel assured His Grace that he would spare no effort to get a draft of his proposed constitution for the Office ready as soon as possible. With luck he would have it ready before the winter was out.

He needed both time and luck. Buckingham was a shrewd politician. He had gathered about him in the Privy Council a group of sharp-witted men: Sir Thomas Clifford from the King's household; Lord Ashley, the brilliant Chancellor of the Exchequer; Lord Arlington, the Secretary of State; and the Earl of Lauderdale, the High Commissioner for Scotland. These men were all ambitious, high-spirited, and independent.

Only one thing held them together—a mutual hatred or distrust of the Catholic Duke of York. Queen Catherine had produced no child in seven years of marriage and the succession seemed to belong to York. To defeat the Duke in anything he undertook and to insure that he would not succeed to the throne when his brother died, they were all willing to bind themselves, for the time being at least, to a policy of opposition under the Duke of Buckingham. The first letters of their names ominously spelled out the word *Cabal*.

With Will Hewer in close attendance, Samuel spent the winter visiting the Rolls Office in Chancery Lane, the Patent Office, the library of the Inner Temple. He called upon all the old officials of the Navy he could find, men who had served the Navy during the reign of Charles I or during the Commonwealth and the Protectorate. He was basing his case upon the principle of precedent. If he could show that the present regulations were as good as those in force during the reign of the martyr king and better than those in force during the rule of Cromwell, the Cabal would have a difficult time making an objection that was not also an insult to the Crown. There was a strong feeling abroad that all the departments of Cromwell's government had been more honest and more efficient than the departments of King Charles II's government. Samuel privately suspected that they were. But he dared not say so aloud. No one dared. And it was his task now to prove that there was nothing inferior in the regulations the Board now used. Their only fault was in the men who executed the rules. With this point he was in hearty agreement.

Through the cold, dreary winter he and Will Hewer slogged from Whitehall to Chancery Lane, from Chancery Lane to the Temple, and from the Temple back to Westminster. It was tedious, eye-straining work, reading the crabbed, faded ink on the old documents, taking meticulous notes, searching through the town for an old officer who could give them a clue of procedure during the Protectorate. Samuel nursed his eyes as best he could, favored his cold feet when he had to wait in the damp for an hour to see an old retired admiral. Will Hewer became gradually less and less the guardian and more and more the trusted clerk and friend. Will would jot down the notes and take them at night to the office to Hayter and Gibson, who would copy them out and file them neatly. Samuel almost forgot his bondage to Elizabeth.

Elizabeth too relaxed her vigilance. She frequently quizzed Will Hewer about their business in town, where they went, what they did, whom they saw; and Will could always give her a detailed report. Sometimes she would accuse Samuel of dreaming of Deb and talking of her in his sleep, but Samuel always denied stoutly that he had even thought of her. This was a lie, for he thought of Deb often and sometimes dreamed of her. But let Elizabeth prove that he had! And he really had not seen her—or tried to. He was over that obsession, rescued by his urgent desire to save the Office from the Duke of Buckingham.

There was one more bad scene, however. He had spent the afternoon with Mr. Wren and had come home alone, well after Will had returned from his duties in Chancery Lane. At supper Elizabeth was sullen, and she snapped at him sharply when he volunteered the information that he had spent his day with Mr. Wren. When he went to bed Elizabeth did not follow him. He was almost asleep before she did come in, but he kept his eyes closed to avoid any more angry words.

He must have been asleep a good two hours when he awoke with a start to see Elizabeth standing over him with the fire tongs in her hand, the tips of it glowing red.

Samuel did not say a word. He was too frightened and miserable. He turned over in the bed and began to sob. Let her pinch him with the tongs, brand him forever with the hot iron. He had spent his total resource for appeasing her. He clutched the pillow and let the sobs rack his body.

Elizabeth watched for a minute in complete bewilderment. Then she returned the tongs to the fireplace and came back to him. She lay down beside him and put her arms around him.

She had no wish to hurt him, she told him softly. She only feared that he would hurt her. It had become too easy to mistrust him, too easy to believe anything she heard reported of him. She had heard that he had not spent the whole afternoon at Whitehall.

Her brother Balty had seen him in Smithfield, and she had believed him.

But that was wrong, she went on gently. Her suspicions always made her fearful and her fears made her mad. She did cruel things when her fear drove her half crazy. But she would torment him no more. She would believe now that he loved her.

Samuel turned in the bed so he could face her. He had not told the whole truth about the afternoon, he confessed. Balty had been right. He had been in Smithfield, and he had seen Balty; but he had thought nothing of it because he knew his business was innocent. He had gone to Smithfield to look at the coaches for sale. He had decided to buy a coach, as a surprise, for Easter. He had only priced them. She was to help him make the choice.

Elizabeth kissed him and said that it was not a coach that she wanted—or not only a coach. She wanted him to resign his office and take her to live in the country, away from London so full of evil.

Samuel held her hands. He could not resign, he told her, not now, there was too much at stake. He had the Navy to think of as well as himself. What he was doing now might make the difference between a good navy and a bad one, and England without a good navy was not England. He owed it to the King and to his country to do what he could do to insure that England would have a good navy, for a long time to come.

When Elizabeth looked downcast Samuel kissed her and told her there was something they might do.

"We can go to France. As soon as my work on the regulations is finished this spring, I can ask a leave, a long leave, for the whole summer, and we can go to Anjou and see the country where your father was born. I need to rest my eyes, and the King will give me leave to go to France to restore my sight."

"A visit to France," Elizabeth said, "will not restore your eyesight. Only retirement from your work will do that. But we will take what we can get. We will go to France for the summer. Let us get the coach first, though, Samuel."

They got the coach. Elizabeth went with Samuel to Smithfield and they selected a trim little vehicle, shiny black and trimmed with silver, as smart and tidy as any that Samuel had ever seen in Hyde Park.

They also got a pair of horses, young, spanking blacks, to match the coach; they hired a coachman and bought livery for him and for the boy who was to ride with the coachman,—fine green serge lined with red. It was all very expensive and very smart, highly suitable for a major officer of His Majesty's Navy.

Samuel did not begrudge the money. He was not sure how much money he had any more. He had enough to live well and that is all that a man ought to have, he decided. Pall was taken care of. John was about to get a living. His father's needs were few. He had obligation now only to his future and to Elizabeth's happiness.

When a linen merchant at the Royal Exchange returned from France with a wealth of fine French goods, Samuel took Elizabeth to the Exchange and let her select a wardrobe—dresses, shoes, gloves, fans—everything she wanted. She would need good clothes for her journey to France.

He also went by the bookshops in Westminster and bought her a whole library of French romances, Scuderi, La Calprenede, Gomberville, D'Urfe, all of them, a trunk full. If he was to have his good library of plays, sermons, music books, scientific treatises, Elizabeth could have her trashy romances.

As the winter of 1669 passed on into its spring, Samuel made good progress with his study of the regulations. In March the Council summoned him to meet with them and advise them what money would be needed to get out the summer fleet. Samuel gathered his figures and gave them the account, down to the shilling. A fleet cost money, but not so much as it had cost in the past when there was no responsible budget, no item-for-item estimate of charges. Sir Thomas Clifford was impressed.

By the middle of April he had his draft of the Regulations of the Navy Office ready. He showed it first to Sir William Coventry, to get his approval, and then he took it to the Duke of York. The Duke spent the afternoon on it, reading it carefully, and when he was through he had only one correction to make. For Samuel's phrase describing the beginning of the Commonwealth government, "upon the rupture between the late King and the Parliament," the Duke required a blunter phrase: "the beginning of the late Rebellion." The Duke wanted no pussyfooting about the Civil Wars. Any party that wanted to give its praise to that government would have to confess himself a man sympathetic to regicide.

Samuel felt uneasy. He felt sure that the Duke did not have him in mind in this talk about regicide—he surely was thinking of Buckingham and the Cabal—but Samuel had always held the Parliament in great respect, felt that Parliament was the only check the people had on a fallible king. And kings were fallible. There was an ineradicable Puritan streak in Samuel that time had only made more cautious. He remembered with discomfort that he had watched the beheading of King Charles I with pious approval. He had always been fearful that some former schoolfellow of his might remember the incident and tell of it. But no one ever had, and he tried to put the memory of the scene out of his mind. He had changed his mind about kings since then. Kings had value; but so had parliaments.

When Samuel arrived at the Palace on Sunday, April 18, the Regulations were ready. Mr. Gibson had spent the weekend copying out Samuel's drafts. The full Council was present, all the Cabal, Prince Rupert, the Duke of Albemarle, and even the Duke of York. If the Council was going to decide the fate of the Navy, the Duke was determined to come out of retirement and defend himself before his enemies.

Samuel entered the chamber, the engrossed and sealed document in his hand. At a nod from York he approached the table and delivered the "Regulations of the Navy Office." The Duke made a little speech thanking the Clerk of the Acts for his good service to the Navy in preparing the revised constitution, and then handed the document to Lord Arlington, the Secretary of State.

"I hope your lordship will read this document at your earliest chance and also make it available to the other members of the Council so they may read it and form whatever opinion of it they desire. I suggest that we all put in writing any faults we find in the constitution as Mr. Pepys has made it. He has labored long and diligently and his labors deserve our thoughtful, *committed* judgments."

Samuel was glad to get away from the presence of those forbidding men. But he was pleased at the neatness of the Duke of York's shrewd strategy. In requesting that they put their objections in writing and stressing the word *committed,* the Duke was insuring that the Cabal put itself on record, officially, either for the government as it was administered during the reign of kings or for it as it was administered during the rule of rebels.

It took three weeks for the lords of the Council to consider the Regulations of the Navy Office. During the interval Samuel relaxed. If the Regulations failed, he failed. His name had become officially associated with the document. If it was blocked, he was as good as out of office. But he did not care too much. His eyes hurt, his bladder troubled him, and he was tired. Brampton now, strangely enough, seemed an oasis of peace and freedom from care.

When word was brought to him, however, that the Duke of Buckingham was high against the constitution and had said publicly that all officeholders ought to be turned out regularly to keep them from becoming tyrants, Samuel was alarmed. He did not want to be turned out by the Duke of Buckingham. He only wanted to retire—voluntarily.

But he was cheered again when he was informed that Sir William Coventry had said in the Parliament that it would cost £10,000 to train a man to replace Mr. Pepys in the Navy Office, and that they would be lucky if they could find a man capable of being trained. Those economy-minded merchants would appreciate the point when it was put to them in terms of pounds, and even Buckingham was not going to move too rapidly against the temper of Parliament.

The first inkling Samuel had that his cause was not lost came when Sir Thomas Clifford went out of his way to accost him in the Matted Gallery to say that he would appreciate it if Mr. Pepys would come to him the next day to discuss the affairs of the Navy. Samuel gave Sir Thomas a vague but pleasant reply and hurried to the Duke of York.

The Duke was pleased at Samuel's news. "Go to him, by all means, Mr. Pepys. Clifford has the best mind of the group. He has more understanding of economy and more respect for diligence than all the others. If he has summoned you, he has something in his mind that we want to hear. Go to him."

Samuel went the next day. He waited an hour in the anteroom of Sir Thomas's chambers, but when he was finally admitted to Clifford's presence, Sir Thomas kept him the rest of the morning. He began by attacking the Regulations as having nothing in them that would prevent a recurrence of the late disgrace of the fleet. Samuel spoke out boldly in defense. The fault of the Navy lay not in its constitution, he said firmly. The fault lay in the quality of the men who administered it. No constitution would be good enough to overcome the weakness or inability of men who did not do their work properly.

Clifford let the Clerk of the Acts talk, listening attentively and making an occasional note. When Samuel was quite through, the Privy Councilor smiled faintly.

"I am inclined to agree with you," he said tersely. "The membership of the Board is what needs improvement, not the Regulations."

Samuel tightened his lips. He had invited this situation. He had exposed himself to this opportunity for Clifford to sack the lot of them. This would be the way the Cabal would demand a cleaning out of the Office, a wholesale dismissal as the price for passing the Duke of York's constitution.

After Clifford had allowed enough time for his words to sink in on his visitor, he proceeded to analyze the virtues and faults of every man on the Board.

"Minnes and Middleton are both too old," he concluded. "Penn is wasted ashore. Brouncker is good, but he spends too much time on his pleasures."

Samuel was impressed. This man knew the qualities of the Board as well as he did himself. Somehow Clifford had learned everything there was to know about his colleagues. The Councilor had said nothing so far about the Clerk of the Acts. All the others were clearly ticketed for removal, but he had not mentioned Mr. Pepys. Samuel waited.

"There are two places on the Board," Sir Thomas went on, "that seem to be in good hands. Osborne and Littleton have made good strides in the short time they have been in office. I think we have nothing to fear in the administration of the Treasury. Also I am told on good authority that no man in England does his work so well for the King as the present Clerk of the Acts. With this good core, I think we can trust the Navy Office to be what it should be. With a little sweeping out, Mr. Pepys, we can make a Board worth the name. Do you agree?"

Samuel relaxed. "Yes, sir, I agree."

So that was it. The Cabal approved him—and not only the Cabal. He had won this approval without being disloyal to the Duke of York. He was now recognized by the Council, the Parliament, the Lord Admiral, and therefore the King. No man could contest his authority in the Navy.

When he learned from the Duke a week later that the Regulations had been passed without objection, he was not surprised. Nor was he surprised at the news that Sir Jeremy Smith had received the King's warrant to succeed Penn. The broom had begun to sweep.

At the office Samuel directed the flow of business with a practiced and easy hand. When the place of Petty Purveyor became vacant, Samuel smoothly engineered the appointment of Mr. Hayter to the job. Hayter deserved the promotion; he was a loyal and capable clerk. He would not rise to the top of the profession, but he would always be a valuable department servant. For Will Hewer there was greater reward, in time. Will's future was assured if he remained confidential clerk to Mr. Pepys. His reward would come.

Samuel moved his seat at the table from his old position near the great fireplace to the other side of the table, with his back to the windows. His eyes could no longer bear the glare of the light from the windows. Lord Brouncker sat at the place of honor, Sir George Carteret's old seat at the head of the table; but the center of authority had moved down the table now to the place occupied by the Clerk of the Acts. It was here, where Samuel sat, that the agenda was established, the order of business set, the quiet, orderly discipline of the office maintained. The Clerk of the Acts was now more than a Clerk of the Acts. He was, in a sense, Secretary of the Navy.

Samuel and Elizabeth went to the theater frequently, but the glare of the blazing candles hurt his eyes almost as much as reading did. He went to the vizard maker in Westminster and ordered a mask to be made to fit the upper part of his face, and into the eye holes of the mask tubes of heavy paper were inserted. He needed something to shield his eyes from the glare of light. The mask made him look like a gargoyle and he refused to look at himself in the mirror while he wore it, but he could manage to read a little in the ugly contraption and he could make entries in his diary and work on his personal accounts.

Finally, under Elizabeth's urging, he applied for his leave. He dictated his petition to Mr. Gibson, explaining to the Duke that his eyesight had come to such a condition that he was moved to request an extended leave of absence from his duties. He proposed a journey of three months to spend the summer in France, to rest and recuperate so that he could return in the fall to devote his life and his service to His Majesty's Navy and to the personal service of the Duke of York.

He had Mr. Gibson make a pretty copy of the letter in fine clerkly script. He told Elizabeth to put on her best new dress, the flowered tabby gown with the good French lace. He ordered the coachman to prepare the horses, currying them until they shone like jet. The coach had just been repainted and the silver scroll-work regilded. Samuel himself put on his colored camlet tunic with the flowered tabby vest and the gold lace at the cuffs. This was an important mission to the Palace, and he wanted to go in state.

The coachman had even exceeded Samuel's desire for elegance. He had tied the manes and tails of the horses with red ribbon, and he had substituted green leather reins for the regular black ones. Now the horses matched the green and red livery of the coachman and the doorboy.

When they entered the coach, Elizabeth insisted that Samuel sit on the backward seat by himself. There was not room on the forward seat for both of them without his rumpling and ruining her full-skirted gown. Samuel complained that riding backward made him dizzy, but Elizabeth said that was nonsense. He only liked to ride in the forward seat so he could admire the horses and the servants in livery.

The elegant coach and the handsome couple rode out of Seething Lane, up Mincing Lane to Fenchurch Street, and then westward toward Whitehall. As they passed through Temple Bar, Samuel saw a face that stopped his heart. It was Deb, walking with a gentleman, down the Strand. He looked at her, hoping to catch her eye without revealing himself to Elizabeth. Deb looked up and saw him, just in time. She smiled quickly, and just as the coach moved on beyond her, Samuel thought he saw her drop her eyelid in a mischievous, saucy wink.

Deb had, he mused, learned something of the world. Now she could walk abroad in the street, accompanied by a fine gentleman, and wink at her first master. Deb would be all right. It made him sigh to think that he would never see her again.

But he was very careful to keep his face immobile. He looked at Elizabeth sitting across from him in the fine coach, her body swaying gently with the motion of the wheels on the cobbled street. She looked almost matronly at twenty-nine, filling her handsome clothes with the plumpness of middle years. She looked rather imperious, too, he thought, holding her head high, conscious of the fine figure she made riding to the Palace in her own coach.

At the Palace Samuel left Elizabeth sitting in the coach while he went into the Duke's chambers to present his petition. Mr. Wren greeted him and took his document straight to the Duke. He was back in a few minutes. Mr. Pepys was to go at once to the Duke.

James Stuart was standing by the fireplace when Samuel entered, the petition in his hand, the seal broken. He waved Samuel to a chair and pulled another for himself close beside him.

"I am distressed, Mr. Pepys, to learn that your eyes have come to this state," His Grace said sympathetically. "The services of the royal physician are available to you if you think they will help."

"I am not sure, your Grace, that anything will help; but I would like to try the rest."

"By all means, rest your eyes. Take the leave and go your journey into France. If you would care for an official excuse for your visit into Europe, you and the Navy could profit by an inspection of King Louis' ships. Would you be willing to go also into Holland and look at the Dutch navy? We can learn much from the Dutch."

"I would be happy to look at something besides the natives of Anjou," Samuel said.

The Duke went in person to the King to get his approval of Mr. Pepys's leave. "His Majesty desires me to tell you that he wishes to be a good master to your eyes, Mr. Pepys," the Duke reported when he returned. "Go to France as soon as you like."

During the last days of May, Samuel cleared up his affairs in London, paid his bills, wrote letters to his family, visited his friends to tell them of his leave. Most important, he went to see the Earl of Sandwich. The Earl had returned from his mission to Spain some time ago, but Samuel had seen little of him. His lordship had been busy and Samuel had been ashamed. He had written him only once in the two years of his absence. There had been a few meetings soon after his lordship returned and a polite rounded himself with new servants, and Samuel was full of busi- exchange of news; but that was all. Lord Sandwich had sur- ness that did not concern or interest the Earl very much.

When Samuel arrived at the Earl's lodgings in Whitehall, only Mr. Sydney Montagu was at home. Sydney had grown up into an imposing young man, bearded, full-chested, talkative. His parents had gone to Hinchingbrooke, he told Samuel, but he was glad to see his old tutor. He recalled to Samuel a week he and his sisters had spent in Seething Lane during the sickness of his brother, and Samuel had taught them the parts of a ship. He had never forgotten, he said; the best teaching he had ever had.

Samuel was flattered at Master Sydney's memory and invited him to come again to Seething Lane and eat dinner with him. He promised to try not to teach him anything this time. Sydney protested that he would come only on the condition that Samuel would bring out his ship models and show them to him again.

Samuel was pleased with the visit. It was good to have his old relationship with the family brought back. He still felt related and warm toward his noble cousins. He had had the old feelings restored without having to face the possibly chilly reception of the

Earl himself. The Earl was a great man and he had made the career of Samuel Pepys possible. Without Edward Montagu there would have been no Samuel Pepys, none worth thinking about. He was grateful to Master Sydney for helping him to preserve what was left of the memory.

On May 29 Samuel and Elizabeth sat in their fine coach and watched the spectacle of the fireworks in celebration of the King's birthday. As the rockets soared and burst high in the air above the Park, Samuel's mind went back to that day nine years ago when he had leaned on the rail of the *Naseby* (or the *Charles* as it was by then) with the Earl of Sandwich and watched the bonfires burning on the cliffs of Dover. It seemed a long time ago—in another world. But those fires on the cliffs had lighted the way to these bursting rockets; that day had led to this. This decade he had just lived through had had a pattern, but he was not quite sure what the pattern was, except that then, nine years ago, he had been a hopeful, ambitious young man, full of eager enthusiasm and woeful ignorance; and now—what was he now? He was Clerk of the Acts of His Majesty's Navy, with a wife, a house, and a coach. It was enough—for the moment, more than he probably deserved, he thought, considering his irrepressibly sinful nature.

Two days later, on the last day of May, he spent the morning giving Will Hewer final instructions. Will was engaged, under Samuel's guidance, in a complete revision of the out-of-date regulations concerning the duties and responsibilities of all line officers. Samuel also told Will to stay in the house in Seething Lane and see that the servants behaved themselves.

In the afternoon he and Elizabeth drove through the Park and watched the Court promenade in the fine May weather. When they came back home from their ride, Elizabeth went up to bed and Samuel went into his study. He took out the book in which he wrote his diary. It was the sixth volume he had filled in the nine and a half years since he had first begun it. The first five volumes were now well bound and safely put away. He would have this one bound too as soon as he was finished. He put on his grotesque mask and sat down at the table. By the light of the two full candelabra he wrote out the brief events of the day, "*Up very betimes,* and so continued all the morning with W. Hewer" and on down to the end: ". . . and so home late."

He looked over the entry, touched up one character to make it clearer, and then skipped a space on the page and began again:

And thus ends all that I doubt I shall ever be able to do with my own eyes in the keeping of my Journal, I being not able to do it any longer, having done now so long as to undo my eyes almost every time that I take a pen in my hand; and, therefore, whatever comes of it, I must forebear; and, therefore, resolve, from this time forward, to have it kept by my people in long-hand, and must therefore be contented to set down no more than is fit for them and all the world to know; or, if there be anything, which cannot be much, now my amours to Deb are past, and my eyes hindering me in almost all other pleasures, I must endeavor to keep a margin in my book open, to add, here and there, a note in short-hand with my own hand.

And so I betake myself to that course, which is almost as much as to see myself go to my grave: for which, and all the discomforts that will accompany my being blind, the good God prepare me!

At the left side of the page he added the date—*May 31, 1669;* and on the right side he wrote his initials—*S. P.* He held the page open a moment to let the ink dry; and then closed the book and passed out of knowledge into history.

As far as my eyes will give

me leave

MR PEPYS *did not go blind. For the rest of his life he suffered from the severe eyestrain that caused him to give up his diary, but he never completely lost his sight. Seventeenth-century lens makers were quite capable of grinding the prescribed strength of convex glass that could have corrected his farsightedness; but unfortunately optometry had not yet learned the secret of dealing with astigmatism. He had to endure the pain, depend upon his clerks, and save his eyes as best he could. Except for a few brief and official occasions he never again took up the diary, in cipher or in longhand; but for thirty-three more years, he gave what sight he had to the service of the Crown and the improvement of the Navy.*

The personal tragedy in his life came from another source— suddenly and without warning. During the last week of their Continental holiday, Elizabeth contracted a fever, possibly typhoid. As soon as they returned to London, she took to her bed and within a few days died, on November 10, in their fine house in Seething Lane. Only imagination can supply the scene of Mr. Pepys's grief, and the diarist on this occasion gave the imagination of posterity nothing to feed upon. We know only that he buried her in the churchyard of St. Olave's across the street, and erected a memorial to her inside the little church where they had for ten years looked down together upon the parish. In elaborate Latin he celebrated her origins, her virtues and, in a daring conceit, even her childlessness: Prolem enixa, quia parem non potuit, nullam.

But the greatest tribute that this most uxorious of men paid to his departed spouse was his preservation of her place in his marriage bed. He took no other wife. It is not to be imagined that he also dedicated his chastity to her memory, but no other woman ever had the honor of sharing his name. The title of Mrs. Samuel Pepys ceased to exist when Elizabeth, at the age of twenty-nine, was committed to the earth that bitter Wednesday, from whence, Samuel memorialized, she "went away again to see a more pleasant world."

Three years later the house itself was burned. The Navy residences that had escaped the great fire of 1666 submitted to the carelessness of Lord Brouncker's household. A fire broke out in the middle of the night in the closet of the Commissioner's mistress and by morning the Navy Office and all the residences were gutted. Mr. Pepys managed to save his books and the presses but very little else. Thereafter he lived no more in Seething Lane.

When the Duke of York was forced to resign his office of Lord High Admiral in the summer of 1673, Mr. Pepys was appointed Secretary of the Admiralty Commission that assumed control of the Navy, and from that time forth lived in Westminster. Here he planned and supervised the construction of thirty great ships-of-the-line which formed the nucleus of the best fleet in Europe. Here he devised the rules and regulations that brought firm discipline for the first time into the English Navy. And here he also felt the shock of Lord Shaftesbury's atrocious antipapist witch hunt. Mr. Pepys was no papist; he was only a Yorkist. But that was enough to bring him under dangerous suspicion and to land him for a few weeks in the Tower under the false accusation of having delivered military secrets to the French.

Not even the machinations of Shaftesbury, however, could prove so preposterous a charge against the impeccable Secretary, and the Lord Chief Justice dismissed the charge. Nor could the whiggish demagogue, in the end, triumph over the King. The sluggish Charles, finally aroused, prorogued the hostile Parliament, broke the back of Shaftesbury's conspiracy, and took command of his own government. The Duke of York came home from Scotland, but Mr. Pepys was placed in charge of the Navy. King Charles invented for him the unique place of Secretary for the Affairs of the Admiralty of England, and in that powerful capacity the former clerk ruled the English Navy for four years, with more authority than any layman, before or since, has ever enjoyed. For four years Mr. Pepys was the English Navy, answerable only to the King; and sometimes when the King forgot one of the inviolable rules which the little Secretary had devised for the tight organization of the fleet, he even rebuked the King— with tact and delicacy, but with firmness.

If King James II had reserved some of his boundless zeal for his religion and devoted it to the dispassionate control of his government with the same implacable industry by which his Secretary of the Navy controlled the fleet, he might have kept his crown and Mr. Pepys might have had the chance to build the Navy into the image of his vision. But from the day he assumed the throne upon his brother King Charles's death, in February, 1685, James Stuart seemed to rule with but one idea in mind—to avenge the wrongs heaped upon him for his Catholicism. His fixation led him from error to error, from angry obduracy to futile indecision, from calm bravery to foolish escape and exile. Within three years he had squandered his inheritance, and his son-in-law, the foreign Prince of Orange, stepped to the throne without a blow being struck or a drop of blood spilled.

Mr. Pepys did not desire to serve his country under the rule of a foreign prince, even if he enjoyed the quasi-legal distinction of joint sovereignty with his wife Mary Stuart and bore the English title William the Third. As soon as the crisis was over, the Secretary of His Majesty's Navy concluded the last detail of his official business and submitted his resignation. According to his friend and fellow diarist, Mr. John Evelyn, "he laid down his office, and would serve no more."

The last half of Mr. Pepys's life, the years in which he made his fame as a Naval administrator, is a public record. The documents of the period are full of his busy affairs, but only occasionally do the letters and the official papers give a glimpse of the private life that the Diary so warmly illumined from 1660 to the summer of 1669. The personal record thereafter is largely a story of the ultimate death of his friends, his family, his servants.

The Earl of Sandwich died aboard his flagship, the Royal

James, *at the battle of Southwold Bay on May 29, 1672. It is somehow satisfactory to the reader of the* Diary *to know that his lordship died fighting the Dutch, in vigorous and courageous action,
and not supine at Hinchingbrooke or Whitehall in the backwaters
of a distinguished but faltering career. He was buried with honors
at Westminster Abbey, his body conducted to his grave by twelve
earls in mourning and six gentlemen bannerolles, the first of
whom was his cousin and former protégé, Mr. Samuel Pepys.*

*Pepys's family continued to be a trial to him for a long time.
Brother John's life was tragic. Samuel obtained for him the Clerkship of Trinity House; and when Samuel himself proceeded
from the Navy Office to the Admiralty, he secured the place of the
Clerk of the Acts for his brother and his old clerk Mr. Hayter
jointly. But John lived only four years to enjoy his comfortable
employment. He died in May of 1677, leaving an unaccountable
indebtedness of over £300 and a tangle of his records at Trinity
House. As he had done for his brother Tom before him, Samuel
assumed the debt and fretted angrily over the mismanaged accounts.*

*In 1680 Samuel's father and his brother-in-law, John Jackson,
died within a month of each other of an ague, leaving Pall a confused widow with an almost bankrupt estate and two young sons
to educate. Samuel took over their education, sending the older
boy, his namesake, Samuel, to sea to learn to make a career in the
Navy, and the younger boy, John, to Cambridge to learn to be a
scholar. Samuel Jackson never learned to please his uncle and
was disinherited for presuming to marry without his approval.
John Jackson was made the heir and received the bulk of Mr.
Pepys's estate, including his valuable library and the priceless*
Diary.

*Poor, unhappy Pall lived on until 1689, widowed, ill, and un-
wanted, a care to her brother, a nuisance to her neighbors, and a
burden to her sons. She had only one achievement in her forty-
nine years of graceless existence; but that, in a way, was the greatest achievement of all. She continued the line—and gave to Samuel the heir he so desperately wanted. She also gave to the world
the means by which the great* Diary *was passed from its creator
to the library of Magdalene College and thence to a grateful*

posterity. It is a nice irony that Pall, who figured so unattractively in her brother's journal, should be the unwitting medium of its preservation.

Mr. Pepys was wont to complain that he was unlucky in his servants. Of Will Hewer he had to make an exception. Surely few men have ever been so fortunate in servant or friend as Mr. Pepys was in the boy he engaged on the first day he moved into his new house in Seething Lane in 1660. Will Hewer went with Mr. Pepys to Whitehall when he left the Navy Office and grew in stature, wealth, and reputation, as Samuel knew he would. He saved his money, invested wisely in real estate, and by the time of the Revolution was worth considerably more in goods and land than his more cautious master. And he never wavered in his loyalty. On the black day in December 1688 when Mr. Pepys went before King William to surrender his office, Hewer wrote him a letter "of great tenderness at a time of difficulty."

"You may rest assured," Will concluded his consolatory note, "that I am wholly yours, and that you shall never want the utmost of my constant, faithful and personal service, the utmost I can do being inconsiderable to what your kindness and favor to me has and does oblige me to. And therefore, as all I have proceeded from you, so all I have and am is and shall be at your service."

And Hewer's action was as good as his sentiment. When he retired from office, Mr. Pepys withdrew from London and the scene of his career in the Navy. He went to Clapham where Will Hewer owned a fine house, and there the two lived together, congenial bachelors, resting in content upon the harvest of their labor and their honors. As a former Master of Trinity House, Mr. Pepys was still consulted from time to time by the great officials of the service. As a former President of the Royal Society, his imprimatur appeared on the title page of Sir Isaac Newton's Philosophiae Naturalis Principia Mathematica, *the celebrated book which announced to the world the idea of universal gravitation.*

On May 26, 1703, Mr. John Evelyn made a solemn entry in his diary: "This day died Mr. Samuel Pepys, a very worthy, industrious and curious person, none in England exceeding him in knowledge of the Navy. . . . He was universally beloved, hospi-

table, generous, learned in many things, skilled in music, a very great cherisher of learned men of whom he had the conversation. . . . Mr. Pepys had been for near forty years so much my particular friend, that Mr. Jackson sent me a complete mourning, desiring me to be one to hold up the pall at his magnificent obsequies; but my indisposition hindered me from doing him this last office."

Mr. Pepys was in his seventy-first year, an exceedingly advanced age for his time.

A SELECTED BIBLIOGRAPHY

Bell, Walter G., *The Great Fire of London in 1666,* London, 1920.

——, *The Great Plague in London in 1665,* rev. ed., London, 1951.

Brett-James, Norman George, *The Growth of Stuart London,* London, 1935.

Bryant, Arthur, *The England of Charles II,* New York, 1935.

——, *King Charles II,* London, 1932.

——, *Samuel Pepys: The Man in the Making,* New York, 1933.

——, *Samuel Pepys: The Years of Peril,* New York, 1935.

——, *Samuel Pepys: The Saviour of the Navy,* New York, 1939.

Chancellor, E. Beresford, *The Pleasure Haunts of London during Four Centuries,* London, 1925.

——, *The West End of Yesterday and To-day,* London, 1926.

Clayton, P. B., and B. R. Leftwich, *The Pageant of Tower Hill,* London, 1933.

Cross, Arthur Lyon, *A Shorter History of England and Great Britain,* New York, 1922.

Dasent, Arthur Irwin, *The History of St. James's Square,* London, 1895.

Digby, Sir Kenelm, *The Closet of Sir Kenelm Digby Knight Opened,* Anne MacDonell (ed.), London, 1910.

Drinkwater, John, *Mr. Charles, King of England,* New York, 1926.

——, *Pepys, His Life and Character,* London, 1930.

Dubreton, J. Lucas, *Samuel Pepys, a Portrait in Miniature,* New York, 1925.

Evelyn, John, *Diary and Correspondence,* William Bray (ed.), 4 vols., London, 1857.

Green, John Richard, *A Short History of the English People,* 2 vols., Everyman Library, London, 1915.

Hamilton, Anthony, *Memoirs of Count Grammont.* Sir Walter Scott (ed.), London, 1897.

Harris, F. R., *The Life of Edward Montagu, K. G., First Earl of Sandwich (1625–1672),* 2 vols., London, 1912.

Heckethorn, Charles William, *Lincoln's Inn Fields and the Localities Adjacent,* London, 1896.

Home, Gordon, *Old London Bridge,* New York, 1931.

Hotson, Leslie, *The Commonwealth and Restoration Stage,* Cambridge, Mass., 1928.

Hyde, Edward, *The Life of Edward, Earl of Clarendon,* 3 vols., Oxford, 1827.

Leake, John, *An Exact Surveigh of the Streets Lanes and Churches Contained within the Ruines of the City of London. Engraved by Wenceslaus Hollar, 1667,* London Topographical Society, 1908.

Mackenzie, Kenneth, *The English Parliament,* Penguin Books, Harmondsworth, 1951.

McAfee, Helen, *Pepys on the Restoration Stage,* New Haven, 1916.

Nicoll, Allardyce, *A History of Restoration Drama,* Cambridge, 1923.

Ogilby, John, and William Morgan, *A Large and Accurate Map of the City of London,* London and Middlesex Archaeological Society, 1895.

Pepys, Samuel, *The Diary of Samuel Pepys,* Henry B. Wheatley (ed.), 10 vols. in 3, London, 1924.

——, *Letters and the Second Diary of Samuel Pepys,* R. G. Howarth (ed.), London, 1932.

——, *The Letters of Samuel Pepys and His Family Circle,* Helen Truesdell Heath (ed.), Oxford, 1955.

Pevsner, Nikolaus, *The Buildings of England: London, except the Cities of London and Westminster,* London, 1952.

Ponsonby, Arthur, *English Diaries: A Review of English Diaries from the Sixteenth to the Twentieth Century with an Introduction on Diary Writing,* 2d ed., London, 1923.

Power, D'Arcy, "An Address on Why Samuel Pepys Discontinued His Diary, Delivered at a meeting of the Samuel Peyps Club held on April 5th, 1911," *The Lancet,* June 24, 1911.

——, "The Medical History of Mr. and Mrs. Samuel Pepys," *The Lancet,* June 1, 1895.

Rocque, John, *A Plan of the Cities of London and Westminster, and the Borough of Southwark; with the Contiguous Buildings, 1746,* London Topographical Society, 1917.

Sheppard, Edgar, *The Old Royal Palace of Whitehall,* London, 1902.

Speed, John, *An Atlas of Tudor England and Wales,* E. G. R. Taylor (ed.), Penguin Books, Harmondsworth, 1951.

Stow, John, *The Survey of London,* Everyman Library, London, 1912.

Strype, John, *A Survey of the Cities of London and Westminster . . .*

*by John Stow . . . Corrected, Improved, and very much Enlarged
. . . by John Strype*, 2 vols., London, 1735.

Summers, Montagu, *Playhouse of Pepys,* London, 1935.

———, *The Restoration Theatre,* New York, 1934.

Taylor, Eric, *The House of Commons at Work,* Penguin Books, Harmondsworth, 1951.

Timbs, John, *Clubs and Club Life in London, with Anecdotes of Its Famous Coffee Houses, Hostelries and Taverns,* London, 1886.

Vertue, G., *A Survey & Ground Plot of the Royal Palace of Whitehall, 1747, from a Survey taken in K. Charles's Reign 1680.*

Wheatley, Henry B., *London, Past and Present . . . Based upon the 'Handbook of London' by the late Peter Cunningham,* 3 vols., London, 1891.

———, *Pepysiana,* Supplementary volume to the *Diary of Samuel Pepys,* London, 1923.

Whitear, Walter H., *More Pepysiana: Being Notes on the Diary of Samuel Pepys,* London, 1927.

Wilson, John Harold, *A Rake and His Times: George Villiers, 2nd Duke of Buckingham,* New York, 1954.

INDEX

This index was planned to serve three purposes: (1) to provide a reference to all persons and places mentioned in the book; (2) to offer the reader a "Cast of Characters" for the chief actors in the story of the Diary; and (3) to make available a chronology of Mr. Pepys's life, which will be found under the entry for Samuel Pepys. All names are entered under the form in which they first appear in the book; subsequent titles or married names are cross-referenced to the original entry. Three abbreviations are used throughout the Index: SP for Samuel Pepys; EP for Elizabeth Pepys; and EM for Edward Montagu, Lord Sandwich.

Bath, city of, SP and family visit, 324, 325

Batten, Elizabeth, Lady, wife of the Surveyor of the Navy Board, 48, 244

Batten, Martha, daughter of the Surveyor, 49, 57

Batten, Admiral Sir William, Surveyor of the Navy Board, 22, 29–30; fond of contractors, 31; attends Coronation parade with SP, 57; jealous of SP's interest in contracts, 77–79; observes hemp tests at Deptford with SP, 88–91; skeptical of SP's association with Coventry, 98; offers his cart to SP to save his goods from the fire, 244; digs a hole in the garden for his wine, 249–250; works with SP in defense against Dutch invasion, 286–290; grieves in the garden with SP, 295–296; dies, 301; *alluded to*, 110, 167, 195, 243

Baynard's Castle, 248

Beale, Mr., 34–36

Becke, Betty, nurses EM at Chelsea, 115–116; injured by gossip, 118, 125

Becke, Mr., EM's landlord at Chelsea, 115 ff., 125

Becke, Mrs., makes cakes for EM, 115; *alluded to,* 125

"The Beggar's Daughter of Bethnal Green," 244

Bell Alley, Westminster, 176

Bergen (harbor), 183, 196, 197

Berkeley, Lord John, of Stratton, Commissioner of the Navy Board, 20, 30; considers house in Seething Lane SP desires, 32–36

Berkeley, William, Rear Admiral, 201, 203

Berkshire, 325

Bess, cookmaid to SP, 148

Bethnal Green, Sir William Rider's house at, 243, 244, 247, 259, 286

Bezan (yacht), 199, 200, 207, 210

Billingsgate, 15, 246

Billingsgate Stairs, 14

Bishopsgate, 293

Black Death. *See* London, plague in

Blackburne, Robert, former Secretary of the Commonwealth Admiralty Commission, uncle of Will Hewer, 28, 273

Bloomsbury, 10

Bloomsbury Square, 174

Bludworth, Sir Thomas, Lord Mayor of London, 167, 229, 238, 240, 241

Bombay, 135

Bowling Green, the, Whitehall, 13

Brahé, Count, Swedish ambassador, 67–68

Brampton, Huntingdonshire, SP inherits his Uncle Robert's estate at, 73; SP's parents and sister go to live at, 73; EP visits, 95, 99, 117–118; SP considers retiring to, 281–282, 286, 312, 350; SP's mother dies at, 283–284; SP sends gold to, 292–295, 300; SP recovers gold from, 302–304; Pall is married at, 321; SP visits, 324–325; *alluded to,* 143, 147, 285, 292

Breckington, Somersetshire, 325

Breda, negotions for peace with the Dutch, 298, 299

Bridewell Prison, 229, 240

Bridges Street, Covent Garden, Theatre Royal in, 138

Bristol, city of, 325, 330

Brooks, Sir Robert, Speaker of the House of Commons, 314–316, 344

Brouncker, William, Viscount, Commissioner of the Navy Board, 159; visits the prize fleet with SP, 197–199, 207; SP considers careless of his duties, 264; quarrels with Penn, 280–281; goes to Pett's aid at Chatham, 290; SP considers butt-headed, 301; in trouble over pay tickets, 305–307; congratulates SP on speech, 316, 317; SP goes to theater with, 322; fearful of SP's new power, 328; his careless-

trimmed, 281; goes to Chatham to aid Pett; overjoyed with SP's speech, 317; *alluded to,* 86, 110, 283, 328

Mitre, The, tavern in Fenchurch Street, 24

Monck, General George, 9; Duke of Albemarle, 17; Serjeant of the King's Scullery, 44–46; member of Tangier Commission, 97; commands Admiralty in York's absence, 162, 164, 167, 170–172, 175, 183, 211–214; in command at Whitehall during plague, 194–197, 208, 215; offers SP place of Surveyor General of the Victual, 215–217; commends SP, 221–223, 263; goes to sea as joint commander with Prince Rupert, 224–228, 230, 231; barricades the Thames against the Dutch, 289, 291; condemns Lord Brouncker, 206; *alluded to,* 219, 220, 261, 349

Montagu, Catherine, infant daughter of EM, 115

Montagu, Sir Edward (later Earl of Sandwich), joint commander of the Restoration fleet, 1, 5; receives the Garter, 2; at Dover, 3; his political philosophy, 4–5; patron of SP, 5–6, 85; obtains place on Navy Board for SP, 18; Charles II rewards, 17–18; receives earldom, 21; becomes First Earl of Sandwich, 28, 47; commander of the fleet, 46; Coronation attire, 53; his family, 54; his enemies, 77, 84–85; brings Queen to England, 80; stores dower gold with SP, 80–81; member of Tangier Commission, 97; recuperating in Chelsea, 113, 115, 118 ff.; is warned of gossip by SP, 122–126; on winter and summer guard against Dutch, 157, 158, 160, 161; at Battle of Lowestoft, 162, 163, 169–173; in sole command of the fleet, 175, 179, 183; negotiates marriage for his daughter Jem, 176–178;

defeats the Dutch, 197–198, 211; disgraced by the business of the prize goods, 200–204, 211–213, 215–217, 219, 220, 222, 224; sent Ambassador to Spain, 227–229, 232; killed at Southwold Bay in Third Dutch War, 360–361; *alluded to,* 157, 190, 262, 264, 275, 291, 306, 355, 356

Montagu, Jemimah, Lady Sandwich, 103, 115, 162, 168, 172, 176, 179, 183, 188, 189

Montagu, Jemimah (Jem), EM's daughter (later Lady Carteret), 116, 176–183, 187–190, 191

Montagu, Sir Sydney, EM's father, 129

Montagu, Sydney, EM's son, 221, 355

Moore, Henry, EM's solicitor, 119, 121–125

Moorfields, 53, 191, 246

Moorgate, 256

More, Sir Thomas, 115

Morrice, Sir William, Secretary of State, 299

Moscovy Court, Tower Hill, 159

Myngs, Sir Christopher, Rear Admiral, 201, 203, 211, 227

Naseby, Battle of, 5

Naseby, EM's flagship, renamed the *Royal Charles,* 116

Navy Board, their office near the Tower, 19; their duties, 19–20; composition, 20, 85; ordered to survey condition of the fleet, 27, 30; SP's first meeting with, 28–29; members, 29–30, 36, 77, 159; their inefficiency, 83, 92; ordered to prepare for war, 158, 213; SP controls, 223, 233, 300, 336; summoned by the Council, 227, 298; Prince Rupert condemns, 228–229; summoned by the Duke of York, 69–70, 260–263; ordered to account for expenditures, 277; resignations begin, 278, 279; morale bad, 280–283;

CECIL ABERNETHY is Professor of English at Birmingham-Southern College in Alabama. Born in Charleston, South Carolina, he attended Birmingham public schools and Birmingham-Southern, taught English for four years at Birmingham's West End High School, and since 1939 has been a member of the faculty of his alma mater. He has also taught at the University of Alabama and holds a master's degree from the University of North Carolina and a Ph.D. from Vanderbilt University.

Professor Abernethy shares with Samuel Pepys a great enthusiasm for that "beguiling, consuming monster," the theater. Besides appearing frequently in college and little-theater productions, he was for ten years faculty director of the Birmingham-Southern college theater. It is only in recent years that the pressures of teaching, research, and writing—in particular, his studies of the life and times of Samuel Pepys—have curtailed his direct involvement with the stage.

Mr. Pepys of Seething Lane marks the culmination of six years of research and writing. Professor Abernethy says of the book: "I have tried to get at the 'truth' of Mr. Pepys without being submerged by the 'facts.' I have referred to no events, I believe, that are not true, but I have taken the novelist's liberty of interpreting the facts in accordance with the image I have of Pepys in my own mind. This is surely not the only image possible, but it is the one that has obsessed me and given the unifying theme of the book: the emergence of a 'new' man at the great moment of transition in English cultural history—nonheroic, efficient, vulnerable. He was a complex of sensuality and primness, idleness and industry, courage and cowardice. But somehow in the *Diary* he resolved the complexity into a portrait of one of the most vivid personalities in history. This book is an attempt to catch that portrait."